Louis ARTHUE.

Matrix Computer Analysis

of Structures.

Moshe   F. Rubinstein.

FRAME ANALYSIS

FRAME ANALYSIS

SECOND EDITION

ARTHUR S. HALL

Associate Professor of Civil Engineering
The University of New South Wales

RONALD W. WOODHEAD

Senior Lecturer in Civil Engineering
The University of New South Wales

JOHN WILEY & SONS, INC.
New York and London

Preface

Before electronic computers were available for general engineering operations, the study of the more complex framed structures was of academic interest only, since the arithmetic work involved is excessive for hand computation. Now, however, the study of the general frame has a practical application. Frames of a three-dimensional nature, composed of members of any shape whatever, with pinned or rigid joints, can be analyzed readily by an extension of the methods previously used for simpler structures.

This exposition of the subject aims at a generality of this kind, within the limitations of a linear behavior of the frame. It will be found that in order to achieve this the demand is not so much for the mastering of difficult techniques as for a clear and thorough understanding of fundamental principles. It follows that the early chapters of the book are of paramount importance, and a careful study of them will repay the reader.

A second objective is the presentation of the subject as a unified whole. Over the last thirty or forty years many special techniques have been devised to provide rapid solutions for particular types of frames. An exhaustive study of these techniques is likely to obscure the essential unity of the subject. In this book the emphasis is therefore upon the general processes of solution. In some instances methods of restricted application are mentioned, but only in order to demonstrate their derivation from the main stream of the subject.

In order to expose the symmetry of form of the subject, a reasonably short treatment is desirable. Some prior acquaintance with elementary parts of frame analysis and with terminology generally has therefore been assumed. The book may be thought of as being addressed mainly to senior students and structural engineers. It aims at laying a foundation for more advanced study.

The purpose would also be difficult to achieve without some use of matrix algebra. It was felt that to assume great fluency in this branch of mathematics would be unrealistic. Instead, therefore, only the most rudimentary knowledge is presupposed, namely, the definitions of the various types of matrix and of the operations of addition, subtraction, multiplication and inversion (division). The definitions of these terms, and a brief treatment of those portions of matrix algebra which are used in the book, are given in an appendix. In any case, an elementary treatment of matrices is now included in many university courses. What engineers find more difficult is an understanding of how these techniques can be used in practice. In the early chapters of this book the subject is developed in longhand form, and the shorter matrix form is given as an alternative. In the later chapters more and more reliance is placed directly on matrices. It is hoped that our book will encourage a transition to the matrix form of expression.

The analysis of complex frames can hardly be undertaken without the assistance of electronic computers. The use of computers is not specifically mentioned in our book, but it is implicit in the more difficult problems. The concise matrix exposition of the subject forms a good preparation for those who wish to use computers in their work. At the same time it is none the less satisfactory for more elementary frames.

A number of simple examples have been provided in order that the principles can be clearly seen. More complex three-dimensional examples are given from time to time, to show that these conform to the same treatment. When special techniques—for example, moment distribution or fixed points—have in the past been developed, each has usually had reference to a particular class of problem. Where such methods are mentioned, the examples must naturally be of a restricted type suitable to the method under discussion. It is of importance to recognize the field of application of each technique, since its use for the analysis of other types of frames will usually lead to a very laborious solution.

The first two chapters discuss the nature of the problem and the principles which are basic to all methods of solution. These principles can be put into operation in two different ways, and all methods of solution can be classified accordingly. One of these classes, the action methods, occupies Part I; the other, the displacement methods, is dealt with in Part II. In many ways there is reciprocity between these two general approaches. For example, where a theorem occurs in Part I there will often be a corresponding theorem in Part II with the terms "action" and "displacement" interchanged. The terms "redundant force" and "degree of freedom" are similarly interchanged. In order to emphasize the reciprocal nature of these two approaches to the subject, a similarity of wording has been used in many places. When reading Part II, the reader should compare the development of the subject with the corresponding development in Part I. For example, Chapter 10 should be compared with Chapter 3.

The general method of treatment followed in Part I has its inspiration in a course of lectures given by Mr. J. C. deC. Henderson in 1953 at the Imperial College, London. Many modifications, including the addition of Part II, have been made by the senior author during postgraduate lectures over several years at the University of New South Wales. We acknowledge helpful suggestions by many members of the structures staff at this university. From our colleagues Professor H. R. Vallentine and Mr. F. E. Archer, as well as from Professor N. A. Mowbray, Professor of Civil Engineering at the University of Auckland, N. Z., we have received invaluable assistance in the form of painstaking criticism and advice. This we acknowledge most sincerely. We also express our appreciation to the University of New South Wales for the use of UTECOM, their DEUCE type computer, in the solution of some of the examples.

A. S. H.
R. W. W.

Sydney, February, 1961

Preface to the
Second Edition

The publication of the second edition has afforded an opportunity for extensive revision of the material. However, care has been taken to preserve the original method of approach, in which the reader is encouraged to appreciate the physical significance of the mathematical processes. Comments on the first edition have confirmed the authors' opinion that this method appeals to students and to engineers alike.

The chapters have been re-arranged to give what we hope is a more orderly progression of the subject. In many places the original text has been amplified by more detailed explanations in order to smooth out difficulties. The material has also been extended to cover more specifically the analysis, both by flexibility and by stiffness, of frames in terms of the properties of the individual components. These extensions and re-arrangements have also permitted the flexibility and stiffness methods to be presented so that their reciprocity is more clearly demonstrated than it was in the first edition.

The original text apparently gave the impression that the solution of simultaneous equations by matrix methods calls for matrix inversion. In fact, some form of systematic elimination is normally used. This is now mentioned in the text. Furthermore a brief description of the Gauss-Jordan technique has been included in the Appendix.

Probably many readers will consider that one of the most important changes is the inclusion of problems at the end of most chapters. The problems vary greatly in difficulty to suit readers at different levels of progress. Some problems have been used to develop points which have received only brief mention in the text.   A number of problems call for computer solution.

Advantage has been taken of the new edition to correct a number of mistakes which occurred in the first edition.   We should like to express our appreciation to those people in many parts of the world who have taken the time and trouble to bring these errors to our attention.

Finally, we acknowledge the assistance of students at Stanford University, the University of Illinois, Texas A. & M., and the University of New South Wales who, from time to time, have submitted solutions to the problems in this book.

A. S. H.
R. W. W.

Contents

Part II DISPLACEMENT STIFFNESS METHODS

Notation

ACTIONS

p actions applied to the end of a member (a release point is considered as a member end)

P Σp

p_0 values of p due to the particular solution only

P_0 Σp_0

N^x axial force

N^y shear force in the y direction

N^z shear force in the z direction

M^x twisting moment

M^y bending moment in the zx plane

M^z bending moment in the xy plane

      (the sign conventions of these actions are shown in Fig. 1.3)

N_0, M_0 internal actions due to applied loads (particular solution only)

n, m internal actions due to unit values of p

W externally applied loads

DISPLACEMENTS

u general symbol for displacement

u displacements of joints or member ends

u_0 values of u due to the particular solution only

$U = \Sigma u$

CO-ORDINATE DATA

$(x \ y \ z)$

or

$(X \ Y \ Z)$ cartesian co-ordinates of a point

λ, μ, ν direction cosines

$X = [X]$ a matrix containing X, Y, Z

$\lambda = [\lambda]$ a matrix containing λ, μ, ν

$R = [R]$ a transformation matrix for rotation of axes

$T = [T]$ a transformation matrix for translation of axes
$A = [A]$ a transformation
matrix for general change of axes

GENERAL SYMBOLS

$B = [B]$ transfer matrix for member ends
$b = [b]$ transfer matrix for unit forces
Q_x, Q_y first moment of area of a plane figure about x and y axes respectively
I_{xx}, I_{yy} second moment of area of a plane figure about x and y axes respectively
I_{xy} product of inertia of a plane figure about x and y axes
$A^x, A^y, A^z,$ geometrical properties
I^x, I^y, I^z of cross-section associated respectively with internal actions N^x, N^y, N^z, M^x, M^y, M^z
d scale factor
e strain
E Young's modulus
$EI = [EI]$ rigidity matrix
$F = [F]$ frame flexibility matrix
f flexibility
f_{CC}^D flexibility of end C of member CD
G shear modulus
$H = [H]$ a transformation matrix
I unit matrix
k stiffness
k_{CC}^D stiffness of end C of a member CD
K Σk
L length of a member
$m = [m]$ matrix relating internal actions to end actions
O null matrix
$\alpha, \beta, \gamma, \delta, \varepsilon$ names of individual primary frames

SUBSCRIPTS, ETC.

Where a double subscript is used the first denotes the location of the effect, while the second denotes the location of the cause, e.g.,

$$u_{rs} = \text{a displacement at } r \text{ caused by some event at } s$$

Usually a matrix is denoted by the same symbol as an element of the matrix, but only a subscript common to all elements is retained, e.g.,

$$u_0 = [u_0] = \{u_{10}\ u_{20}\ u_{30}\ \cdots\ u_{n0}\}$$

Thus for a row or column matrix, the matrix symbol usually will have one less subscript than an individual element, while for a rectangular (or square) matrix it will have two less.

The presence of $\sim$ above a symbol indicates a scaled value of the quantity referred to. $\tilde{p}$ is a scaled value of p.

The presence of $-$ above a symbol indicates a change of axes.

FRAME ANALYSIS

CHAPTER 1

Definitions

1.1 SCOPE

It is possible to classify a structure as one-dimensional, two-dimensional or three-dimensional according to the character of its components. To a first approximation a beam may be represented by its centroidal axis and analyzed as if it were a line structure. Because of this it can be regarded as a one-dimensional structure even though the line itself may be curved as in the case of an arch or helix.

On the other hand a flat plate or a curved shell is represented, for the purpose of analysis, by its middle surface. Whatever the shape of this surface, a small element of it will possess the characteristic of extension in two dimensions. Plates and shells are accordingly classified as two-dimensional structures. Although many bodies are three-dimensional in reality, few are analyzed as such.

A structure whose components are all one-dimensional is usually called a framed structure. This book deals only with structures of this type. It is to be understood that the frame as a whole may, and often does, extend in three dimensions, and in this respect the treatment in this book is intended to be quite general.

The methods of analysis presented here are based on the assumption that a linear relationship exists between the applied actions and the resulting displacements. This assumption requires, first, that the material of the frame shall behave in a Hookean manner at all points and throughout the range of loading considered. Second, it assumes that the changes in the geometry of the structure are small enough to be neglected when the internal actions are calculated.

The fundamental methods of flexibility and stiffness analysis will be treated from the point of view of a three-dimensional frame of a general nature.   In order to illustrate these methods examples of both simple and complex frames are used.   Special techniques, which apply only to particular types of frame, are of necessity treated only in relation to their field of application.

1.2 OBJECTIVE OF ANALYSIS

The objective in analyzing a structure is the determination of stresses and displacements of all points of the material.   In the analysis of frames this result is reached by certain well-defined stages.   In the first place the actions and displacements at the ends of each member are found.   The term "actions" is used to denote collectively forces and couples, while the term "displacements" includes both translations and rotations.·

When the end conditions of a member are known, the member can be analyzed in isolation from the remainder of the frame.   Provided the length of the member is fairly large compared with the dimensions of the cross section, such an analysis can be based on the engineers' beam theory. This theory will be assumed in this book.   In this stage of the analysis a single set of displacement components (six for a general member) and a single set of actions, often called stress resultants, are computed for each cross-section of the member.   Possible distortion of the cross-section and the distribution of stresses across the section are ignored at this stage.

Last, the stresses at the various points on a given cross-section are determined from the total internal actions on the section, which are now known.   The relative displacement of the various parts of the section can also be found.   This final phase of the calculation will not be dealt with in this book.   The analysis will be regarded as complete when the internal actions and displacements have been determined for each cross-section.

1.3 AXES

For the consideration of the frame as a whole, a single set of axes will be required, the choice of which usually presents no problem.   In dealing with an individual member, it is convenient to allow the axes to vary from point to point.   At a particular cross-section the direction of the centroidal axis will be taken as the x axis, while the two principal axes of the cross-section will constitute the y and z axes.   These will be called the axes of the member at that section.   Clearly, if the member is curved, the direction of at least two of the member-axes will vary along its length.

1.4 DISPLACEMENTS

Displacements will be represented by the symbol u.   When the six components of displacement at one point are being referred to, translations in the x, y and z directions will be denoted by u_1, u_2 and u_3 respectively, and positive displacements will be taken to mean displacements in the positive directions of the axes.

Rotations around the x, y and z axes will be denoted by u_4, u_5 and u_6 respectively, and positive directions for these quantities will be governed by the right-hand screw rule.   This rule signifies a clockwise rotation looking in the positive direction of the axis.   Alternatively, if the y axis is rotated through $90°$ to the z direction, the direction of its movement specifies positive rotation about the x axis.   Similar definitions hold for rotations around the y and z axes provided x, y, z are always used in cyclic order.

1.5 EXTERNAL ACTIONS

If by external actions we signify the actions external to a particular member of the frame, these comprise first the applied loading which is external to the frame as a whole, and second the forces and couples applied to the end faces of the member.   These latter, which will be called "end actions," are exerted upon the member in question by other parts of the frame.   It might be noted that a frame member has actions of this sort applied only to its ends, and in this respect it differs from what have been called two-dimensional and three-dimensional components (see Section 1.1).

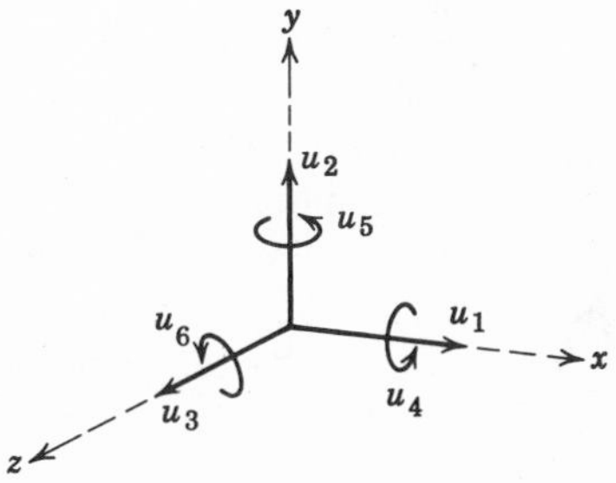

Fig. 1.1

End actions will be denoted by p (or P where they occur in summation). For the six component actions at one point, forces in the x, y and z directions will be denoted by p_1, p_2 and p_3 respectively.   Couples acting around the x, y and z axes will be denoted by p_4, p_5 and p_6 respectively. In each case the positive direction will be specified in the same way as for the corresponding displacement (see Fig. 1.1).

The external loads applied to the frame will be denoted by W and specified according to the same sign convention. That is to say, each load W will be resolved into components along and around the axes x, y, z at the point where the load is supposed to be applied. The signs of these components then follow directly from the directions of the member axes at this point.

1.6 INTERNAL ACTIONS

At any position along a member there will occur certain "internal actions," or stress resultants, which are induced by the forces acting externally upon the member. A distinction between these internal actions and the end actions is not always explicitly made, but it is convenient to make it at least for the purpose of sign convention.

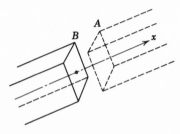

Fig. 1.2

At a given section there will be six component internal actions, namely, the axial force, two shears, a torsion moment and two bending moments. Each of these actions consists essentially of a pair of opposed actions which cause deformation of an elemental length of the member. The torsion moment is a pair of couples which twist the element about its axis. The bending moment in the xy plane is a pair of couples which cause the element to bend in the xy plane. The axial force is a pair of opposed forces which extend the element in a longitudinal direction.

The axial force will be denoted by N^x, and the two shears by N^y and N^z. The twisting moment will be called M^x, and the two bending moments M^y and M^z. The superscript indicates the axis along which the forces act, or around which the couples act.

Often we have occasion to apply to a structure unit values, or specimen values, of a force. In such instances, the resulting internal actions will be denoted by n^x, n^y, n^z, m^x, m^y and m^z. Thus if we apply the whole of some external load W to a frame, the axial force at any point will be denoted by N^x. However, if we apply a unit load at the same location as W it will cause an axial force denoted by n^x. Then $N^x = W \cdot n^x$.

If the member is cut at a particular cross-section (Fig. 1.2), the x axis will be directed outwards from one cut face (B), which will be called the *left-hand side* of the cut, and inwards upon the other (A), which will be the right-hand side. If the actions exerted on the left-hand face B are

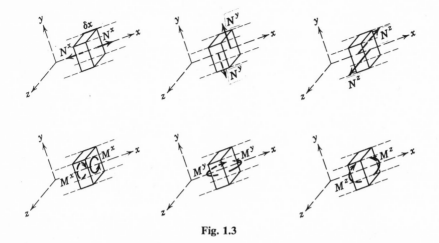

Fig. 1.3

in the positive directions as defined in Fig. 1.1, the internal actions at the given section will be regarded as positive.

Figure 1.3 shows an elemental length, dx, of the member subjected to each of the internal actions in turn, the positive sense being chosen in each case. The type of distortion which each of these actions will produce can be seen from the diagram. If the equilibrium of the element is examined it will be seen that the shear force and bending moment in the xy plane obey the relationship

$$N^y = -\frac{dM^z}{dx}$$

while for the shear force and bending moment in the xz plane

$$N^z = +\frac{dM^y}{dx}$$

If end actions are applied to the right-hand end of a member (that is, the end where x is algebraically greatest) they will induce, at an adjacent cross-section, internal actions each of which is equal to the corresponding end action. At the left-hand end of the member a similar condition prevails except that the internal actions are opposite in sign to the end actions. As shown in the curved beam of Fig. 1.4, the direction of the x axis defines the left-hand end, A, and the right-hand end, B. At A an end force p_1 is applied in the positive direction, and in the immediate vicinity the axial force N^x is $-p_1$ (compressive). At B an end force p_1 is applied, again in the positive direction, and in this case it produces an axial force

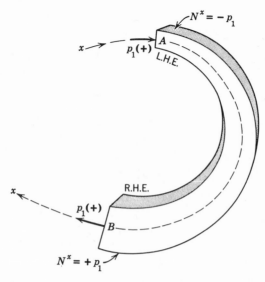

Fig. 1.4

N^x equal to $+p_1$ (tensile). Similar relationships would be observed if any of the other end actions $p_2 \ldots p_6$ were applied.

1.7 PRIMARY AND SECONDARY ACTIONS

In many frames some of the six internal actions or stress resultants contribute greatly to the distortion of the elements, while others contribute a negligible amount. The actions are accordingly classified as primary and secondary. For instance, in triangulated frames with slender members the major frame distortion stems from direct extension of the members. Axial force is therefore the primary action while bending and shear are secondary. Such frames are often analyzed approximately by assuming the joints to be pinned, which is equivalent to ignoring the smaller effects. Again, in frames which depend for their stability upon joint rigidity, bending (and sometimes torsion) is the major factor, while axial force contributes little to the deformation.

In the general methods of analysis all actions or displacements can be included with equal facility in the solution, though some may have a negligible effect upon the result. On the other hand, some of the special methods are only readily applicable in cases where one particular action is predominant. An attempt to extend such a method to deal with other conditions will often lead to undue complexity.

Where the distinction between primary and secondary effects is known from experience, the secondary actions are often ignored ab initio, thereby reducing the calculation. This is merely a matter of omitting certain terms from the general solution.

1.8 SECTION PROPERTIES

When the engineer's beam theory is used, and if the stresses are assumed to be within the proportional range, the expressions for the deformation of an elemental length dx of a member due to the various internal actions are all of the same form. Thus, due to bending, the deformation is $M\,dx/EI$, while the deformation due to axial force is $N^x\,dx/EA$. The product EI is a measure of the flexural rigidity of the element, while EA is a measure of its axial rigidity. Associated with each of the six internal actions we have a similar rigidity product of which the first term is a property of the material, either Young's modulus, E, or the shear modulus, G. The second term is a function of the shape and size of the cross-section. These section properties can be evaluated as integrals which are discussed in textbooks on strength of materials.

The integrals depend upon the manner in which the stresses are distributed over the section and, while some yield properties which occur in other fields of engineering, others are peculiar to this subject. For instance, the expression associated with the axial force is the *area* which is a commonly used property, but associated with the shears we have functions of a special character. The latter have the dimensions of length^2 and frequently have numerical values not very different from that of the area, for which reason they are often regarded as modified values of A. However, in the following work the functions will be recognized as separate entities, and the symbols A^x, A^y and A^z will denote the properties associated with the forces N^x, N^y and N^z respectively. The function A^x is the area of the cross-section.

In the same way we have, associated with the bending moments, integrals which can be recognized as the moments of inertia (more correctly termed "second moments of area") of the cross-section about the principal axes. But in connection with the twisting moment we have another special property often called the torsion constant. Any attempt to regard this as a modified polar moment of inertia would be misleading since, for structural shapes, the two are very different. Instead, the symbols I^x, I^y and I^z will be used to denote the properties associated with the internal actions M^x, M^y and M^z respectively. I^y and I^z are the second moments of area about the y and z axes while I^x is the torsion constant. All these quantities have the dimensions of length^4.

Table 1.1
Symbols for Actions, Displacements and Rigidities

Quantity	Along axes			Around axes		
	x	y	z	x	y	z
End actions	p_1	p_2	p_3	p_4	p_5	p_6
Displacements	u_1	u_2	u_3	u_4	u_5	u_6
Internal actions	N^x	N^y	N^z	M^x	M^y	M^z
Rigidities	EA^x	GA^y	GA^z	GI^x	EI^y	EI^z

The product of a section property with an elastic modulus will be called a rigidity. For convenience the symbols used for actions, displacements and rigidities are summarized in Table 1.1.

CHAPTER 2

Basic Concepts

2.1 COMPONENTS OF THE FRAME

For the purpose of analysis, a frame is regarded as being composed of members and joints, which often correspond to physical entities in the real frame. In a roof truss a "member" usually signifies a single bar of metal or timber, while the joint of analysis has its counterpart in a welded or bolted joint in the actual structure.

This correspondence, however, is not essential. In any case the real member has to be represented in the idealized structure by a single line, which follows the centroidal axis of the member concerned. A joint is a point at which it is convenient, for analytical purposes, to terminate a member. Consider an unsymmetrical arch whose shape is that of two circular arcs of different radii meeting tangentially at the crown. Physically, the arch could well be built as a single monolithic member, but analytically it might be more convenient to regard it as two members with a joint at the crown. If the arch is regarded so, the joints are chosen for mathematical convenience, and the members are defined by the location of the joints.

Consider also a welded portal frame consisting of two columns and a beam of the same section. Here the real structure is thought of as three members and four joints (including the feet of the column). Analytically this frame could be treated as a single member and regarded as an arch with two discontinuities in the axis.

A joint, sometimes referred to as a node point, is the junction point of two or more members. A member, which has a joint only at each end, is a frame component which joins two node points. Actions are exerted upon a joint by the adjacent members, and equal and opposite reactions are exerted on the members by the joint. Under reactions of this nature at its ends any given member will suffer deformation. The behavior of the frame components is based on three fundamental considerations, namely, equilibrium, compatibility and the relationship between the forces applied to a component and the distortion produced thereby.

2.2 EQUILIBRIUM

Each joint is in equilibrium under the actions exerted upon it by the members meeting there, together with any external loads which are applied directly to the joint. Typical actions are shown dashed in Fig. 2.1. In general there will be three forces and three couples exerted upon the joint by each member. The reactions, which are exerted by the joint on the member, are shown by full arrows in Fig. 2.1. These also constitute a system in equilibrium, or more generally a system with a resultant equal to any load applied at the joint. In the text the joint equilibrium will be expressed in terms of these reactive forces which have already been defined as end actions on the members.

The equilibrium of a joint provides a set of equations relating the actions on adjacent member ends, and in general there will be six independent equations for each joint.

Each member is also in equilibrium under the joint reactions applied at its ends together with any external loads applied directly to the member. In general there will be six independent equations for each member, and these equations provide relationships between the joint actions at the two

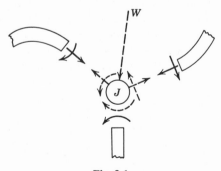

Fig. 2.1

ends of the member concerned. These equations are rarely stated explicitly but are implied in certain processes employed. Thus, in the solution of a pin-jointed frame we proceed with the analysis from joint to joint. The determination of the forces at joint A leads to a knowledge of one of the forces at B, supposing that A and B are connected by a member. This knowledge implies equilibrium of member AB, which is, however, frequently not stated.

Methods such as slope deflection or moment distribution require a knowledge of "carry-over" effects from one joint to another. These are member properties, and for their determination the member equilibrium equations are needed.

2.3 COMPATIBILITY

In order that the continuity of the frame shall be maintained in the manner dictated by its physical construction the displacements of the ends of the members must be related in some way. In other words, after distortion the members must "fit together." This condition, known as compatibility, is expressed by a series of compatibility equations.

If two members meet at a node point before and after the frame is loaded, the displacements of the two member ends must be equal in respect to each of the three components of translation, and hence three compatibility conditions are involved. If a third member is also connected to the joint, its end must undergo similar components of translation and three further conditions are implied. Thus for an n-member joint, compatibility in respect of translation is expressed by $3(n - 1)$ equations.

Furthermore, relative rotation may be prevented between any pair of member ends and in respect of any of the three components of rotation. If three members are joined by a pin whose axis lies in the x direction, relative rotation between the members is possible around the x axis but not around the y or z axis. If two of these members are now joined by a weld, one further compatibility condition is imposed. A fully rigid joint is one in which complete equality of rotation is demanded among all the members concerned. For an n-member joint this would be expressed by $3(n - 1)$ equations in addition to those required for compatibility of translation.

At certain joints, the frame must be supported in some manner, either by a foundation or by some other structure the analysis of which is regarded as outside the present problem. The manner of support at such joints as these will dictate the number of degrees of joint freedom and hence the compatibility conditions for the adjacent members.

2.4 ACTION-DISPLACEMENT RELATIONS

Under the actions applied to its ends a member undergoes deformation. For any member, relationships will exist between the end actions, p, and end displacements, u, and these will be functions of the shape, size and elastic properties of the member. A straight member sustaining axial forces at its ends will suffer extension or contraction, the extent of which will depend upon its length, area of cross-section and Young's modulus. Under the action of end torsional moments the relative end rotations will depend on the length, torsion constant and shear modulus. For a non-prismatic member the relations will be of the same kind but more complex.

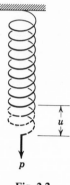

Fig. 2.2

Perhaps the simplest relationship of this kind is illustrated by a spring under a tensile end force. Figure 2.2 shows a spring which extends a distance u under a load p. The force required to produce unit extension is called the spring stiffness k. Thus $k = p/u$. Alternatively we can speak of the spring flexibility f as the displacement produced by unit force. In this case we have $f = u/p$.

Again we might consider the cantilever AB of Fig. 2.3. The end A may be regarded as supported in some manner by a structure whose characteristics are not important for the purpose of definition. The cantilever need not necessarily be straight or even lie in one plane.

If the end B is given a rotation of unity, other displacements at this end being prevented, a number of end actions at A and B will thereby be induced. These are known as *stiffness coefficients*. In general, a stiffness is an action induced by a unit displacement.

Alternatively, if a unit couple is applied at B, other actions being zero, a number of end displacements at A and B will result. These are called *flexibility coefficients*. In general a flexibility coefficient is a displacement produced by a unit action.

Fig. 2.3

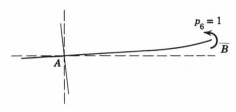

Fig. 2.4

Thus there are two ways of stating the relationship between p and u: by expressing p as a function of u, and by expressing u as a function of p.

In the structure shown in Fig. 2.2, where the force produces a single component of displacement, the flexibility is the reciprocal of the stiffness. In a somewhat more general situation the force might cause more than one displacement. Such a situation is illustrated in Fig. 2.4, where the couple produces both rotation and vertical displacement at B. Then the above relationships would define more than one flexibility coefficient and more than one stiffness coefficient. The relationship between stiffness and flexibility would then be more complex. This relationship will be discussed more fully in Chapter 13.

2.5 THE PROCESS OF SOLUTION

The considerations of the last three sections give rise to three distinct sets of equations: (1) equilibrium equations, (2) compatibility equations, and (3) action-displacement relations. The variables in these equations are the displacements of, and the actions upon, the ends of the members. The first set contains only the actions, and the second set only the displacements. The third set provides a relationship between the two.

The problem is similar to that of determining elastic stresses in a solid body, where the same three sets of equations serve as the basis. The only difference is that in a solid body the members consist of infinitesimal elements while in a frame they assume a finite size and are contiguous only at their ends.

If the equilibrium equations alone are sufficient to determine the end actions, the frame is said to be statically determinate. End displacements are then obtained from the third set of equations. The fact that the compatibility equations are not required in such a situation signifies that the members will fit together irrespective of their deformations.

If the equilibrium equations are insufficient to determine the end actions, the frame is said to be statically indeterminate. Then the compatibility equations are required, and furthermore the three sets of equations are interrelated.

Although it would be possible to separate the frame into its individual elements and to write, for each, all the necessary equations, such a procedure leads to an unnecessarily large number of operations. It is more customary to approach the solution in two stages. The frame is temporarily modified in such a way as to allow a simple solution under the given system of external loading. The modified frame is called the *primary frame*, and its solution (that is, the displacements and internal actions under the given loading) may be termed the *particular solution*. The restoration of the frame to its original form introduces a further set of displacements and internal actions which may be called the *complementary solution*. The modification may take one of two forms.

First, the continuity may be destroyed at a number of places sufficient to render the frame statically determinate. The particular solution can be obtained by the application of the laws of statics to the primary frame. In this method the complementary solution would be required to restore the continuity. The temporary destruction of continuity at a point is accompanied by the elimination of one or more of the internal actions at that point. For example, if a rigid joint at the end of a beam is replaced by a pinned joint, rotational continuity is no longer maintained and at the same time the bending moment at that point is eliminated. The actions so removed are called *redundant actions* or simply *redundants*. The complementary solution determines the magnitude of these redundants necessary to restore continuity.

Second, a sufficient number of joint displacements may be inhibited such that each member can be analyzed in isolation from its neighbors. The analysis of a single member under the given loads either assumes a standard form or else is carried out as a preliminary calculation. This calculation then constitutes the particular solution. The prevention of joint displacement violates joint equilibrium, which has to be restored by the complementary solution. The complementary solution determines the magnitude of the joint displacements necessary to restore equilibrium.

These two alternative approaches to the problem indicate a duality which exists between actions and displacements. In the first approach certain actions are temporarily removed; these actions are the unknowns in the simultaneous equations which lead to the complementary solution. Methods of solution using this principle are called *action methods* or *flexibility methods*. In the second approach certain displacements are prevented or "removed"; these displacements are now the unknowns in the simultaneous equations. Methods of solution using this principle are called *displacement methods* or *stiffness methods*.

Action methods are developed in Part I of this book; displacement methods are dealt with in Part II.   The treatment is designed to show the reciprocity which exists between the two approaches so that the essential unity of the whole subject is preserved.   In the earlier portions of Part I and Part II the same layout has been used, and they should be compared. To pursue this aspect too far would lead to unreality, since structures are usually to be analyzed for externally imposed *forces* and not externally imposed displacements, so that in this important aspect the interchange of terms is not adhered to.

In each method of solution, the final result is obtained as the sum of two partial solutions, called the *particular solution* and the *complementary solution*.   It should be emphasized that these methods will therefore be applicable only so long as the principle of superposition is valid.   In frames that, for one reason or another, behave in a non-linear manner, it may be necessary to write the equilibrium, compatibility and action-deformation equations out in full.

The two principles of solution can be illustrated by a simple example in which only one degree of redundancy and only one degree of joint freedom exist.

Example 2.1   The propped cantilever in Fig. 2.5 has a constant value of EI. Assume that only bending distortions are significant.   Solve for the bending moment and deflection at all points.   (In this simple problem the symbols I and M will be used instead of I^z and M^z.)

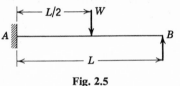

Fig. 2.5

Solution 1 (Action Method).   Let the right-hand reaction, regarded as the redundant, be removed.   The structure then becomes statically determinate (Fig. 2.6a).   The particular solution for this condition, shown in Fig. 2.6, is obtained by using the laws of *equilibrium*.   Owing to the external loading, the vertical deflection, u_0, of the end B is

$$u_0 = -\frac{5}{48}\frac{WL^3}{EI} \tag{2.1}$$

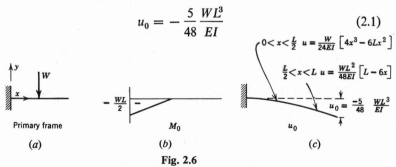

Primary frame

(a) M_0 (b) u_0 (c)

Fig. 2.6

PARTICULAR SOLUTION

The deflection of the cantilever at B caused by unit value of the reaction is then found. This is a coefficient of flexibility for the end B and is denoted by f.

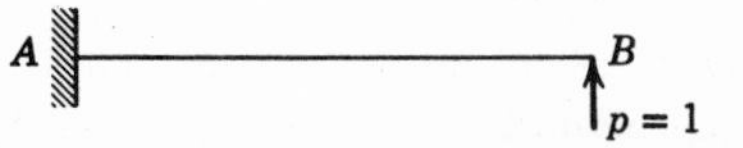

A
B
p = 1

$$f = \frac{1}{3}\frac{L^3}{EI} \tag{2.2}$$

The flexibility coefficients are properties of the structure and not of the loading. The only one required in this problem is given by equation 2.2. This coefficient can be used to express the action-displacement relation since, if the deflection due to the true value, p, of the redundant is u_n,

$$u_n = fp$$

For *compatibility* the total deflection of B must be zero, so that

$$u_0 + u_n = 0 \tag{2.3}$$

and substituting in this compatibility equation for u_n in terms of the action p by using the action-displacement relation, we have

$$u_0 + fp = 0 \tag{2.4}$$

Using the particular values of u_0 and f for this problem, we obtain

$$-\frac{5}{48}\frac{WL^3}{EI} + \frac{1}{3}\frac{L^3}{EI}p = 0$$

and

$$p = \tfrac{15}{48}W$$

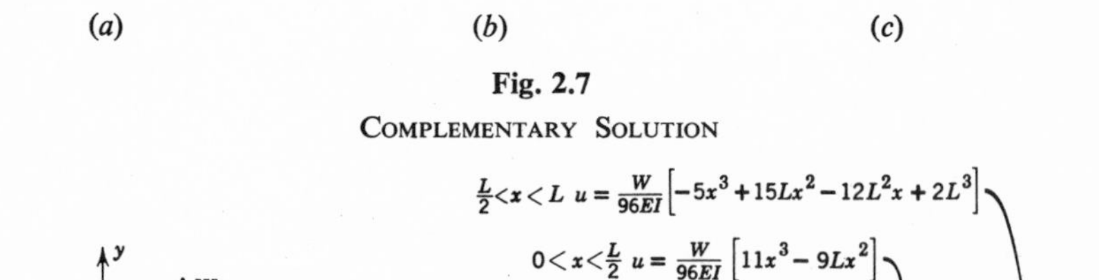

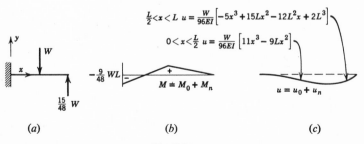

y
x
15/48 W
15/48 WL
+
M_n
0<x<L u = 5W/96EI [3Lx² − x³]
u_n = + 5/48 WL³/EI
+
u_n

(*a*) (*b*) (*c*)

Fig. 2.7

COMPLEMENTARY SOLUTION

L/2<x<L u = W/96EI [−5x³ + 15Lx² − 12L²x + 2L³]
0<x<L/2 u = W/96EI [11x³ − 9Lx²]
y
W
x
15/48 W
−9/48 WL
+
−
M = M_0 + M_n
u = u_0 + u_n

(*a*) (*b*) (*c*)

Fig. 2.8

COMPLETE SOLUTION

The bending moment and deflection due to the redundant p constitute the complementary solution and are given in Fig. 2.7.

The true solution, shown in Fig. 2.8, is then the sum of the particular solution and the complementary solution.

In this method of analysis, equilibrium is at all stages satisfied. The compatibility condition (equation 2.3), after being re-expressed in terms of the unknown action p, provides the complementary solution.

Solution 2 (Displacement Method). Let the rotation of the end B, the unrestrained end movement, be inhibited.

The member is now fixed-ended and yields the particular solution shown in Fig. 2.9.

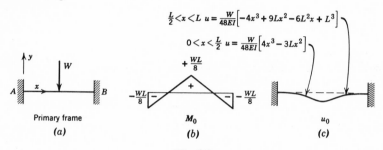

$$\tfrac{L}{2} < x < L \quad u = \frac{W}{48EI}\left[-4x^3 + 9Lx^2 - 6L^2x + L^3\right]$$

$$0 < x < \tfrac{L}{2} \quad u = \frac{W}{48EI}\left[4x^3 - 3Lx^2\right]$$

Primary frame
(a)

M_0
(b)

u_0
(c)

Fig. 2.9

PARTICULAR SOLUTION

The couple, p_0, which has to be applied by the support B to the end of the member in order to prevent B from rotating, is, for this loading

$$p_0 = -\frac{WL}{8} \tag{2.5}$$

In the real structure joint B is free to rotate so that under the above system it is not in equilibrium. This is sometimes expressed by saying that an "external restraint" must be temporarily introduced.

The couple which must be applied to the member in order to cause unit rotation is then found. This is a coefficient of stiffness of the end B and is denoted by k.

$$k = \frac{4EI}{L} \tag{2.6}$$

The stiffness coefficients are properties of the structure and not of the loading. The only one required in this problem is given by equation 2.6. This coefficient can be used to express the action-displacement relation since, if the couple induced on the member end by the true rotation, u, is p_n, then

$$p_n = ku$$

For *equilibrium* the sum of the couples exerted by joint B must be zero, so that

$$p_0 + p_n = 0 \qquad (2.7)$$

and substituting in this equilibrium equation for p_n in terms of the displacement u by using the action-displacement relation, we have

$$p_0 + ku = 0 \qquad (2.8)$$

Using the particular values of p_0 and k for this problem, we have

$$-\frac{WL}{8} + \frac{4EI}{L} u = 0$$

and

$$u = \frac{1}{32} \frac{WL^2}{EI}$$

The bending moment and deflection caused by the displacement u constitute the complementary solution and are given in Fig. 2.10.

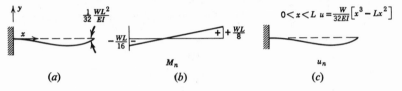

Fig. 2.10

COMPLEMENTARY SOLUTION

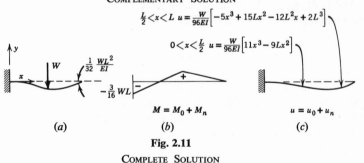

Fig. 2.11

COMPLETE SOLUTION

The true solution, shown in Fig. 2.11, is then the sum of the particular solution and the complementary solution.

In this method of analysis, compatibility is at all stages satisfied. The equilibrium condition (equation 2.7), after being re-expressed in terms of the unknown displacement u, provides the complementary solution.

The two solutions outlined here are the prototypes of the two categories of solution of all indeterminate structures. The equations to be solved, namely $u_0 + fp = 0$ in one case and $p_0 + ku = 0$ in the other case, are typical.   In more complex problems these single equations are replaced by sets of linear simultaneous equations, which still retain the same form as above, provided that the terms are interpreted as matrices.

The equilibrium equations and compatibility equations are so simple in their most basic form that they are frequently not explicitly stated. For instance, the compatibility equation 2.3, namely $u_0 + u_n = 0$, would usually be omitted and the form $u_0 + fp = 0$ stated directly.   For the purpose of understanding the principles fully it should be clearly recognized that this latter form has already involved the substitution of an action-displacement equation, and the consequent change from the original displacement unknown u_n to the new action variable p.

The action-displacement relations are expressed in terms of flexibility coefficients in one type of solution and stiffness coefficients in the other, and the evaluation of these coefficients often requires considerable computation.   The remainder of this book will be concerned largely with methods of obtaining these coefficients and with the solution of the resulting equations.

ACTION FLEXIBILITY METHODS

PART 1

ACTION FLEXIBILITY PROVIDER

CHAPTER 3

Principle of Flexibility Analysis

3.1 RELEASES

The method of influence coefficients is the most general of the action methods. It is not really distinct from other techniques which employ this action approach, but differs from them only in being more general so that they can be derived from the influence coefficient method. In principle it follows the first solution of Example 2.1, but it is now necessary to extend the exposition to include frames with multiple redundancies.

The frame is rendered statically determinate by temporarily releasing a sufficient number of actions. The suppression of each internal action at a given cross-section of the frame corresponds to one release. In order to assist the conception of a release it is often supposed that mechanical articulations have been introduced. Thus the introduction of a hinge signifies the suppression of one bending moment. A roller support corresponds to the elimination of one force component. The introduction of a ball and socket joint in a beam would indicate the suppression of two bending moments and the torque and would thus correspond to three releases. If the frame has n degrees of redundancy, n releases will be required to render it statically determinate.

It is important to realize that more than one release can be effected at a given cross-section. The term "release" signifies not only the place at which the modification is made but also which of the actions is suppressed. The number assigned to a release signifies not only the position of the release within the frame, but also the direction in which the displacement is permitted to take place.   Thus, at a cross-section C the removal of the axial force might be called release 1, while the removal of the shear force at the same section might constitute release 2.   A unit action at release 1 would then imply a unit axial force at C, and a unit action at release 2 would mean a unit shear force at C.   In a three-dimensional frame, complete separation at a cross-section will require six releases.

3.2   PARTICULAR SOLUTION

When the given external loads are applied to the primary frame, which is statically determinate, the internal actions at all points can be obtained by using the laws of equilibrium, and the displacements can then be determined provided the section rigidities are known.   These values constitute the particular solution.

At each release a discontinuity will in general occur.   Where a hinge has been introduced, the application of the external loads to the frame will result in an angular discontinuity.   That is to say, the cross-section to one side of the hinge will undergo a displacement relative to that on the other side.   If a shear force N^y has been released, the two sides of the release will become relatively displaced in the y direction.

We say that the particular solution results in a relative displacement, or discontinuity at each release.   The displacement at release 1 will be denoted by u_{10}, that at release 2 by u_{20} and so on.   The first subscript describes the release: the second signifies that the displacements are caused by the applied loads.

3.3   COMPLEMENTARY SOLUTION

The actions which have been temporarily suppressed at the various releases are called "redundant actions" or simply "redundants."   Their true values, which at this stage of the analysis are unknown, will be denoted by $p_1, p_2, p_3 \ldots p_n$.   Considering the frame still in its modified, or statically determinate, condition, we can suppose that an action equal to p_1 is applied at release position 1.   This would cause displacements throughout the frame, and in particular it would induce displacements, or, strictly speaking, relative displacements, at the releases.   These displacements will be called $u_{11}, u_{21}, u_{31} \ldots u_{n1}$, where the first subscript indicates the position and direction at which the displacement occurs, and the second signifies that the displacements are caused by p_1.

In a similar way, the application of redundant p_2 at release 2 will result in displacements $u_{12}, u_{22}, u_{32} \ldots u_{n2}$ at the release points. In the general case, u_{rs} will denote "the displacement at release r caused by the redundant p_s acting at release s."

The actions and displacements throughout the frame due to all the redundants acting together constitute the complementary solution.

3.4 COMPATIBILITY EQUATIONS

When the external loads and the redundants are applied together, the total displacement at release 1 is

$$u_1 = u_{10} + u_{11} + u_{12} \cdots + u_{1n}$$

where the first term, u_{10}, is caused by the loading (particular solution) and the others are caused by the respective redundants. Similarly, the total displacement at 2 is

$$u_2 = u_{20} + u_{21} + u_{22} \cdots + u_{2n}$$

and so on for the other release points.

For compatibility the discontinuities $u_1, u_2 \ldots u_n$ must all be zero in the final solution. This condition is expressed by the compatibility equations

$$
\begin{aligned}
u_{10} + u_{11} + u_{12} \quad &\cdots + u_{1n} = 0 \\
u_{20} + u_{21} + u_{22} \quad &\cdots + u_{2n} = 0 \\
&\cdot \\
&\cdot \\
&\cdot \\
u_{n0} + u_{n1} + u_{n2} \quad &\cdots + u_{nn} = 0
\end{aligned}
\tag{3.1}
$$

3.5 FLEXIBILITY COEFFICIENTS

The displacements, other than those caused by the external loads, are re-expressed in terms of the unknown redundants, using action-displacement relations in the form of flexibility coefficients. A typical flexibility coefficient f_{rs} is defined by

$$f_{rs} = \text{the displacement at } r \text{ induced by the application}$$
$$\text{of unit action at release } s$$

At each release in turn unit value of the relevant redundant is applied. The unit value of p_1 causes displacements $f_{11}, f_{21}, f_{31} \ldots f_{n1}$ at the release points.

The displacements due to the true values of the redundants are expressed in terms of these coefficients. For instance, the displacement at r caused by applying an action p_s at s is

$$u_{rs} = f_{rs}p_s \tag{3.2}$$

Substituting expressions of this type into the compatibility equations 3.1 we obtain

$$u_{10} + f_{11}p_1 + f_{12}p_2 \quad \cdots \quad + f_{1n}p_n = 0$$
$$u_{20} + f_{21}p_1 + f_{22}p_2 \quad \cdots \quad + f_{2n}p_n = 0$$
$$\begin{array}{c} \cdot \\ \cdot \\ \cdot \end{array} \tag{3.3}$$
$$u_{n0} + f_{n1}p_1 + f_{n2}p_2 \quad \cdots \quad + f_{nn}p_n = 0$$

3.6 DISPLACEMENT AT ANY POINT

The procedure used for finding the displacements at the releases can be used equally well for calculating the displacement of any point of the frame. At any location the total displacement is the sum of the partial displacements caused successively by the applied loads and by the n redundants. The compatibility equations 3.3 can be regarded as part of a set which extends indefinitely,

$$u_{10} + f_{11}p_1 \quad \cdots \quad + f_{1n}p_n = 0$$
$$u_{20} + f_{21}p_1 \quad \cdots \quad + f_{2n}p_n = 0$$
$$\begin{array}{c} \cdot \\ \cdot \\ \cdot \end{array} \tag{3.4}$$
$$u_{n0} + f_{n1}p_1 \quad \cdots \quad + f_{nn}p_n = 0$$
$$u_{A0} + f_{A1}p_1 \quad \cdots \quad + f_{An}p_n = u_A$$
$$u_{B0} + f_{B1}p_1 \quad \cdots \quad + f_{Bn}p_n = u_B$$

and so on. Here u_A and u_B are the displacements, in specified directions, of any points A and B on the frame. The coefficient f_{A1} is the displacement at A caused by unit p_1. Provided the necessary flexibility coefficients are computed, the displacement of any point can be found in this way.

Of all the displacements evaluated in this way, those corresponding to releases are required to be zero for compatibility, and these yield n equations from which the unknown redundants $p_1 \ldots p_n$ are determined. These values can be used in the remaining equations for the calculation of displacements at other locations.

3.7 EXPRESSION IN MATRIX FORM

If the sets of equations are written in matrix form the relationship of the general case to the simple case of Example 2.1 is more readily seen.

Let $[u_0]$ represent the displacements under the particular solution and $[u_n]$ the displacements under the complementary solution. Then

$$[u_0] = \begin{bmatrix} u_{10} \\ u_{20} \\ \cdot \\ \cdot \\ \cdot \\ u_{n0} \end{bmatrix} \quad \text{and} \quad [u_n] = \begin{bmatrix} (u_{11} + u_{12} & \cdots & + u_{1n}) \\ (u_{21} + u_{22} & \cdots & + u_{2n}) \\ \cdot \\ \cdot \\ \cdot \\ (u_{n1} + u_{n2} & \cdots & + u_{nn}) \end{bmatrix}$$

By using the rule for matrix addition (Appendix, p. 278), the compatibility equations 3.1 can be written as

$$[u_0] + [u_n] = 0 \qquad (3.5)$$

(cf. equation 2.3).

If $[p]$ is the column matrix of the redundants and $[f]$ is the flexibility matrix,

$$[p] = \begin{bmatrix} p_1 \\ p_2 \\ \cdot \\ \cdot \\ \cdot \\ p_n \end{bmatrix} \quad \text{and} \quad [f] = \begin{bmatrix} f_{11} & f_{12} & \cdots & f_{1n} \\ f_{21} & & & \\ \cdot & & & \\ \cdot & & & \\ \cdot & & & \\ f_{n1} & f_{n2} & \cdots & f_{nn} \end{bmatrix}$$

By using the rule for matrix multiplication (Appendix, p. 280),

$$[f][p] = \begin{bmatrix} f_{11} & f_{12} & \cdots & f_{1n} \\ f_{21} & & & \\ \cdot & & & \\ \cdot & & & \\ \cdot & & & \\ f_{n1} & f_{n2} & \cdots & f_{nn} \end{bmatrix} \begin{bmatrix} p_1 \\ p_2 \\ \cdot \\ \cdot \\ \cdot \\ p_n \end{bmatrix} = \begin{bmatrix} (f_{11}p_1 + f_{12}p_2 & \cdots & + f_{1n}p_n) \\ (f_{21}p_1 + f_{22}p_2 & \cdots & + f_{2n}p_n) \\ \cdot \\ \cdot \\ \cdot \\ (f_{n1}p_1 + f_{n2}p_2 & \cdots & + f_{nn}p_n) \end{bmatrix}$$

and the action-displacement relations can therefore be written as

$$[u_n] = [f][p] \tag{3.6}$$

Substituting for $[u_n]$ in equation 3.5 gives

$$[u_0] + [f][p] = 0 \tag{3.7}$$

This is the matrix expression of equations 3.3, and at the same time it is identical in form with equation 2.4, except that the symbols now represent matrices instead of single quantities. This emphasizes the fact that the set of equations 3.3 and the single equation 2.4 have the same significance.

In order to put this method of analysis into effect it is necessary to compute the flexibility coefficients, which are the elements of f, and then to solve the set of equations 3.3 or the matrix equivalent 3.7.

CHAPTER 4

Flexibility Analysis of Simple Frames

4.1 DISPLACEMENT AT ANY POINT

The determination of the displacement at any point of a frame due to a given system of loading is a problem of fundamental importance in the analysis of the frame.

Two symbols will be used to denote such a displacement. The symbol u_{rs} will be used to signify the displacement in the position and direction denoted by r, caused by a load or force (W, say) at a position and direction denoted by s. On the other hand, if we apply a *unit value* of the load at s, the displacement caused at r will be denoted by f_{rs}, which is a flexibility coefficient. Then $u_{rs} = f_{rs} \cdot W$.

In the first instance we shall consider the displacements of statically determinate frames. It is convenient to think of the consequences of loading as taking place in three stages:

(1) The applied loads give rise to internal actions throughout the frame.

(2) Each small element undergoes deformation as a result of the actions arising from step (1).

(3) Deformation of each element causes alteration in the geometry of the whole structure and thus contributes to the displacement at any given point.

We can calculate the effects in that order.

29

With regard to step 1 we note that the calculation of the internal actions makes use of the equations of statics. The first step thus employs the principle of *equilibrium*. The process will be taken for granted. The six actions will be denoted by N^x, N^y, N^z, M^x, M^y and M^z. In the event that we are calculating flexibility coefficients, the loading will consist of unit forces and the internal actions will then be denoted by n^x, $n^y \ldots m^z$. Otherwise, the procedure is precisely the same.

In step 2, the deformation of any particular element, of length dx, is determined from the actions found in the previous step. This calculation embodies the *action-deformation* relationship. In this book the deformations will be computed according to the engineers' beam theory, and linear elastic behavior will be assumed. This results in the following expressions:

deformation of the
    element due to

$$N^x = du_1 = \left(\frac{dx}{EA^x}\right)N^x$$

,,

$$N^y = du_2 = \left(\frac{dx}{GA^y}\right)N^y$$

,,

$$N^z = du_3 = \left(\frac{dx}{GA^z}\right)N^z$$

,,

$$M^x = du_4 = \left(\frac{dx}{GI^x}\right)M^x$$

,,

$$M^y = du_5 = \left(\frac{dx}{EI^y}\right)M^y$$

,,

$$M^z = du_6 = \left(\frac{dx}{EI^z}\right)M^z$$

The computation of the change of shape of the frame in step 3 from the elemental deformations is essentially a problem in geometry. It is based on the principle of *compatibility* of deformations. In simple structures, finding the displacement of point A due to the deformation of an element at B (Fig. 4.1) presents no difficulty. In less simple problems the use of geometry alone often leads to a tedious solution. It is convenient then

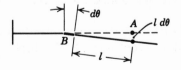

Fig. 4.1

to make use of the fact that the principles of the geometry of displacements are related to the principles of the equilibrium of forces. In view of this relationship it is frequently advantageous to replace a geometrical problem by the analogous statics problem. Sometimes the reverse process is required.

The relationship referred to is based on the theorem of virtual work:

If a rigid body, acted upon by a system of forces in equilibrium, undergoes a displacement during which the equilibrium is not disturbed, the total work done by the forces is zero.

This follows from the fact that the sum of the work done by the forces is equal to the work done by the resultant, which is zero.

Suppose it is required to find the displacement (u_A) in a given direction at a point A in a frame (Fig. 4.2a) caused by the bending deformation of an isolated element at another point B in the frame.

In reality the frame is unloaded and the objective is to find the geometrical relationship between the bending of the element at B and the displacement of the point A. This implies that all other elements of the frame remain perfectly rigid and undergo rigid-body displacements only.

Before we actually bend the element at B let us introduce a force p_A at A acting in the direction of the dashed line (Fig. 4.2a). This may be regarded as an imaginary force, or *virtual force*, introduced only so that work will be done when the frame is deformed. This virtual force gives rise to a bending moment p_B at B and other internal actions which can all be calculated by statics.

The frame comprises a flexible body (the element at B) and two rigid bodies CB_1 and B_2DA. All these bodies are in equilibrium, so if we now bend the element at B (Fig. 4.2b) the total work done by all the forces

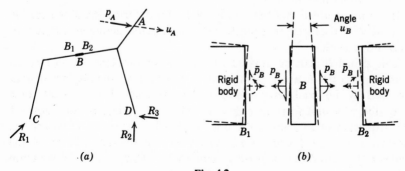

(a)   (b)

Fig. 4.2

acting on the *rigid* bodies will be zero. Since the supports do not yield, and therefore the reactions if any do no work, we can say

(Work done by p_A) + (Work done by forces on faces B_1 and B_2) = 0

Now the forces acting on the flexible element at B (Fig. 4.2*b*) are equal and opposite to those on faces B_1 and B_2. Hence we might equally well say

(Work done by p_A) = (Work done by forces acting on element B)

But the type of deformation we have imposed on the element B is such that the only stress resultant which does any work is the bending moment p_B, and it does work equal to $p_B u_B$.

Hence we have

$$p_A u_A = p_B u_B \tag{4.1}$$

The bending moment p_B is related to the force p_A by statics. Suppose that

$$p_B = h_{BA} p_A \tag{4.2a}$$

Then from equation 4.1

$$u_A = h_{BA} u_B \tag{4.2b}$$

Since the displacements in equation 4.2*b* occur in the reverse order to the forces in equation 4.2*a*, the forces and displacements are said to transform *contragrediently*.

If we require to find the displacement at A due to an *axial deformation* of the element B, we should let p_B denote the *axial force* at B. Under the given deformation, the axial forces would be the only ones to do work, and equation 4.1 would still apply. Equations similar to equations 4.2*a* and 4.2*b* would follow, the only difference being that the constant h_{BA} would have a different value.

It should be noted that the positive sense for deformation of the flexible element B is taken such that positive stress resultants acting *on the element* do positive work.

This principle can be applied to the present problem. Consider an element of length dx at a typical point Q, and consider the displacement at r caused by the axial deformation of this element. Let the axial force at Q due to a unit force at r be denoted by n_r^x. Then by equation 4.1 the displacement at r due to a unit axial deformation at Q is also n_r^x. However, by steps 1 and 2 we have found that the deformation of the element Q due to the actual load system is $(dx/EA^x)N^x$. This deformation will therefore cause a displacement $n_r^x(dx/EA^x)N^x$ at r.

The three steps referred to on page 29 may be summarized as follows

Step 1:   Axial force on typical element $= N^x$

Step 2:   Axial deformation of typical element $= \left(\dfrac{dx}{EA^x}\right)N^x$

Step 3:   Displacement at r due to axial deformation

       of typical element $= n_r^x\left(\dfrac{dx}{EA^x}\right)N^x$

Thus the product is developed from right to left as the steps proceed. It will be seen later that this has significance in regard to matrix formulation.

The element at Q suffers five other modes of deformation, the effects of which can be found in a similar manner. Since the various forms of deformation are assumed to be independent, the displacement at r caused by the six deformations of the element Q is

$$u_r = n_r^x\left(\frac{dx}{EA^x}\right)N^x + n_r^y\left(\frac{dx}{GA^y}\right)N^y + n_r^z\left(\frac{dx}{GA^z}\right)N^z$$

$$+ m_r^x\left(\frac{dx}{GI^x}\right)M^x + m_r^y\left(\frac{dx}{EI^y}\right)M^y + m_r^z\left(\frac{dx}{EI^z}\right)M^z$$

Since the deformation of each element of the frame contributes likewise to the displacement at r, the total displacement at r can be found by summing the foregoing expressions for all elements. This gives the expression

$$u_r = \int_F \frac{n_r^x N^x}{EA^x}\,dx + \int_F \frac{n_r^y N^y}{GA^y}\,dx + \int_F \frac{n_r^z N^z}{GA^z}\,dx$$

$$+ \int_F \frac{m_r^x M^x}{GI^x}\,dx + \int_F \frac{m_r^y M^y}{EI^y}\,dx + \int_F \frac{m_r^z M^z}{EI^z}\,dx \quad (4.3)$$

where $\displaystyle\int_F$ signifies integration round the whole frame.

It should be noted that equation 4.3 always yields the value of a *relative* displacement. If r represents the position and direction of a unit load reacted by a fixed foundation, then equation 4.3 determines the displacement at r, due to some given load system, *relative* to the foundation.

On the other hand, if r is a release, unit value of the force at r will signify a unit value of a pair of opposed actions (sometimes called a self-equilibrating system). In such a case u_r represents the displacement of one cross-section relative to the adjacent one, namely the discontinuity at the release caused by the applied load.

4.2 DISPLACEMENT OF THE PRIMARY FRAME
DUE TO APPLIED LOADS

We now apply the above procedure to the problem of finding the displacements of the primary frame under the action of externally applied loads. At present we shall consider that the external loads are applied in full to the frame (as distinct from being applied in the form of unit loads later to be multiplied by the numerical values of the actual loads). Consequently the internal actions caused by these loads are denoted by N_0^x, N_0^y, N_0^z, M_0^x, M_0^y and M_0^z. These values together with the resulting displacements of the primary frame constitute the particular solution.

With these terms inserted, equation 4.3 yields the value of u_{r0}, which is the displacement at any point r due to the *applied loads*.

$$u_{r0} = \int\limits_F \frac{n_r^x N_0^x}{EA^x}\, dx + \int\limits_F \frac{n_r^y N_0^y}{GA^y}\, dx \cdots + \int\limits_F \frac{m_r^z M_0^z}{EI^z}\, dx \qquad (4.4)$$

The equation 4.4 can be used to find the relative displacement, or discontinuity, at any release r provided the terms n_r^x, n_r^y ... m_r^z result from the application of unit redundant p_r. If n_r^x, n_r^y ... represent actions caused by the application of unit external action at a point r other than a release, the equation gives the corresponding displacement at that point.

4.3 FLEXIBILITY COEFFICIENTS

Any coefficient that represents the displacement at r due to a *unit* force at s is called a flexibility coefficient and is denoted by f_{rs}. When both r and s are release locations, f_{rs} is a release flexibility coefficient. For a frame which is n times redundant, the matrix of n^2 release flexibility coefficients is called the flexibility matrix, f, of the chosen primary frame. However, we can also determine as many other flexibility coefficients as we please.

The internal actions produced by unit p_s, this being the only action acting on the frame, have been defined as n_s^x, n_s^y, ... m_s^z. Hence, using these terms in equation 4.3 in place of N^x, N^y, etc., we get

$$f_{rs} = \int\limits_F \frac{n_r^x n_s^x}{EA^x}\, dx + \int\limits_F \frac{n_r^y n_s^y}{GA^y}\, dx \cdots + \int\limits_F \frac{m_r^z m_s^z}{EI^z}\, dx \qquad (4.5)$$

Although equations 4.4 and 4.5 each contain six integrals, some of these integrals often have a relatively small value in practical frames, in which case they can be neglected.   In a pin-jointed frame, with external loads all acting at the joints, the only internal action is axial force and all integrals except the first are zero.

Where several of the integrals are significant, and where in addition the functions themselves are complicated, a considerable amount of computation is entailed and the problem may be impracticable without the use of a computer.   This aspect will be mentioned again in Chapter 6. In the present chapter, simple illustrative examples will be used in which the members are straight and of constant section.   In such cases the section properties, EA^x, GA^y and so on, are constant, and the integrals of equation 4.5 can be modified accordingly.   The first integral can be written as $\dfrac{1}{EA^x} \int n_r^x n_s^x \, dx$, and each remaining term can be put into a similar form.   The integrand terms n_r^x, n_s^x, n_r^y, $n_s^y \ldots m_r^z, m_s^z$, arising as they do from the application of a single force and its reaction, will either be constant along the length of a straight member or, in the case of the bending-moment terms, they may vary linearly.   This permits each integral, for a given member, to be regarded as being the volume of a solid having the same length as the member and having a rectangular cross-section at any point.   The area of this cross-section is to represent the product under the integral sign.   The volume of the solid of Fig. 4.3a will be $\int_0^L n_r^x n_s^x \, dx$.   Figure 4-3b illustrates a solid whose volume is $\int_0^L m_r^y m_s^y \, dx$ where m_r^y varies but m_s^y is constant.   Table 4.1 gives the volumes of all solids of this type.

For frames with prismatic members, the integrals of equation 4.4 can be similarly evaluated except that the functions N_0^x, $N_0^y \ldots M_0^z$, which depend upon the loading, are not necessarily linear.

When evaluating the integrals, attention must be paid to the sign of the

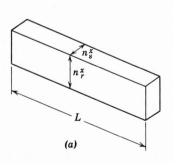

(a)

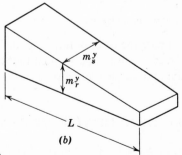

(b)

Fig. 4.3

functions n_r (or m_r) and n_s (or m_s). In the following examples the work is set out in tabular form. Each load condition occupies one column, and the different internal actions n^x, $n^y \ldots m^z$ occupy successive rows. This indicates the affinity of the different cases and also foreshadows the matrix expression of these quantities.

Table 4.1

Volume Integrals

n_s or m_s → / n_r or m_r ↓	a ▭ L	a ◹ L	a ▱ b L
c ▭ L	Lac	$\dfrac{Lac}{2}$	$\dfrac{Lc(a+b)}{2}$
c ◺ L	$\dfrac{Lac}{2}$	$\dfrac{Lac}{3}$	$\dfrac{Lc(2a+b)}{6}$
◿ c L	$\dfrac{Lac}{2}$	$\dfrac{Lac}{6}$	$\dfrac{Lc(a+2b)}{6}$
c ▱ d L	$\dfrac{La(c+d)}{2}$	$\dfrac{La(2c+d)}{6}$	$\dfrac{La(2c+d)+Lb(c+2d)}{6}$
Parabolic c d e L d = central ordinate	$\dfrac{La(c+4d+e)}{6}$	$\dfrac{La(c+2d)}{6}$	$\dfrac{La(c+2d)+Lb(2d+e)}{6}$

From the form of the integrals in equation 4.5 it is evident that $f_{rs} = f_{sr}$, a fact which is also attested by Maxwell's reciprocal law. It follows that the matrix f is symmetrical.

4.4 ILLUSTRATIVE EXAMPLES

Example 4.1 The gabled portal of Fig. 4.4 is completely built in both at A and at E. For loadings in the plane of the frame each support is

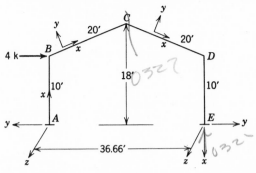

Fig. 4.4

capable of developing three components of reaction, two forces and a couple.

It is assumed that EI is constant throughout, and that all effects other than bending produce negligible distortions of the frame. It is required to find the internal actions at all sections of the frame and the horizontal displacement of the point D.

Solution. Since the frame (for loads in its own plane) is threefold statically indeterminate, three releases are made. This will be done by completely severing member DE adjacent to the support E, thus releasing all three component actions at that point, and leaving the frame cantilevered from A. The vertical force at E will be considered as redundant p_1, the horizontal force as p_2 and the couple as p_6. These redundants are not in fact the most convenient ones from the arithmetical point of view, but they provide a simple illustration of the principles. The question of choice of redundants is discussed in Chapter 9.

The particular solution will comprise the bending moments and deflections in the cantilever $ABCDE$ under the action of the 4-kip load at B.

Since we have to find the horizontal deflection at D, we require flexibility coefficients relating the releases to the horizontal displacements at D. For this purpose we introduce a *unit* force $w_D = 1$ at D. The five load conditions, namely, 4 kips, $p_1 = 1$, $p_2 = 1$, $p_6 = 1$ and $w_D = 1$, produce the bending-moment diagrams M_0^z, m_1^z, m_2^z, m_6^z and m_D^z of Table 4.2 (in which the units are *kip-feet*). Since a redundant consists of a *pair* of actions applied mutually between two adjacent cross-sections, the pairs are shown for completeness in Table 4.2, although here the force acting on the abutment produces no effect.

Combination of the M_0^z diagram with each of the others in turn produces the displacements at the releases and at D, namely, u_{10}, u_{20}, u_{60} and u_{D0}. The various combinations of m_1, m_2, m_6 and m_D diagrams among themselves yield the flexibility coefficients f. The value of f_{DD} is not required since there is no actual load at D.

Table 4.2

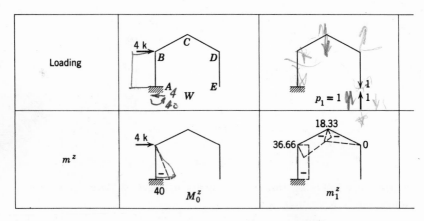

Table 4.3

Integral	Member	u_{10}	u_{20}	u_{60}	u_{D0}	f_{11}
$\dfrac{1}{EI^z}\displaystyle\int m_r^z m_s^z\,dx$	AB	+7332	−667	−200	+1333	+13439.5
	BC	0	0	0	0	+15679.5
	CD	0	0	0	0	+2240.0
	DE	0	0	0	0	0
Sum		+7332	−667	−200	+1333	+31359

The volume method based on Table 4.1 is used, the members being considered separately. Since EI is constant for all members, it is given the arbitrary value of unity.

In Table 4.3 only the final value of the integral for each member is given. The first entry concerns the member AB and the bending-moment diagrams m_1^z and M_0^z. The first of these diagrams is a rectangle (see Table 4.2) and the second is a triangle, and they comprise the two elevations of the solid concerned. By reference to Table 4.1 we note that the value of the integral is therefore $Lac/2$, where $L = 10$, $a = 36.66$ and $c = 40$. Since both diagrams are negative we obtain the figure +7332. The remaining figures in Table 4.3 are determined in a similar manner.

A negative sign in the foregoing terms signifies that the relative displacement is in a direction opposed to that specified by the arrow in the first row of Table 4.2.

Table 4.2 (continued)

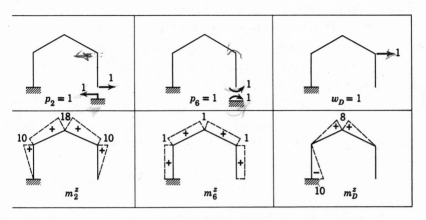

Table 4.3 (continued)

$f_{12} = f_{21}$	$f_{16} = f_{61}$	f_{D1}	f_{22}	$f_{26} = f_{62}$	f_{D2}	f_{66}	f_{D6}
−1833.0	−366.6	+1833.0	+333.3	+50	−166.7	+10	−50
−7454.2	−549.9	−1955.2	+4026.7	+280	+1226.7	+20	+80
−2810.6	−183.3	−977.6	+4026.7	+280	+1226.7	+20	+80
0	0	0	+333.3	+50	0	+10	0
−12098	−1100	−1100	+8720	+660	+2287	+60	+110

Each of the values above should be multiplied by $1/EI$.

The compatibility equations are

$$+7332 + 31359p_1 - 12098p_2 - 1100p_6 = 0$$
$$-667 - 12098p_1 + 8720p_2 + 660p_6 = 0 \qquad (4.6)$$
$$-200 - 1100p_1 + 660p_2 + 60p_6 = 0$$

The constant multiplier $1/EI$ has been omitted in these equations.
These equations give

$$p_1 = -0.327 \qquad p_2 = -1.050 \qquad p_6 = +8.878$$

The complementary solution comprises the actions and displacements arising from the application of these three redundants to the primary frame. For the sake of brevity, internal actions other than M^z will not be determined. The bending moments due to $p_1 = -0.327$ will be -0.327 times those designated m_1^z in Table 4.2. The deflection at D will be -0.327 times the flexibility coefficient f_{D1}. Proceeding similarly with the other two redundants, we find that the bending moments and deflection at D arising from the complementary solution are

$$M^z_{\text{c.s.}} = m^z_1 p_1 + m^z_2 p_2 + m^z_6 p_6$$

$$u_{D_{\text{c.s.}}} = f_{D1} p_1 + f_{D2} p_2 + f_{D6} p_6$$

and the total bending moments and deflection are

$$M^z = M^z_0 + m^z_1 p_1 + m^z_2 p_2 + m^z_6 p_6 \tag{4.7}$$

$$u_D = u_{D0} + f_{D1} p_1 + f_{D2} p_2 + f_{D6} p_6 \tag{4.8}$$

The bending moments are plotted in Fig. 4.5. The horizontal displacement of D is

$$u_D = \frac{1}{EI}\,[1333 - 1100(-0.327) + 2287(-1.050) + 110(8.878)]$$

$$= \frac{267.9}{EI}\,\text{ft} \qquad (EI \text{ in kip, foot units})$$

The compatibility equations could be written in the matrix form

$$\begin{bmatrix} +7332 \\ -667 \\ -200 \end{bmatrix} + \begin{bmatrix} +31359 & -12098 & -1100 \\ -12098 & +8720 & +660 \\ -1100 & +660 & +60 \end{bmatrix} \begin{bmatrix} p_1 \\ p_2 \\ p_6 \end{bmatrix} = 0 \tag{4.9}$$

$$u_0 \qquad + \qquad\qquad\quad fp = 0$$

The equations could be solved by inversion of the matrix f. Usually it is more efficient to obtain the solution by a reduction process such as Gauss-Jordan elimination (Appendix, p. 296). This method is equally effective when a number of loading conditions is to be investigated. In such a case the matrix u_0 contains several columns, one for each system of loading. The method of solving the equations is explained in the Appendix (p. 297). In this example, only one integral of equation 4.5 was taken into account, namely, $\displaystyle\int \frac{m^z_r m^z_s}{EI^z}\,dx$. Where distortions due to other internal

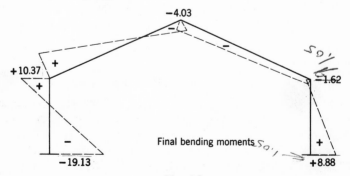

Fig. 4.5

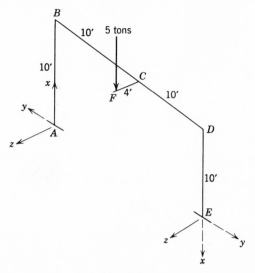

Fig. 4.6

actions have an appreciable effect upon the solution it is necessary to make tabulations similar to Tables 4.2 and 4.3 but extended to include the additional integrals.

Example 4.2   The three-dimensional frame of Fig. 4.6 has supports at A and E which are capable of developing six reaction components. The frame is therefore six times statically indeterminate.

The sectional properties of the members are

Columns AB, ED $\quad GI^x = \dfrac{1}{5} \quad$ Beam $BCD \quad GI^x = \dfrac{2}{5}$

$$EI^y = 3 \qquad\qquad EI^y = 6$$

$$EI^z = 1 \qquad\qquad EI^z = 2$$

Solution.   The necessary six releases can be made in a variety of ways. A complete separation of the frame at some section is perhaps the easiest to visualize, and noting that the preservation of symmetry will simplify the arithmetic, we make the cut at C. This cut leads to a frame in which some of the redundants can be evaluated by inspection. However, this simplification will be ignored. A complete solution having been made, symmetry will be used to provide a check.

Table 4.4 shows the twisting moments and the two bending moments produced by each of the seven cases of loading. The shear and axial force distortions have been neglected. Since none of the redundant actions produces stress in the cantilever CF, the redundants are independent of the bending moments caused in CF by the load, and this member is therefore omitted from Table 4.4.

Table 4.4

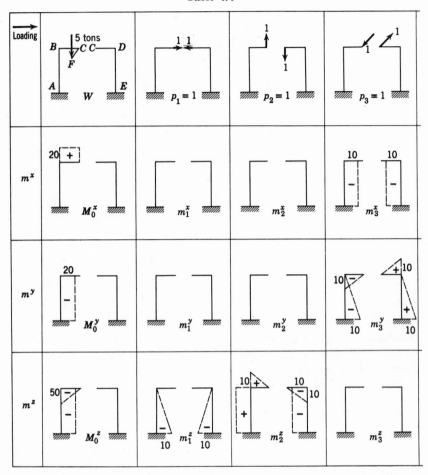

Table 4.5 gives the values of the various integrals. In evaluating integrals of this type two points should be noted. First, the product of two symmetrical or two anti-symmetrical functions, taken over the whole frame, produces a symmetrical integrand only half of which need be evaluated. Second, the product of a symmetrical with an anti-symmetrical function or diagram produces an anti-symmetrical integrand whose integral is zero. In the present problem, where an integral is zero for the latter reason, the remark $\oint \times A/S$ is inserted in Table 4.5. Otherwise the integrals are computed for each member separately as in the previous example.

Table 4.4 (continued)

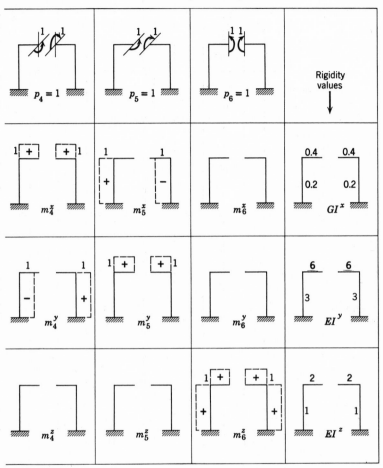

The compatibility equations are then

$$
\begin{aligned}
+2500 + 677p_1 \quad\quad\quad\quad\quad\quad\quad\quad\quad\quad\; - 100p_6 &= 0 \quad (a)\\
-5833 \quad\quad\quad + 2333p_2 \quad\quad\quad\quad\quad\quad\quad\quad\quad &= 0 \quad (b)\\
+333 \quad\quad\quad\quad\quad\quad\quad + 10333p_3 + 33p_4 \quad\quad\quad &= 0 \quad (c)\\
+567 \quad\quad\quad\quad\quad\quad\quad + \quad 33p_3 + 57p_4 \quad\quad\quad &= 0 \quad (d)\\
0 \quad\quad\quad\quad\quad\quad\quad\quad\quad\quad\quad\quad\quad\quad + 103p_5 \quad\; &= 0 \quad (e)\\
-625 - 100p_1 \quad\quad\quad\quad\quad\quad\quad\quad\quad\quad\quad + 30p_6 &= 0 \quad (f)\\
&\quad\quad\quad\quad (4.10)
\end{aligned}
$$

giving $p_1 = -1.25, p_2 = +2.50, p_3 = 0, p_4 = -10.00, p_5 = 0, p_6 = +16.67.$

Table 4.5

Integral	Member	u_{10}	u_{20}	u_{30}	u_{40}	u_{50}	u_{60}	f_{11}	f_{21} $=f_{12}$	f_{31} $=f_{13}$	f_{41} $=f_{14}$	f_{51} $=f_{15}$	f_{61} $=f_{16}$
$\dfrac{1}{GI^x}\int m_r^x m_s^x\,dx$	AB												
	BC				+500								
	CD												
	DE												
$\dfrac{1}{EI^y}\int m_r^y m_s^y\,dx$	AB			+333	+67								
	BC												
	CD												
	DE												
$\dfrac{1}{EI^z}\int m_r^z m_s^z\,dx$	AB	+2500	−5000				−500	+333					−50
	BC		−833				−125						
	CD							$\$ \times A/S$					
	DE							+333					−50
Sum		+2500	−5833	+333	+567	0	−625	+667	0	0	0	0	−100

Table 4.5 (continued)

f_{22}	f_{32} $=f_{23}$	f_{42} $=f_{24}$	f_{52} $=f_{25}$	f_{62} $=f_{26}$	f_{33}	f_{43} $=f_{34}$	f_{53} $=f_{35}$	f_{63} $=f_{36}$	f_{44}	f_{54} $=f_{45}$	f_{64} $=f_{46}$	f_{55}	f_{65} $=f_{56}$	f_{66}
					+5000							+50		
										+25				
							\$ × A/S			+25				
					+5000							+50		
					+111	+16.7			+3.3					
					+55.5							+1.7		
					+55.5		\$ × A/S					+1.7		
					+111	+16.7			+3.3					
+1000														+10
+167														+5
+167				\$ × A/S										+5
+1000														+10
+2333	0	0	0	0	+10,333	+33	0	0	+57	0	0	+103	0	+30

45

The torsion moment at any part of the frame is now found from the equation

$$M^x = M^x_0 + m^x_1 p_1 + m^x_2 p_2 + m^x_3 p_3 + m^x_4 p_4 + m^x_5 p_5 + m^x_6 p_6 \quad (4.11)$$

and the bending moments M^y and M^z from similar expressions involving m^y and m^z.

An interesting feature of equations 4.10 is that they fall into two independent groups, a, b and f containing the variables p_1, p_2 and p_6, and c, d and e containing p_3, p_4 and p_5. This feature is governed by the f coefficients, indicating that it is a property of the frame and not of this particular loading. The three redundants p_1, p_2 and p_6 act in the plane of the portal and produce, at the releases, displacements only in that plane. The other three redundants do not act in, nor do they produce displacements in, the xy plane. Any load could be resolved into a group of components in the xy plane and a group of components perpendicular to it. Each group would induce only three of the redundants. In the present instance the 5-ton load could be replaced by a 5-ton load at C together with a 20-ton-foot couple. The former would give redundants p_1, p_2 and p_6, and the latter would produce p_3, p_4 and p_5.

Example 4.3 The frame of Fig. 4.7 is pin-jointed. The only sectional property required for analysis is EA^x, which has the relative values 1, 2 and 4 for vertical, diagonal and horizontal members respectively.

Solution. The only internal action which has a non-zero value in this frame is the axial force. Furthermore, throughout any given member the axial force is constant, and it is therefore specified in Table 4.6 by a numerical value beside the member in place of a graph as in previous examples.

Since only axial force is present, the complete cutting of a member constitutes only one release in this case. The frame is twice redundant, and is rendered statically determinate by cutting members 3 and 8. The releases will be called A and B instead of 1 and 2 as previously.

The solution is presented in the same form as for the two previous examples. Table 4.6 shows the axial forces arising from the different cases of loading. Table 4.7 gives the values of the displacement integrals

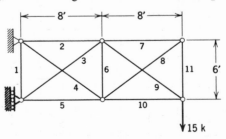

Fig. 4.7

Table 4.6

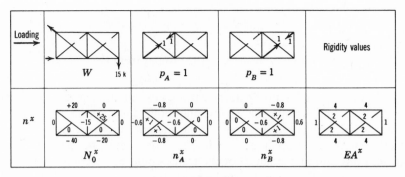

Table 4.7

Integral	Member	u_{A0}	u_{B0}	f_{AA}	$f_{BA} = f_{AB}$	f_{BB}
	1			+2.16		
	2	−32		+1.28		
	3			+5.00		
	4	+125		+5.00		
	5	+64		+1.28		
$\dfrac{1}{EA^x}\displaystyle\int n_r^x n_s^x \, dx$	6	+54	+54	+2.16	+2.16	+2.16
	7					+1.28
	8					+5.00
	9		+125			+5.00
	10		+32			+1.28
	11					+2.16
Sum		+211	+211	+16.88	+2.16	+16.88

for the various members.   In this problem, since the axial force is always
constant along the length of a member, we have

$$\frac{1}{EA^x}\int_0^L n_r^x n_s^x \, dx = \frac{n_r^x n_s^x L}{EA^x}$$

The compatibility equations are

$$211 + 16.88p_A + 2.16p_B = 0$$
$$211 + 2.16p_A + 16.88p_B = 0 \qquad (4.12)$$

whence $p_A = p_B = -11.08$.

The axial force in any member is then found from the equation

$$N^x = N_0^x + n_A^x p_A + n_B^x p_B \qquad (4.13)$$

In the discussion of more extensive frames the numbering of the releases 1, 2, 3 ... suffers from the disadvantage that the number of a release gives no indication of its location. If the internal actions are distinguished by the numbers 1, 2, 3, 4, 5, 6 as described on page 3, the release of the torsion moment at a point D of the frame could be described as release $D4$. The redundant would then be p_{D4} and so on.

The following example, although not very extensive, will serve to illustrate the nomenclature. The same problem will also be solved by several other methods in later chapters, so that comparisons can be drawn between the forms of solution.

Example 4.4 The frame of Fig. 4.8 is plane and has rigid joints at B, D and F. The supports A and C are fixed, while E is pinned so that as a plane frame it is five times statically indeterminate. The moment of inertia, I^z, of the beam is twice that of the columns. It is assumed that E is constant and that deformations due to shear and axial force are negligible.

Solution. The two reactions at E and the three at A are released, resulting in a statically determinate frame which is symmetrical and cantilevered from C.

The axes chosen for each member are shown in Fig. 4.8. The x axis lies along the member in each case, the direction of the y axis being arbitrary.

Tables 4.8 and 4.9 are arranged in the same way as for previous examples. Table 4.8 shows the bending-moment diagrams for the various cases of loading. The displacements at the releases and the coefficients of flexibility are computed in Table 4.9.

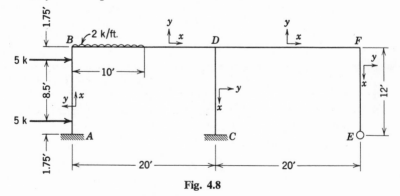

Fig. 4.8

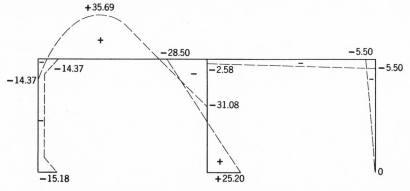

Fig. 4.9

The compatibility equations are:

$$-95083 + 6133p_{A1} + 2640p_{A2} - 340p_{A6} + 4800p_{E1} - 1440p_{E2} = 0$$
$$-46582 + 2640p_{A1} + 2592p_{A2} - 264p_{A6} + 1440p_{E1} - 576p_{E2} = 0$$
$$+5637 - 340p_{A1} - 264p_{A2} + 34p_{A6} - 240p_{E1} + 72p_{E2} = 0$$
$$-72000 + 4800p_{A1} + 1440p_{A2} - 240p_{A6} + 6133p_{E1} - 2640p_{E2} = 0$$
$$+23040 - 1440p_{A1} - 576p_{A2} + 72p_{A6} - 2640p_{E1} + 2592p_{E2} = 0$$

$$(4.14)$$

Upon solution these give

$$P_{A1} = +14.17, p_{A2} = +5.07, p_{A6} = +15.18, p_{E1} = -0.15, p_{E2} = -0.46$$

The final bending moments are given by

$$M = M_0 + p_{A1} \cdot m_{A1} + p_{A2} \cdot m_{A2} + p_{A6} \cdot m_{A6} + p_{E1} \cdot m_{E1} + p_{E2} \cdot m_{E2}$$

$$(4.15)$$

and this yields the bending-moment diagram of Fig. 4.9.

If matrices are used, the flexibility matrix of the frame is

$$f = \begin{bmatrix} f_{A1 \cdot A1} & f_{A1 \cdot A2} & f_{A1 \cdot A6} & f_{A1 \cdot E1} & f_{A1 \cdot E2} \\ f_{A2 \cdot A1} & f_{A2 \cdot A2} & f_{A2 \cdot A6} & f_{A2 \cdot E1} & f_{A2 \cdot E2} \\ f_{A6 \cdot A1} & f_{A6 \cdot A2} & f_{A6 \cdot A6} & f_{A6 \cdot E1} & f_{A6 \cdot E2} \\ f_{E1 \cdot A1} & f_{E1 \cdot A2} & f_{E1 \cdot A6} & f_{E1 \cdot E1} & f_{E1 \cdot E2} \\ f_{E2 \cdot A1} & f_{E2 \cdot A2} & f_{E2 \cdot A6} & f_{E2 \cdot E1} & f_{E2 \cdot E2} \end{bmatrix}$$

$$= \begin{bmatrix} 6133 & 2640 & -340 & 4800 & -1440 \\ 2640 & 2592 & -264 & 1440 & -576 \\ -340 & -264 & 34 & -240 & 72 \\ 4800 & 1440 & -240 & 6133 & -2640 \\ -1440 & -576 & 72 & -2640 & 2592 \end{bmatrix}$$

Table 4.8

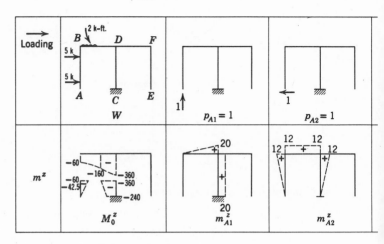

Table 4.9

Integral	Member	$u_{A1 \cdot 0}$	$u_{A2 \cdot 0}$	$u_{A6 \cdot 0}$	$u_{E1 \cdot 0}$	$u_{E2 \cdot 0}$	$f_{A1 \cdot A1}$	$f_{A2 \cdot A1} = f_{A1 \cdot A2}$	$f_{A6 \cdot A1} = f_{A1 \cdot A6}$
$\frac{1}{EI^z}\int m_r^z m_s^z\, dx$	AB		−2342	+270					
	CD	−72000	−23040	+3600	−72000	+23040	+4800	+1440	−240
	EF								
	BD	−23083	−21200	+1767			+1333	+1200	−100
	DF								
Sum		−95083	−46582	+5637	−72000	+23040	+6133	+2640	−340

while the matrix of release displacements for this particular load condition is

$$u_0 = \begin{bmatrix} u_{A1\cdot 0} \\ u_{A2\cdot 0} \\ u_{A6\cdot 0} \\ u_{E1\cdot 0} \\ u_{E2\cdot 0} \end{bmatrix} = \begin{bmatrix} -95{,}083 \\ -46{,}582 \\ 5{,}637 \\ -72{,}000 \\ 23{,}040 \end{bmatrix}$$

The compatibility condition is expressed by the matrix equation

$$u_0 + fp = 0$$

giving

$$p = -f^{-1}u_0 \qquad (4.16)$$

Table 4.8 (continued)

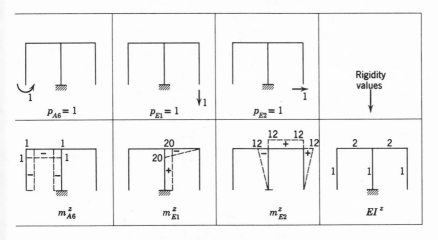

			Rigidity values
$p_{A6}=1$	$p_{E1}=1$	$p_{E2}=1$	
m^z_{A6}	m^z_{E1}	m^z_{E2}	EI^z

Table 4.9 (continued)

$f_{E1\cdot A1} = f_{A1\cdot E1}$	$f_{E2\cdot A1} = f_{A1\cdot E2}$	$f_{A2\cdot A2}$	$f_{A6\cdot A2} = f_{A2\cdot A6}$	$f_{E1\cdot A2} = f_{A2\cdot E1}$	$f_{E2\cdot A2} = f_{A2\cdot E2}$	$f_{A6\cdot A6}$	$f_{E1\cdot A6} = f_{A6\cdot E1}$	$f_{E2\cdot A6} = f_{A6\cdot E2}$	$f_{E1\cdot E1}$	$f_{E2\cdot E1} = f_{E1\cdot E2}$	$f_{E2\cdot E2}$
		+576	−72			+12					
+4800	−1440	+576	−72	+1440	−576	+12	−240	+72	+4800	−1440	+576
											+576
		+1440	−120			+10					
									+1333	−1200	+1440
+4800	−1440	+2592	−264	+1440	−576	+34	−240	+72	+6133	−2640	+2592

Solution of equation 4.16 gives the values of the redundants as follows:

$$\begin{bmatrix} p_{A1} \\ p_{A2} \\ p_{A6} \\ p_{E1} \\ p_{E2} \end{bmatrix} = \begin{bmatrix} +14.17 \\ +5.07 \\ +15.18 \\ -0.15 \\ -0.46 \end{bmatrix}$$

Owing to the particular choice of redundants, the compatibility equations are ill-conditioned. As a consequence, a considerable number of significant figures is required in order to obtain reasonable accuracy. The matter of the choice of suitable releases is discussed further in Chapter 9.

The values of the redundants are substituted, as before, into equation 4.15 to obtain the final bending moments.

In the last example, the notation employed for the subscripts clearly indicates, for any coefficient, the location of both cause and effect.

$$
f = \begin{bmatrix}
f_{A1 \cdot A1} & f_{A1 \cdot A2} & f_{A1 \cdot A6} & f_{A1 \cdot E1} & f_{A1 \cdot E2} \\
f_{A2 \cdot A1} & f_{A2 \cdot A2} & f_{A2 \cdot A6} & f_{A2 \cdot E1} & f_{A2 \cdot E2} \\
f_{A6 \cdot A1} & f_{A6 \cdot A2} & f_{A6 \cdot A6} & f_{A6 \cdot E1} & f_{A6 \cdot E2} \\
\hline
f_{E1 \cdot A1} & f_{E1 \cdot A2} & f_{E1 \cdot A6} & f_{E1 \cdot E1} & f_{E1 \cdot E2} \\
f_{E2 \cdot A1} & f_{E2 \cdot A2} & f_{E2 \cdot A6} & f_{E2 \cdot E1} & f_{E2 \cdot E2}
\end{bmatrix}
=
\begin{bmatrix}
f_{AA} & f_{AE} \\
\hline
f_{EA} & f_{EE}
\end{bmatrix}
$$

(displacements caused by $p_{A1} = 1$; displacements caused by $p_{E1} = 1$; displacements at $A1$ due to various loads; displacements at $E2$ due to various loads)

When the releases are made at more than one cross-section of the frame, as in this case, such a notation seems to distinguish the coefficients which relate a cause and effect located at the same cross-section of the frame, for example, $f_{A2 \cdot A6}$, from the coefficients relating cause and effect at different places, for example, $f_{A2 \cdot E2}$. In fact, the flexibility matrix can be divided into submatrices as shown.

The elements of submatrix f_{AE} give displacements at A caused by unit loads at E. Submatrices f_{AE} and f_{EA} can be called *carry-over* matrices.

It should be clearly understood that the elements of f_{AE} and f_{EA} are not essentially different from the elements of f_{AA} and f_{EE}.

4.5 SCALE FACTORS

In the examples of the last section, the flexibility coefficients were calculated on the basis of unit values of the redundants. In fact, any arbitrary values could have been used, and the compatibility equations would then give not the absolute values of the redundants but their values relative to the assumed arbitrary figures. In this respect, the process resembles a change of unit. If, when the unit of force is 1 pound, a given redundant is found to have a magnitude of 400 units, then, if the unit of force is taken as 1000 pounds we should expect the redundant to have a magnitude of 0.400 unit.   On this basis it is clear that to change the scale for all redundants would be merely to change the units, and a corresponding change of magnitude would result.   The possibility of a separate scaling effect for each unknown requires consideration.

Suppose that, at the various releases, actions d_1, $d_2 \ldots d_n$ are applied. The action d_r is regarded as a unit action multiplied by a numerical scale factor d_r.   At any general point of the frame, the internal actions produced by the unit p_r have been called n_r^x, $n_r^y \ldots m_r^y$, m_r^z.   Consequently the internal actions produced by d_r will be $(d_r n_r^x)$, $(d_r n_r^y) \ldots (d_r m_r^z)$.   Similarly the actions n_s^x, $n_s^y \ldots$ will become $(d_s n_s^x)$, $(d_s n_s^y) \ldots$.

In its basic form a flexibility coefficient f_{rs} is given by

$$f_{rs} = \int \left[\frac{n_r^x n_s^x}{EA^x} + \frac{n_r^y n_s^y}{GA^y} + \cdots + \frac{m_r^z m_s^z}{EI^z} \right] dx$$

The scaled value will be denoted by $\tilde{f}_{rs}$, and its value will be

$$\tilde{f}_{rs} = \int \left[\frac{(d_r n_r^x)(d_s n_s^x)}{EA^x} + \frac{(d_r n_r^y)(d_s n_s^y)}{GA^y} + \cdots + \frac{(d_r m_r^z)(d_s m_s^z)}{EI^z} \right] dx$$

$$= d_r d_s \times f_{rs} \qquad\qquad\qquad (4.17)$$

In general every coefficient involving release r is multiplied by d_r, and every coefficient involving release s is multiplied by d_s.   The effect of scaling upon all the coefficients can be expressed in matrix form.

Let d be a scaling matrix consisting of a diagonal matrix (Appendix, p. 286) whose diagonal contains all the scale factors d_1 d_2 $\ldots$ d_n appertaining to the n releases.   The other elements of the matrix are zero.

$$d = \begin{bmatrix} d_1 & & & & & & & \\ & d_2 & & & & & & \\ & & \ddots & & & & & \\ & & & d_r & & & & \\ & & & & d_s & & & \\ & & & & & \ddots & & \\ & & & & & & d_n \end{bmatrix}$$

Then $\tilde{f}$, the matrix of scaled coefficients, is given by

$$\tilde{f} = dfd =$$

$$
\begin{bmatrix} d_1 & & & & & \\ & d_2 & & & & \\ & & \ddots & & & \\ & & & d_r & & \\ & & & & d_s & \\ & & & & & \ddots \\ & & & & & & d_n \end{bmatrix}
\begin{bmatrix} f_{11} & f_{12} & \cdots & f_{1n} \\ f_{21} & f_{22} & & \\ & & \vdots & \\ & & \vdots & \\ & & \vdots & \\ f_{n1} & f_{n2} & \cdots & f_{nn} \end{bmatrix}
\begin{bmatrix} d_1 & & & & & \\ & d_2 & & & & \\ & & \ddots & & & \\ & & & d_r & & \\ & & & & d_s & \\ & & & & & \ddots \\ & & & & & & d_n \end{bmatrix}
$$

$$(4.18)$$

Premultiplication of f by d causes each *row* to be multiplied by the appropriate factor. The rth row is multiplied by d_r. Postmultiplication by d causes each *column* to be multiplied by the appropriate factor. The sth column is multiplied by d_s. A typical element f_{rs} is thus multiplied by d_r and by d_s, as required by equation 4.17.

Displacement of any point of the primary frame under the action of applied loads involves only one scale factor, since the applied loads retain their natural values.

$$u_{r0} = \int \left[\frac{n_r^x N_0^x}{EA^x} + \frac{n_r^y N_0^y}{GA^y} \cdots + \frac{m_r^z M_0^z}{EI^z} \right] dx$$

Using the scaled values $(d_r n_r^x)$, $(d_r n_r^y)$, etc., we have

$$\tilde{u}_{r0} = \int \left[\frac{(d_r n_r^x) N_0^x}{EA^x} + \frac{(d_r n_r^y) N_0^y}{GA^y} \cdots + \frac{(d_r m_r^z) M_0^z}{EI^z} \right] dx$$

$$= d_r u_{r0} \tag{4.19}$$

The effect upon all the u_0 values at the releases can be expressed in matrix form.

$$
\tilde{u}_0 = du_0 =
\begin{bmatrix} d_1 & & & & & \\ & d_2 & & & & \\ & & \ddots & & & \\ & & & d_r & & \\ & & & & d_s & \\ & & & & & \ddots \\ & & & & & & d_n \end{bmatrix}
\begin{bmatrix} u_{10} \\ u_{20} \\ \vdots \\ u_{r0} \\ u_{s0} \\ \vdots \\ u_{n0} \end{bmatrix}
\tag{4.20}
$$

The scaled values of $\tilde{f}$ and $\tilde{u}_0$ can be used to determine redundants and displacements throughout the frame. In terms of unscaled values we know that the total displacement at the releases is given by the matrix equation

$$u = u_0 + fp$$

Premultiplying throughout by d, we get

$$du = du_0 + dfp$$
$$= du_0 + (dfd)\, d^{-1}p$$
$$\tilde{u} = \tilde{u}_0 + \tilde{f}\tilde{p} \tag{4.21}$$

where
$$\tilde{p} = d^{-1}p \tag{4.22}$$

The inverse of the diagonal matrix d (Appendix, p. 291) consists of a diagonal matrix whose elements are the reciprocals of those of d, namely $1/d_1, 1/d_2 \ldots 1/d_n$. The scaled values $\tilde{p}$ are therefore equal to the original values each *divided* by the appropriate factor.

The final displacements at the releases are zero, and equation 4.21 yields the compatibility equations

$$\tilde{u} + \tilde{f}\tilde{p} = 0 \tag{4.23}$$

Thus, when the scaled values of u_0 and f are used in the usual manner they will provide inversely scaled values of the redundants.

The true value, p, of any redundant can be obtained from $\tilde{p}$ by *multiplying* by its corresponding factor. However, the true value is not usually required. The final internal actions at any section can be computed just as well from $\tilde{p}$. For instance, the final axial force at any point is given by

$$N^x = N_0^x + p_1 n_1^x + p_2 n_2^x \cdots + p_n n_n^x \tag{4.24}$$

The use of scaled values results in the expression

$$N^x = N_0^x + \tilde{p}_1(d_1 n_1^x) + \tilde{p}_2(d_2 n_2^x) \cdots + \tilde{p}_n(d_n n_n^x)$$
$$= N_0^x + \left(\frac{p_1}{d_1}\right)(d_1 n_1^x) + \left(\frac{p_2}{d_2}\right)(d_2 n_2^x) \cdots + \left(\frac{p_n}{d_n}\right)(d_n n_n^x) \tag{4.25}$$

which is the same as equation 4.24.

Scaled values $\tilde{p}$ can also be used to determine the frame displacement at any point. The matrix equation 4.21 can be extended to provide the displacement at any point, in the manner described in Section 3.6. For the displacement at a point A, coefficients are required which involve the use of a unit force at A. Suppose that a scale factor d_A is employed with this unit force; then from the relationship given in equation 4.21 we shall have

$$\tilde{u}_A = \tilde{u}_{A0} + \tilde{f}_{A1}\tilde{p}_1 + \tilde{f}_{A2}\tilde{p}_2 \cdots + \tilde{f}_{An}\tilde{p}_n \tag{4.26}$$

But $\tilde{u}_A$ is $d_A u_A$. That is to say, the calculated value $\tilde{u}_A$ is only scaled by the scale factor employed at the point A, and is unaffected by the use of factors at the release points. These factors are compensated by the corresponding change in the redundants $\tilde{p}$.

By reference to the examples of the last section it will be seen that the use of unit redundants often leads to flexibility coefficients which are very large since they involve the linear dimensions of the frame. Where problems are being solved by hand or with a desk calculator the use of scale factors nearly always simplifies the calculation of these coefficients and results in smaller values. This is turn assists in the solution of the simultaneous equations.

Table 4.10

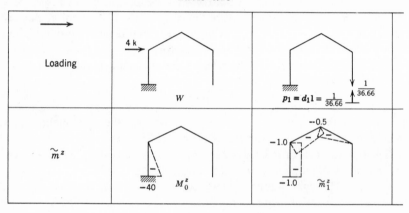

Table 4.11

Integral	Member	$\tilde{u}_{10}$	$\tilde{u}_{20}$	$\tilde{u}_{60}$	$\tilde{u}_{D0}$	$\tilde{f}_{11}$	$\tilde{f}_{21}$ $= \tilde{f}_{12}$
	AB	$+200$	-66.67	-200	$+133.33$	$+10$	-5
$\dfrac{1*}{EI^z} \displaystyle\int \tilde{m}_r^z \tilde{m}_s^z \, dx$	BC					$+11.67$	-20.33
	CD					$+1.67$	-7.67
	DE						
Sum		$+200.00$	-66.67	-200.00	$+133.33$	$+23.33$	-33.00

* I/EI^z has been taken as unity.

If the compatibility equations prove to be ill-conditioned, they can sometimes be improved by using scaled values of f.

The effect of using scale factors will be illustrated by reworking Example 4.1.

Example 4.5   Re-solve Example 4.1 using scale factors.   The horizontal deflection of point D is required as before.

Solution.   The same releases are adopted as in the first solution of this problem, namely, three releases at point E.   The redundants will be called p_1, p_2 and p_6 as before.   Scale factors are chosen so that the salient values in the bending-moment diagram m_1, m_2 and m_6 are unity (see Table 4.10).   The factors are governed by the frame dimensions and are

Table 4.10 (continued)

Table 4.11 (continued)

$\tilde{f}_{61}$ $= \tilde{f}_{16}$	$\tilde{f}_{D1}$	$\tilde{f}_{22}$	$\tilde{f}_{62}$ $= \tilde{f}_{26}$	$\tilde{f}_{D2}$	$\tilde{f}_{66}$	$\tilde{f}_{D6}$
-10	$+5$	$+3.33$	$+5$	-1.67	$+10$	-5
-15	-5.33	$+40.27$	$+28$	$+12.27$	$+20$	$+8$
-5	-2.67	$+40.27$	$+28$	$+12.27$	$+20$	$+8$
		$+3.33$	$+5$		$+10$	
-30.00	-3.00	$+87.20$	$+66.00$	$+22.87$	$+60.00$	$+11.00$

respectively $1/36.66$, $1/10$ and 1. Grouped into a scaling matrix these give

$$d = \begin{bmatrix} \dfrac{1}{36.66} & 0 & 0 \\ 0 & \dfrac{1}{10} & 0 \\ 0 & 0 & 1 \end{bmatrix}$$

The compatibility equations are now

$$\frac{1}{EI^z} \begin{bmatrix} +200.00 \\ -66.67 \\ -200.00 \end{bmatrix} + \frac{1}{EI^z} \begin{bmatrix} +23.33 & -33.00 & -30.00 \\ -33.00 & +87.20 & +66.00 \\ -30.00 & +66.00 & +60.00 \end{bmatrix} \begin{bmatrix} \tilde{p}_1 \\ \tilde{p}_2 \\ \tilde{p}_6 \end{bmatrix} = 0 \qquad (4.27)$$

$$+\tilde{u}_0 \qquad + \qquad \tilde{f} \qquad\qquad \tilde{p} \quad = 0$$

These give

$$\tilde{p}_1 = -12.000 \qquad \tilde{p}_2 = -10.502 \qquad \tilde{p}_3 = +8.886$$

The final bending moments are given by

$$M^z = M_0^z + (-12.000)\tilde{m}_1^z + (-10.502)\tilde{m}_2^z + (+8.886)\tilde{m}_6^z \quad (4.28)$$

which results in the bending-moment diagram of Fig. 4.10. These values agree with those obtained previously (see Fig. 4.5).

Although the true values of the redundants are rarely required, they are obtained as follows:

$$p_1 = \tilde{p}_1 \times d_1 = -12.000 \times \frac{1}{36.66} = -0.327$$

$$p_2 = \tilde{p}_2 \times d_2 = -10.502 \times \frac{1}{10} \quad = -1.050$$

$$p_6 = \tilde{p}_6 \times d_6 = \ +8.886 \times 1 \quad\ = +8.886$$

The scaled value of the horizontal displacement of D is obtained by the use of equation 4.26:

$$\tilde{u}_D = \tilde{u}_{D0} + \tilde{f}_{D1}\tilde{p}_1 + \tilde{f}_{D2}\tilde{p}_2 + \tilde{f}_{D6}\tilde{p}_6$$

$$= [+133.33 - 3.00(-12.000) + 22.87(-10.502) + 11.0(+8.886)]\frac{1}{EI^z}$$

$$= 26.88/EI^z$$

But
$$\tilde{u}_D = d_D u_D = \tfrac{1}{10} u_D$$

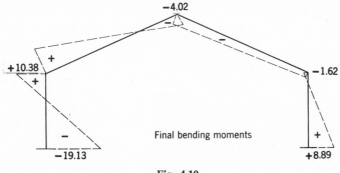

Fig. 4.10

The true displacement is therefore

$$u_D = 268.8 \times \frac{1}{EI^z} \text{ ft.}$$

4.6   TEMPERATURE CHANGE, SHRINKAGE AND MISFIT

Hitherto, the particular solution has been referred to as the solution of a statically determinate primary frame under the action of externally applied loads.   The particular solution is not necessarily confined to the behavior of the primary frame under external loads.   Any agency that causes deformation of the primary frame will produce a particular solution. Other than loads, the most common causes of deformation are temperature change, shrinkage and misfit of prefabricated elements.   In a statically determinate frame the elements are free to deform (within limits) without inducing internal actions in the frame.   Hence the effect of temperature change or shrinkage upon the primary frame is to produce release displacements but no internal actions.

These release displacements will constitute the particular solution. If the actual frame is statically indeterminate a complementary solution, which will restore compatibility, is then calculated in the usual manner.

If, at any cross-section Q, the temperature increase is uniform across the section of a member, an elemental length dx will undergo an axial extension equal to $\alpha T \, dx$, where α is the coefficient of linear expansion and T is the temperature rise.   If the axial force at Q due to unit value of redundant p_r is n_r^x, then the displacement at release r due to the deformation at Q is $n_r^x \alpha T \, dx$.   The *axial* force n_r^x at Q is required because the deformation at Q is an *axial* deformation. The total displacement at release r will be

$$u_{r0} = \int\limits_F n_r^x \alpha T \, dx \tag{4.29}$$

The temperature strain is assumed to be uniform across any given section, but not necessarily the same at all sections.

Example 4.6   In the frame of Fig. 4.4, the members CD and DE undergo a temperature rise of 40°F while the temperature of members AB and BC remains constant.   Find the bending moments induced in the frame.
    Take $E = 4 \times 10^6$ psi, $I = 0.8$ ft.⁴, $\alpha = 6 \times 10^{-6}$ per °F.
    Solution.   The same primary frame will be used as in Example 4.5. The members CD and DE experience an *axial* deformation due to thermal strain.   For each member the deformation in length dx is

$$du_1 = \alpha T \, dx = 2.4 \times 10^{-4} \, dx$$

For the particular solution we shall now require the *axial* force due to arbitrary values of the redundants, i.e., n_1^x, n_2^x and n_6^x.
    Scaling factors will be used, and these will be the same as those of Example 4.5.   The calculation is set out in two tables to preserve the form used in previous examples.   Apart from the effect of scaling, the value of u_{10} would simply be the vertical displacement of E due to temperature rise in CDE.   For more complex frames, and particularly if scaling factors are used, the tabular layout is probably worthwhile.
    Using the frame flexibility as found in Example 4.5, we can now write the compatibility equations.

$$\begin{bmatrix} +1.18 \times 10^{-4} \\ +1.20 \times 10^{-4} \\ 0 \end{bmatrix} + \frac{1}{EI^z} \begin{bmatrix} +23.33 & -33.00 & -30.00 \\ -33.00 & +87.20 & +66.00 \\ -30.00 & +66.00 & +60.00 \end{bmatrix} \begin{bmatrix} \tilde{p}_1 \\ \tilde{p}_2 \\ \tilde{p}_6 \end{bmatrix} = 0 \tag{4.30}$$

It should be noted that the factor $1/EI^z$ does not occur in the particular solution because these deformations are not caused by stresses.   We

Table 4.12

	du_1	$\tilde{n}_1^x$	$\tilde{n}_2^x$	$\tilde{n}_6^x$
AB	0	−0.027	0	0
BC	0	−0.011	+0.092	0
CD	$2.4 \times 10^{-4} \, dx$	+0.011	+0.092	0
DE	$2.4 \times 10^{-4} \, dx$	+0.027	0	0

Table 4.13

Integral	Member	$\tilde{u}_{10}$	$\tilde{u}_{20}$	$\tilde{u}_{60}$
$\int u_r^x \, du_1$	AB	0	0	0
	BC	0	0	0
	CD	$+5.24 \times 10^{-5}$	$+1.20 \times 10^{-4}$	0
	DE	$+6.55 \times 10^{-5}$	0	0
Sum		$+1.18 \times 10^{-4}$	$+1.20 \times 10^{-4}$	0

must therefore evaluate EI^z. Since u_0 is expressed in feet and radians, EI^z must be expressed in feet units.

$$EI = 4.61 \times 10^5 \text{ kip-ft.}^2$$

The equations 4.30 are now solved for the scaled values of $\tilde{p}_1$, $\tilde{p}_2$ and $\tilde{p}_6$. The bending moments will be due to the redundants only.

A temperature change which varies from one side of a member to the other will result in a varying thermal strain, which in turn will cause both elongation and curvature of the element. The element will thus undergo axial-type deformation, du_1, and bending deformation, du_6.

Figure 4.11 shows a small element, Q, of a beam of depth D. The temperature rise varies linearly from T_1 at the top to T_2 at the bottom. The extension of the fibers therefore varies from $\alpha T_1 \, dx$ to $\alpha T_2 \, dx$.

The deformation of the element can be described as the sum of an *axial* deformation du_1, where

$$du_1 = \alpha \left(\frac{T_1 + T_2}{2} \right) dx$$

and a *bending* deformation du_6, where

$$du_6 = \alpha \left(\frac{T_1 - T_2}{D} \right) dx$$

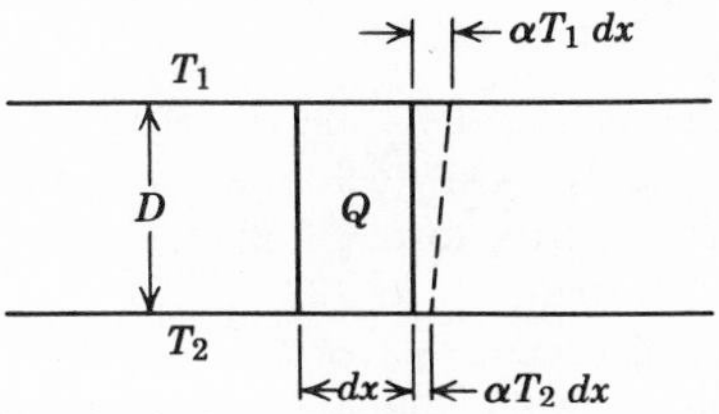

Fig. 4.11

If unit value of the redundant p_r causes an axial force n_r^x and a bending moment m_r^z at Q, then the displacement at r due to the deformation of the element Q is $(n_r^x \, du_1 + m_r^z \, du_6)$. The total displacement at release r will be

$$u_{r0} = \int_F n_r^x \alpha \left(\frac{T_1 + T_2}{2} \right) dx + \int_F m_r^z \alpha \left(\frac{T_1 - T_2}{D} \right) dx \qquad (4.31)$$

For a given problem, the particular solution can be found as in Example 4.6 except that the second integral must also be evaluated.

Shrinkage strains can give rise to the same types of element deformation as temperature strains. These can therefore be dealt with by expressions similar to those of equation (4.31).

Initial misfit of a member can be regarded as an overall deformation of the member. The corresponding release displacements can be calculated in the usual way, and these will then constitute the particular solution u_0.

PROBLEMS

†**4.1.** Solve the frame of Fig. P4.1 by the flexibility method. Select a primary frame by making a complete cut at some point. Find the flexibility matrix, considering bending deformations only.

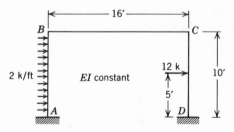

Fig. P4.1

For the given loading calculate the stress-resultants at a point 4 feet above D and the horizontal deflection at C.

4.2. In the portal frame of Fig. P4.2, the EI of the sloping members is twice that of the vertical members. Only deformation due to bending need be considered. For a unit value of the force W_1 alone, find:
  (a) the vertical displacement, u_D, of D.
  (b) the horizontal displacement, u_E, of E.
  (c) the bending moment at the midpoint of each of the columns.
Calculate the same information for unit values of W_2 and W_3.

Hence express the displacements u_D and u_E for any combination of W_1, W_2 and W_3 in the form

$$\begin{bmatrix} u_D \\ u_E \end{bmatrix} = [H] \begin{bmatrix} W_1 \\ W_2 \\ W_3 \end{bmatrix}$$

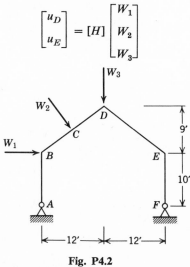

Fig. P4.2

Express the two bending moments as linear functions of the loads in a similar form.

4.3. The rigid jointed frame of Fig. P4.3 has constant section properties along all members, and deformation due to shear and axial force is negligible compared with that due to bending. Find the bending moment, shear force and

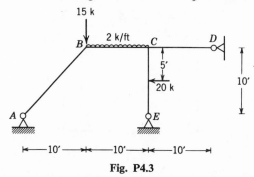

Fig. P4.3

axial force at the midpoint of *BC* for each of the three loads separately. Obtain the three solutions simultaneously by employing multiple constant terms (multiple R.H.S.) in the compatibility equations.

4.4. In the pin-jointed frame of Fig. P4.4 the cross-section stiffness of members 7, 8, 9 and 10 is *EA*; that of members 6, 12, 13 and 11 is 2*EA*; and that of members 1, 2, 3, 4 and 5 is 3*EA*.

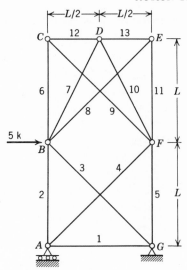

Fig. P4.4

Find the horizontal deflection of E, in terms of EA and L, due to the 5-kip load at B.   Also find the horizontal deflection at E due to shortening of 1 millimeter of the member BE.

4.5. Draw the bending-moment diagram for the frame of Fig. P4.5.   Use suitable factors to reduce the magnitude of the flexibility coefficients.

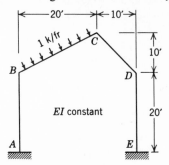

Fig. P4.5

4.6. A frame (Fig. P4.6) consists of a tripod each leg of which is in the shape of an L, the three legs being at $120°$ to one another.   Member ABG has a cross-section 1 inch square; CDG has a cross-section 1.2 inches square; EFG has a cross-section 1.4 inches square.   Joints B, D, F and G are rigid.   The material is homogeneous and isotropic.   The bases A, C and E are universal joints capable of supplying three force components but no component couples.   A vertical load of 1 kip acts at G, and a horizontal load of 1 kip at B in the direction BG.   Find the internal actions at the midpoint of FG.   Take $G = 1$ and $E = 2.5$.

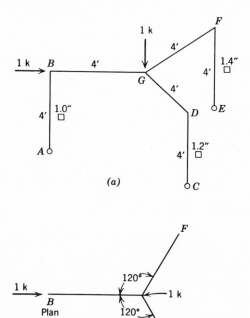

Fig. P4.6

4.7. Fig. P4.7 shows a rigid jointed frame composed of four members each 10 feet long and having a rectangular cross-section 12 inches × 6 inches. *AB*, *BC* and *BD* are horizontal, while *DE* is inclined at 45° to the horizontal. *B*, *D* and *E* lie in the vertical plane about which *AC* is symmetrical. In every member the cross-section is oriented so that the long side lies in a vertical plane.

The supports *A*, *C* and *E* are all completely fixed. A vertical 5-kip load acts at *D*.

The properties of the cross-section are:

$$I^x = 598 \text{ in.}^4 \quad \text{(torsion constant)}$$
$$I^y = 216 \text{ in.}^4$$
$$I^z = 864 \text{ in.}^4$$

Assume that $E = 2.5G$.

State the number of degrees of redundancy of the frame. If use is made of symmetry, how many simultaneous equations would occur in a flexibility analysis?

Solve the frame by flexibility methods and draw the bending-moment and twisting-moment diagrams for the members.

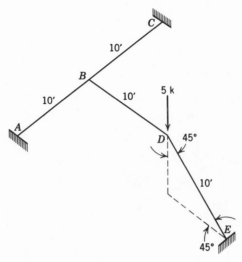

Fig. P4.7

4.8. In the rigid frame of Fig. P4.8, the support *A* is completely fixed. The supports *C* and *E* are restrained against translation, but are free to rotate about all axes. The relative properties of the members are as follows:

	Columns	Beams
GI^x	0.5	1
EI^y	4	2
EI^z	4	8

For the loading shown, find the six internal stress resultants at the top of each column. In the flexibility matrix, indicate by partitioning lines which of the releases occur at a given section of the frame.

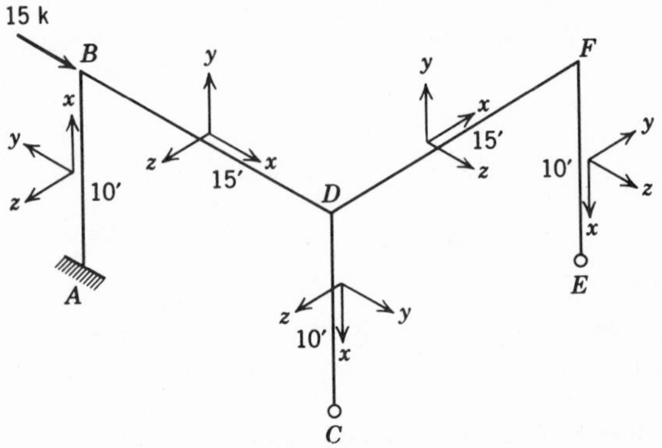

Fig. P4.8

4.9. The plane frame of Fig. P4.9 has rigid joints at *B* and *C*, and the supports at *A*, *D* and *E* are pinned.   All members have the same cross-section and the same length.   Find the vertical displacement of the midpoint of *BC* if the support *A* moves 0.2 inch horizontally.

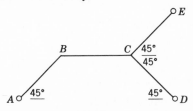

Fig. P4.9

4.10. In the portal frame of Fig. P4.10, the *EI* value of each member is the same and only bending deformations are to be considered.
  (*a*) Find the bending moment at *B* caused by the unit load at *A*.
  (*b*) Without making use of the principle of virtual work (i.e., by geometrical considerations alone) find the vertical displacement at *A* which will result from a unit angular discontinuity (kink) introduced at *B*.

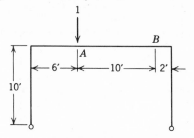

Fig. P4.10

4.11. Figure P4.11 shows a gabled portal, the columns of which are stepped at

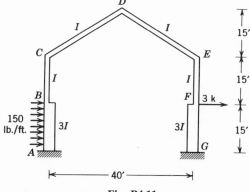

Fig. P4.11

midheight and fixed at the base.

$$I = 200 \text{ in.}^4$$
$$E = 30 \times 10^6 \text{ psi}$$
$$\alpha = 12 \times 10^{-6} \text{ per } {}^\circ\text{F}$$

Find the bending moment at the point E.

(a) For a temperature rise of 50°F.

(b) For the loading shown.

Only deformations due to bending are to be taken into account (note that E and I are given in inch and pound units).

4.12. In the pin-jointed frame of Problem 4.4, members 6, 7, 8, 9, 10, 11, 12 and 13 undergo a temperature rise of 80°F. Find the forces in all members due to this change if the coefficient of linear expansion of the material is 0.14×10^{-4} per °F and $E = 10^4$ ksi. The cross-sectional area is 0.5 in.² for members 7, 8, 9, 10; 1.0 in.² for members 6, 12, 13, 11; and 1.5 in.² for members 1, 2, 3, 4 and 5.

4.13. In the pin-jointed frame of Fig. P4.13, member 8 is manufactured 0.01 foot short and is forced into position. Determine the forces induced in the members by this lack of fit.

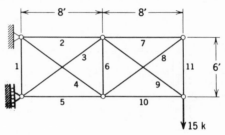

Fig. P4.13

The areas of the vertical, diagonal and horizontal members are respectively 1 in.², 2 in.² and 4 in.². Take $E = 30 \times 10^3$ ksi.

CHAPTER 5

Axis Transformations

5.1 CHANGE OF AXES

A system of forces acting at a single point A can be described in terms of component forces acting along three given axes x, y, z and component couples acting around these axes. By choosing different axes $\bar{x}$, $\bar{y}$, $\bar{z}$ the description of the force system will clearly be changed. In effect we shall now be expressing a set of forces in the axes $\bar{x}$, $\bar{y}$, $\bar{z}$ which are statically equivalent to those in the axes x, y, z. Although they are equivalent from the point of view of equilibrium, the two systems are not equal in all respects.

Suppose that the cantilever of Fig. 5.1a is acted upon by a single vertical force W_2 at the point A. In a new set of axes with origin at B it is

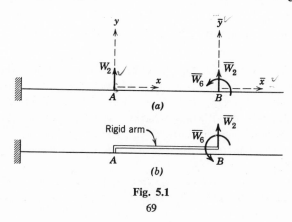

Fig. 5.1

69

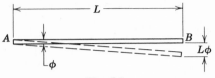

Fig. 5.2

possible to find a force $\overline{W}_2$ and a couple $\overline{W}_6$ which are statically equivalent to W_2.   If applied at B, the two actions $\overline{W}$ would have a different effect upon the deformation of the structure from that produced by W_2 applied at A.   In order to avoid this alteration, it is supposed that the new system of forces is still applied at A, and to assist this conception the idea is introduced of a perfectly rigid bar connecting B with the point of application A (Fig. 5.1b).   Being infinitely rigid, this bar undergoes no deformation.   By such a device we may picture the force at A replaced by an equivalent system in any axes whatsoever but still applied to the structure at A.

A similar transformation can be made with regard to displacements. Where the origin is shifted, it is again convenient to imagine the two origins as being physically connected.   The relationships developed below are based on the assumption of small displacements.   For instance, in Fig. 5.2, if the end A of the rigid bar AB (joining origins A and B) is given a small rotation ϕ, the displacement of end B is taken to be a rotation ϕ together with a vertical translation $L\phi$.   The latter value can be used only if ϕ is small.

Axis transformation is of fundamental importance to the subject of frame analysis.   Expressions will be developed for the effect of translation and rotation of axes on a system of forces acting at a point and also upon a set of displacements which take place at a point in a structure.

5.2   TRANSLATION OF AXES

Suppose that forces p_1, p_2 and p_3 act along the axes x, y, z whose origin is at O (Fig. 5.3), and couples p_4, p_5 and p_6 act around these axes.   New axes $\bar{x}$, $\bar{y}$, $\bar{z}$, parallel to x, y, z have their origin at O', which has coordinates (X, Y, Z) with respect to the original axes.   It is required to find the values of forces $\bar{p}_1$, $\bar{p}_2$ and $\bar{p}_3$ acting along $\bar{x}$, $\bar{y}$, $\bar{z}$, and couples $\bar{p}_4$, $\bar{p}_5$ and $\bar{p}_6$ acting around these axes, such that the system of actions $\bar{p}$ is statically equivalent to the system p.

The two systems are resolved parallel to $\bar{x}$, $\bar{y}$ and $\bar{z}$ in turn, and moments are taken around $\bar{x}$, $\bar{y}$ and $\bar{z}$.   Equating the components of the two systems

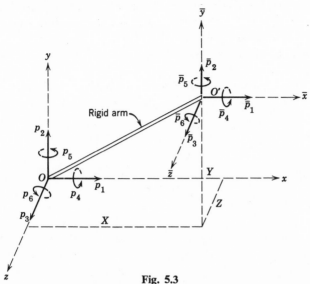

Fig. 5.3

in each case, we have

$$\bar{p}_1 = p_1$$

$$\bar{p}_2 = p_2$$

$$\bar{p}_3 = p_3$$

$$\bar{p}_4 = p_4 + Zp_2 - Yp_3$$

$$\bar{p}_5 = p_5 + Xp_3 - Zp_1$$

$$\bar{p}_6 = p_6 + Yp_1 - Xp_2$$

These equations can be expressed in matrix form:

$$
\begin{bmatrix} \bar{p}_1 \\ \bar{p}_2 \\ \bar{p}_3 \\ \bar{p}_4 \\ \bar{p}_5 \\ \bar{p}_6 \end{bmatrix}
=
\begin{bmatrix}
1 & 0 & 0 & 0 & 0 & 0 \\
0 & 1 & 0 & 0 & 0 & 0 \\
0 & 0 & 1 & 0 & 0 & 0 \\
0 & +Z & -Y & 1 & 0 & 0 \\
-Z & 0 & +X & 0 & 1 & 0 \\
+Y & -X & 0 & 0 & 0 & 1
\end{bmatrix}
\begin{bmatrix} p_1 \\ p_2 \\ p_3 \\ p_4 \\ p_5 \\ p_6 \end{bmatrix}
$$

This defines a transformation matrix T such that

$$\bar{p} = Tp \tag{5.1}$$

If a further shift of origin is made to O'' involving a transformation matrix T_1, the system of forces $\bar{p}$ at O'' will be given by

$$\bar{\bar{p}} = T_1\bar{p} = T_1Tp$$

In the particular case where the second translation restores the origin to O, $\bar{p} = p$ and $T_1 T = I$. Moreover, since the second shift is the reverse of the first, T_1 will be similar to T with X, Y and Z reversed in sign. Consequently, reversing the sign of X, Y and Z in matrix T forms the inverse T^{-1}.

It is often convenient to refer to T by its submatrices (Appendix, p. 279). If we let

$$X = \begin{bmatrix} 0 & +Z & -Y \\ -Z & 0 & +X \\ +Y & -X & 0 \end{bmatrix} \tag{5.2}$$

we can write

$$T = \left[\begin{array}{c|c} I & O \\ \hline X & I \end{array} \right] \tag{5.3}$$

where I is a unit matrix of order (3×3) and O is a null matrix of order (3×3). The inverse of T can be written

$$T^{-1} = \begin{bmatrix} I & O \\ -X & I \end{bmatrix} = \begin{bmatrix} I & O \\ X^T & I \end{bmatrix} \tag{5.4}$$

since transposing X has the same effect as changing its sign.

To transform the displacements, we suppose that the origins O and O' (Fig. 5.3) are joined by a rigid arm and displacements $u_1 \ldots u_6$ are imposed at O. Provided the rotations u_4, u_5 and u_6 are small, the resulting displacements of the end O' will be

$$\bar{u}_1 = u_1 + Zu_5 - Yu_6$$
$$\bar{u}_2 = u_2 + Xu_6 - Zu_4$$
$$\bar{u}_3 = u_3 + Yu_4 - Xu_5$$
$$\bar{u}_4 = u_4$$
$$\bar{u}_5 = u_5$$
$$\bar{u}_6 = u_6$$

In matrix form

$$\begin{bmatrix} \bar{u}_1 \\ \bar{u}_2 \\ \bar{u}_3 \\ \bar{u}_4 \\ \bar{u}_5 \\ \bar{u}_6 \end{bmatrix} = \begin{bmatrix} 1 & 0 & 0 & 0 & +Z & -Y \\ 0 & 1 & 0 & -Z & 0 & +X \\ 0 & 0 & 1 & +Y & -X & 0 \\ 0 & 0 & 0 & 1 & 0 & 0 \\ 0 & 0 & 0 & 0 & 1 & 0 \\ 0 & 0 & 0 & 0 & 0 & 1 \end{bmatrix} \begin{bmatrix} u_1 \\ u_2 \\ u_3 \\ u_4 \\ u_5 \\ u_6 \end{bmatrix}$$

Recognizing this square matrix as the transpose of T^{-1}, we can write these equations as

$$\bar{u} = (T^{-1})^T u \tag{5.5}$$

5.3 CONTRAGREDIENCE

Once we had obtained the transformation rule for forces, (equation 5.1), the rule for the transformation of displacements could have been derived very quickly by using the *principle of contragredience*. This principle, which follows directly from the virtual work theorem, will now be explained.

In Section 4.1 we found, by the use of virtual work, that if forces at A and B were related by the equation

$$p_B = h_{BA} \cdot p_A$$

then the corresponding displacements would be related by the equation

$$u_A = h_{BA} \cdot u_B$$

This relationship can be extended to the situation where p_A and p_B each represents groups of forces. We suppose that forces $p_{A1}, p_{A2} \ldots p_{An}$ act at locations $A_1, A_2 \ldots A_n$. Each of these gives rise to forces at points $B_1, B_2 \ldots B_m$. If the forces at B points are linearly related to the forces at the A points, then by superposition we can write

$$p_{B1} = h_{11}p_{A1} + h_{12}p_{A2} + \cdots + h_{1n}p_{An}$$

$$\cdot$$
$$\cdot$$
$$\cdot$$

$$p_{Bm} = h_{m1}p_{A1} + h_{m2}p_{A2} + \cdots + h_{mn}p_{An}$$

or
$$\underset{(m \times 1)}{p_B} = \underset{(m \times n)}{H_{BA}} \underset{(n \times 1)}{p_A} \tag{5.6}$$

where the matrix H_{BA} is of order $(m \times n)$.

We now discuss the effect of displacements $u_{B1}, u_{B2} \ldots u_{Bm}$ introduced at the B points. By the virtual work theorem the displacement u_{B1} will cause displacements $h_{11}u_{B1}, h_{12}u_{B1}, h_{13}u_{B1} \ldots h_{1n}u_{B1}$ at the various A points. The effect of each of the u_B displacements individually can be derived from the previous theorem. Then by superposition we can write

$$u_{A1} = h_{11}u_{B1} + h_{21}u_{B2} + \cdots + h_{m1}u_{Bm}$$
$$u_{A2} = h_{12}u_{B1} + h_{22}u_{B2} + \cdots + h_{m2}u_{Bm}$$
$$\cdot$$
$$\cdot$$
$$\cdot$$

$$u_{An} = h_{1n}u_{B1} + \cdots \qquad + h_{mn}u_{Bm}$$

or
$$[u_A] = [H_{BA}]^T [u_B] \tag{5.7}$$

For multiple forces and displacements in the A and B system we therefore have that

$$\text{if} \quad p_B = H_{BA}p_A \tag{5.8a}$$

$$\text{then} \quad u_A = H_{BA}^T u_B \tag{5.8b}$$

For single quantities the matrix H becomes a scalar and transposition is of no account.

The relationship of equations 5.8a and 5.8b is expressed by saying that forces and displacements transform contragrediently.

Applying this principle to the transformations of section 5.2, we see that since

$$\bar{p} = Tp$$
$$u = T^T \bar{u}$$

and since T is square in this case

$$\bar{u} = (T^{-1})^T u$$

5.4 ROTATION OF AXES

As before, suppose that a system of six actions $p_1 \ldots p_6$ acts in the axes x, y, z. Without change of origin, the axes are rotated to the directions $\bar{x}$, $\bar{y}$, $\bar{z}$ whose direction cosines relative to the original axes are $(\lambda_1 \, \mu_1 \, \nu_1)$, $(\lambda_2 \, \mu_2 \, \nu_2)$ and $(\lambda_3 \, \mu_3 \, \nu_3)$ respectively (Fig. 5.4). In the new axes a system of forces $\bar{p}_1 \ldots \bar{p}_6$ is found which is statically equivalent to the original system. The equivalence is determined as before by resolving parallel to $\bar{x}$, $\bar{y}$, $\bar{z}$ and taking moments around these axes. In this way we obtain

$$\bar{p}_1 = \lambda_1 p_1 + \mu_1 p_2 + \nu_1 p_3$$
$$\bar{p}_2 = \lambda_2 p_1 + \mu_2 p_2 + \nu_2 p_3$$
$$\bar{p}_3 = \lambda_3 p_1 + \mu_3 p_2 + \nu_3 p_3$$
$$\bar{p}_4 = \lambda_1 p_4 + \mu_1 p_5 + \nu_1 p_6$$
$$\bar{p}_5 = \lambda_2 p_4 + \mu_2 p_5 + \nu_2 p_6$$
$$\bar{p}_6 = \lambda_3 p_4 + \mu_3 p_5 + \nu_3 p_6$$

In matrix form

$$
\begin{bmatrix} \bar{p}_1 \\ \bar{p}_2 \\ \bar{p}_3 \\ \bar{p}_4 \\ \bar{p}_5 \\ \bar{p}_6 \end{bmatrix}
=
\begin{bmatrix}
\lambda_1 & \mu_1 & \nu_1 & 0 & 0 & 0 \\
\lambda_2 & \mu_2 & \nu_2 & 0 & 0 & 0 \\
\lambda_3 & \mu_3 & \nu_3 & 0 & 0 & 0 \\
0 & 0 & 0 & \lambda_1 & \mu_1 & \nu_1 \\
0 & 0 & 0 & \lambda_2 & \mu_2 & \nu_2 \\
0 & 0 & 0 & \lambda_3 & \mu_3 & \nu_3
\end{bmatrix}
\begin{bmatrix} p_1 \\ p_2 \\ p_3 \\ p_4 \\ p_5 \\ p_6 \end{bmatrix}
$$

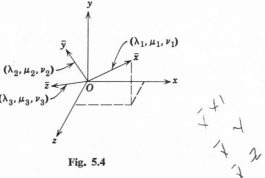

Fig. 5.4

which defines a transformation matrix R such that

$$\bar{p} = Rp \tag{5.9}$$

The inverse of R can be found by resolving along, and taking moments around, axes x, y, z, thus obtaining a relationship in the form

$$p = R^{-1}\bar{p}$$

Such a procedure would show that R^{-1} is the transpose of R. The truth of this may be checked by multiplying R by its transpose. It is to be noted that for each axis $\lambda^2 + \mu^2 + \nu^2 = 1$. Furthermore, because $\bar{x}$ and $\bar{y}$ are perpendicular directions $\lambda_1\lambda_2 + \mu_1\mu_2 + \nu_1\nu_2 = 0$. Similar equations apply to $\bar{y}$ and $\bar{z}$, and to $\bar{z}$ and $\bar{x}$.

As with the matrix of translation, T, the matrix of rotation can be conveniently expressed in terms of submatrices. Putting

$$\lambda = \begin{bmatrix} \lambda_1 & \mu_1 & \nu_1 \\ \lambda_2 & \mu_2 & \nu_2 \\ \lambda_3 & \mu_3 & \nu_3 \end{bmatrix} \tag{5.10}$$

we can write

$$R = \left[\begin{array}{c|c} \lambda & O \\ \hline O & \lambda \end{array}\right] \tag{5.11}$$

The inverse of R is then

$$R^{-1} = R^T = \left[\begin{array}{c|c} \lambda^T & O \\ \hline O & \lambda^T \end{array}\right] \tag{5.12}$$

For the transformation of the displacements we can apply contragredience which, from equation 5.6, gives

$$u = R^T\bar{u}$$
$$= R^{-1}\bar{u}$$

so that

$$\bar{u} = Ru \tag{5.13}$$

5.5 ROTATION AND TRANSLATION OF AXES

If the axes undergo both translation and rotation, the translation being effected first, a force system p will be finally changed to

$$\bar{p} = RTp \tag{5.14}$$

The product of the matrices R and T will define a single axis transformation matrix which will be denoted by A.

$$\bar{p} = Ap \tag{5.15}$$

Since, in terms of (3×3) submatrices,

$$R = \begin{bmatrix} \lambda & O \\ O & \lambda \end{bmatrix} \quad \text{and} \quad T = \begin{bmatrix} I & O \\ X & I \end{bmatrix}$$

then

$$A = \begin{bmatrix} \lambda & O \\ O & \lambda \end{bmatrix} \begin{bmatrix} I & O \\ X & I \end{bmatrix} = \begin{bmatrix} \lambda & O \\ \hline \lambda X & \lambda \end{bmatrix} \tag{5.16}$$

We can also obtain A^{-1} in similar terms

$$A^{-1} = (RT)^{-1}$$

$$= T^{-1}R^{-1}$$

$$= \begin{bmatrix} I & O \\ X^T & I \end{bmatrix} \begin{bmatrix} \lambda^T & O \\ O & \lambda^T \end{bmatrix} = \begin{bmatrix} \lambda^T & O \\ \hline X^T\lambda^T & \lambda^T \end{bmatrix} \tag{5.17}$$

It is, of course, permissible to perform the rotational transformation first, in which case we should have $\bar{p} = TRp$ and $A = TR$. However, the rotation having been effected, it would be necessary to determine the position of the new origin O' with respect to the rotated axes before carrying out the translation. Normally, it is advantageous to perform the translation first so that the co-ordinates of O' relative to the original axes, namely XYZ, can be used in the matrix T. The two methods are illustrated in Example 5.1.

The combined effect of translation and rotation of axes upon a system of displacements can also be expressed by means of a single transformation matrix. Assuming that the translation is effected first, we have, from equation 5.15 and the principle of contragredience,

$$\bar{u} = (A^{-1})^T u \qquad (5.18)$$

The matrix $(A^{-1})^T$ can be written in terms of its submatrices by transposing each side of equation 5.17, giving

$$(A^{-1})^T = \left[\begin{array}{c:c} \lambda & \lambda X \\ \hdashline O & \lambda \end{array}\right] \qquad (5.19)$$

The relationship of this matrix to the matrix A (equation 5.16) should be noted.

When a system of forces or displacements in the xy plane is transformed to another system in the same plane, only the first, second and sixth rows and columns of the various matrices are significant, and by omitting the others each matrix can be reduced to order (3×3).

Example 5.1   Figure 5.5 shows a coplanar system of forces acting at O. It is required to find the statically equivalent system acting in the axes $\bar{x}\bar{y}$ at O' whose co-ordinates relative to xy are $(4, 4)$.   The axes are rotated 20° anti-clockwise.

Solution 1.   If the translation is performed first, the origin is shifted to the point $X = 4$, $Y = 4$.   If rows 3, 4 and 5 are omitted from T and the corresponding columns, T becomes

$$T = \begin{bmatrix} 1 & 0 & 0 \\ 0 & 1 & 0 \\ Y & -X & 1 \end{bmatrix} = \begin{bmatrix} 1 & 0 & 0 \\ 0 & 1 & 0 \\ 4 & -4 & 1 \end{bmatrix}$$

The direction cosines of $\bar{x}$ are (cos 20°, sin 20°, 0) and the direction cosines of $\bar{y}$ are (−sin 20°, cos 20°, 0).   Omitting the irrelevant rows and

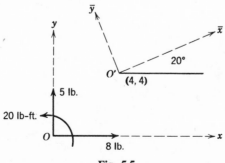

Fig. 5.5

columns from R, we have

$$R = \begin{bmatrix} \lambda_1 & \mu_1 & 0 \\ \lambda_2 & \mu_2 & 0 \\ 0 & 0 & 1 \end{bmatrix} = \begin{bmatrix} \cos 20° & \sin 20° & 0 \\ -\sin 20° & \cos 20° & 0 \\ 0 & 0 & 1 \end{bmatrix}$$

$$A = RT = \begin{bmatrix} 0.9397 & 0.3420 & 0 \\ -0.3420 & 0.9397 & 0 \\ 0 & 0 & 1 \end{bmatrix} \begin{bmatrix} 1 & 0 & 0 \\ 0 & 1 & 0 \\ 4 & -4 & 1 \end{bmatrix}$$

$$= \begin{bmatrix} 0.9397 & 0.3420 & 0 \\ -0.3420 & 0.9397 & 0 \\ 4 & -4 & 1 \end{bmatrix}$$

Now the original actions are

$$p = \begin{bmatrix} p_1 \\ p_2 \\ p_6 \end{bmatrix} = \begin{bmatrix} +8 \\ +5 \\ +20 \end{bmatrix}$$

Therefore

$$\bar{p} = Ap = \begin{bmatrix} 0.9397 & 0.3420 & 0 \\ -0.3420 & 0.9397 & 0 \\ 4 & -4 & 1 \end{bmatrix} \begin{bmatrix} +8 \\ +5 \\ +20 \end{bmatrix} = \begin{bmatrix} +9.23 \\ +1.96 \\ +32.00 \end{bmatrix}$$

Solution 2.   Alternatively, if the rotation is carried out first, the matrix R is unaltered but, it is now necessary to calculate the co-ordinates, $X_1 Y_1$, of O' relative to axes $x_1 y_1$ (Fig. 5.6).

$$X_1 = 4 \cos 20° + 4 \sin 20° = 5.1268$$

$$Y_1 = -4 \sin 20° + 4 \cos 20° = 2.3908$$

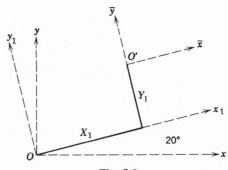

Fig. 5.6

The translation matrix is then

$$
T = \begin{bmatrix} 1 & 0 & 0 \\ 0 & 1 & 0 \\ Y_1 & -X_1 & 1 \end{bmatrix} = \begin{bmatrix} 1 & 0 & 0 \\ 0 & 1 & 0 \\ 2.3908 & -5.1268 & 1 \end{bmatrix}
$$

$$
A = TR = \begin{bmatrix} 1 & 0 & 0 \\ 0 & 1 & 0 \\ 2.3908 & -5.1268 & 1 \end{bmatrix} \begin{bmatrix} 0.9397 & 0.3420 & 0 \\ -0.3420 & 0.9397 & 0 \\ 0 & 0 & 1 \end{bmatrix}
$$

$$
= \begin{bmatrix} 0.9397 & 0.3420 & 0 \\ -0.3420 & 0.9397 & 0 \\ 4.0000 & -4.0000 & 1 \end{bmatrix}
$$

Then $\bar{p} = Ap$ as before.

It is seen that both methods lead to the same value of A, but if the calculations of A in the two solutions are compared, the disadvantages of the second method are obvious. The disadvantages are emphasized in a more complex problem. In certain problems, however, it may be easier to perform the rotation first.

Example 5.2 Figure 5.7 shows a three-dimensional force system acting at O in axes xyz. The origin is to be shifted to the point $(3, -1, 4)$. The

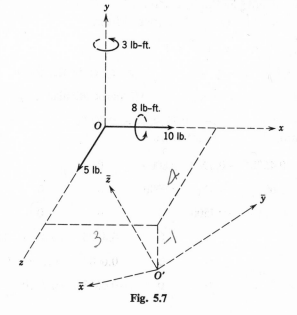

Fig. 5.7

axes are to be rotated to $\bar{x}\bar{y}\bar{z}$. Axis $\bar{y}$ has direction cosines of 0.6 with both x and z; its direction cosine with y is positive.   Axis $\bar{z}$ lies in a plane parallel to xy, and has a negative direction cosine with axis x.

Solution.   The translation matrix T has the value

$$T = \begin{bmatrix} 1 & 0 & 0 & 0 & 0 & 0 \\ 0 & 1 & 0 & 0 & 0 & 0 \\ 0 & 0 & 1 & 0 & 0 & 0 \\ 0 & 4 & 1 & 1 & 0 & 0 \\ -4 & 0 & 3 & 0 & 1 & 0 \\ -1 & -3 & 0 & 0 & 0 & 1 \end{bmatrix}$$

Considering the direction of $\bar{y}$, we are given that $\lambda_2 = 0.6$ and $\nu_2 = 0.6$. The value of μ_2 can be calculated from

$$\lambda_2^2 + \mu_2^2 + \nu_2^2 = 1$$

giving $\mu_2 = 0.5292$.

Considering the direction of $\bar{z}$, we are given that $\nu_3 = 0$.   The values of λ_3 and μ_3 are found from

$$\lambda_3^2 + \mu_3^2 + \nu_3^2 = 1$$

and $\lambda_2\lambda_3 + \mu_2\mu_3 + \nu_2\nu_3 = 0$ ($\bar{z}$ perpendicular to $\bar{y}$)

giving $\lambda_3 = -0.6615$ and $\mu_3 = 0.7500$.

The direction of $\bar{x}$ can now be obtained from

$$\lambda_1^2 + \mu_1^2 + \nu_1^2 = 1$$

$$\lambda_1\lambda_2 + \mu_1\mu_2 + \nu_1\nu_2 = 0 \qquad (\bar{x} \text{ perpendicular to } \bar{y})$$

$$\lambda_1\lambda_3 + \mu_1\mu_3 + \nu_1\nu_3 = 0 \qquad (\bar{x} \text{ perpendicular to } \bar{z})$$

giving $\lambda_1 = -0.4500$, $\mu_1 = -0.3969$, $\nu_1 = 0.8000$.

The rotation matrix R is therefore

$$R = \begin{bmatrix} -0.4500 & -0.3969 & 0.8000 & 0 & 0 & 0 \\ 0.6000 & 0.5292 & 0.6000 & 0 & 0 & 0 \\ -0.6615 & 0.7500 & 0 & 0 & 0 & 0 \\ 0 & 0 & 0 & -0.4500 & -0.3969 & 0.8000 \\ 0 & 0 & 0 & 0.6000 & 0.5292 & 0.6000 \\ 0 & 0 & 0 & -0.6615 & 0.7500 & 0 \end{bmatrix}$$

and by matrix multiplication

$$A = RT = \begin{bmatrix} -0.4500 & -0.3969 & 0.8000 & 0 & 0 & 0 \\ 0.6000 & 0.5292 & 0.6000 & 0 & 0 & 0 \\ -0.6615 & 0.7500 & 0 & 0 & 0 & 0 \\ +0.7876 & -4.2000 & -1.6407 & -0.4500 & -0.3969 & 0.8000 \\ -2.7168 & 0.6000 & 2.1876 & 0.6000 & 0.5292 & 0.6000 \\ -3.0000 & -2.6459 & 1.5884 & -0.6615 & 0.7500 & 0 \end{bmatrix}$$

The original actions are

$$p = \begin{bmatrix} +10 \\ 0 \\ +5 \\ +8 \\ +3 \\ 0 \end{bmatrix}$$

The statically equivalent system in axes $\bar{x}\bar{y}\bar{z}$ is therefore

$$\bar{p} = Ap = \begin{bmatrix} -0.50 \\ 9.00 \\ -6.61 \\ -5.10 \\ -9.84 \\ -25.10 \end{bmatrix}$$

The transformation of forces and displacements can be summarized. Suppose we are effecting a change of axes from C to D. The forces at D are given by the transformation

$$p_D = A_{\overleftarrow{DC}} p_C \qquad (5.20)$$

That is to say, the forces have been transformed from the axes represented by the second subscript (of the matrix A) to the axes represented by the first subscript.

On the other hand, displacements at D are given by the transformation

$$u_D = A_{\overrightarrow{CD}}^T u_C \qquad (5.21)$$

That is to say, the displacements have been transformed from the axes represented by the first subscript to those represented by the second subscript. Also, in the case of displacements, the A matrix is transposed.

The matrix A_{DC} is interpreted as a matrix of the form given by equation 5.16, in which the axes at D (first subscript) are expressed in terms of those at C (second subscript), which are regarded as the initial axes. The matrix A_{CD} is a matrix expressing the axes at C in terms of those at D. Alternatively, A_{CD} can be regarded as A_{DC}^{-1}.

It should be noted that an arrow placed above the subscripts merely emphasizes the source and destination of the quantities being transformed. In any case, the A matrix is written with the *second* subscript regarded as that of the original axes.

Suppose we transform a set of forces first from C to D, and subsequently from D to E. The two transformations can be written

$$p_D = A_{DC}p_C$$

and

$$p_E = A_{ED}p_D$$

Hence

$$p_E = A_{ED} \cdot A_{DC}p_C$$

From physical considerations it is clear that a direct transformation from C to E must produce the same result. Since the direct change would be written

$$p_E = A_{EC}p_C$$

it follows that

$$A_{EC} = A_{ED}A_{DC} \tag{5.22}$$

The displacement transformation, if performed in two stages, will be

$$u_E = A_{DE}^T A_{CD}^T u_C$$

If the transformation were made directly from C to E we would have

$$u_E = A_{CE}^T u_C$$

This implies that

$$A_{CE}^T = A_{DE}^T A_{CD}^T$$
$$= (A_{CD}A_{DE})^T$$

and this agrees with equation 5.22.

Clearly this relationship could be extended so that a single change of axes could be expressed in terms of a number of intermediate steps. An interesting case results when the component steps are all identical. For instance, suppose that $A, B, C \ldots$ are equally spaced points around a helix (Fig. 5.8). If, at each point, the x axis is tangential to the helix and the z axis is horizontal, the change from each set of axes to the next is the same, that is,

$$A_{BA} = A_{CB} = A_{DC} = \cdots$$

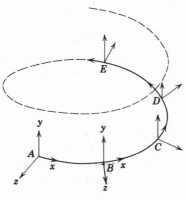

Fig. 5.8

Then
$$A_{EA} = A_{ED}A_{DC}A_{CB}A_{BA}$$
$$= A_{BA}A_{BA}A_{BA}A_{BA}$$
$$= [A_{BA}]^4 \tag{5.23}$$

If a set of actions p_C is transformed from axes C to axes D and afterwards back again to axes C, the actions will revert to their original values. Thus

$$p_D = A_{DC}p_C$$

and
$$p_C = A_{CD}p_D$$
$$= A_{CD}A_{DC}p_C$$

Since this identity must hold for any values of p_C, it follows that the product $(A_{CD}A_{DC})$ must be a unit matrix, so that

$$A_{DC} = A_{CD}^{-1} \tag{5.24}$$

The transformations developed in this chapter are used extensively in the remainder of the book.

PROBLEMS

5.1. The column vector $\{2, 10, -5, 6.2, 8.1, -11.3\}$ represents a system of forces p_A expressed in axes at A, and in units of kips and feet. B is a point whose co-ordinates relative to A are $(-4, -16, 0)$. The axis z_B is parallel to z_A and x_B makes an angle of $-25°$ with x_A. Determine the system of forces p_B which is statically equivalent to p_A.

5.2. A three-dimensional system of forces is expressed in certain axes. Write down the matrices which will transform these forces (1) when the axes are rotated by $+20°$ about the z axis and (2) when the axes are rotated by $-10°$ about the y axis.

5.3. A two-dimensional force system is expressed in axes $(x_A \, y_A)$ at A. The origin is transferred to B (3, 8) and the axes rotated so that x_B is $-90°$ from x_A. Write down the matrix which will transform p_A to an equivalent set p_B.

5.4. A system of forces 10 pounds, 0 pounds, -8 pounds, 2 pound-feet, -3 pound-feet, 0 pound-feet acts in orthogonal axes at a point A. The point B has co-ordinates (1, 2, 8) relative to the axes at A. The y axis at B is parallel to the y axis at A. The x axis at B has direction cosines of (0.6, 0, 0.8) with the axes at A. Find the system of forces in the axes at B which is statically equivalent to the given system at A.

5.5. A system of forces p_A is expressed in axes (x, y, z) at A (Fig. P5.5). The axes are rotated to $(\bar{x}, \bar{y}, \bar{z})$ at B in two stages: (1) a rotation about a line parallel to z through C (0, -12, 0), and (2) a rotation of $-10°$ about the new $\bar{y}$ axis.

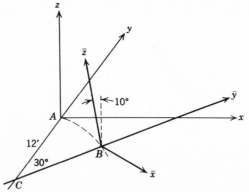

Fig. P5.5

If $p_B = A \cdot p_A$, derive the matrix A as the product of three transformation matrices, each of which represents either a pure translation or a pure rotation.

5.6. A and B are two points on a rigid body. The point B has co-ordinates (100, 150, 120) inches relative to the axes at A. The axis y_B is parallel to the axis y_A and x_B has direction cosines (0.6, 0, 0.8) with the axes at A. If the point A undergoes displacements represented, in inches and radians, by the vector (0.25, 0.8, -0.1, 0.002, -0.0032, -0.0015), find the displacement of the point B expressed in the axes at B.

5.7. A set of small displacements are expressed in axes (x, y, z) at A. Re-express these displacements in terms of axes $(\bar{x}, \bar{y}, \bar{z})$ at A, such that $\bar{x}$ coincides with $-y$ and $\bar{y}$ coincides with $+z$.

5.8. A rigid bar AB lies in the xy plane, the co-ordinates of B relative to axes $(x_A \, y_A)$ at A being (2, 8) in feet. The axes at B are at $+30°$ to those at A. If A is given displacements of $u_1 = +0.5$ foot, $u_2 = -1.2$ feet and $u_6 = +20°$, calculate the true displacements of B in the axes at B, and the error involved when these displacements are calculated according to small-displacement theory.

CHAPTER 6

Flexibility Analysis of a Single Member

Of special interest is the expression for the flexibility of one end of a single member, the other end of which is completely fixed. A member fixed at both ends and having an axis not lying in one plane is sixfold statically indeterminate. If the member is entirely separated from the support B (Fig. 6.1), leaving it cantilevered from A, the six component actions at B will comprise the redundants. The free end of the cantilever is capable of six displacements. The six actions at B are related to the six displacements at B by thirty-six flexibility coefficients in the form of a (6×6) matrix, which will be denoted by f_{BB}.

In the first instance the natural axes of the member at B will be employed for the expression of f_{BB}. In some cases other axes will suggest themselves as being more convenient, and the re-expression of the flexibility in these axes will be discussed.

Fig. 6.1

6.1 END FLEXIBILITY OF A MEMBER

The flexibility coefficients can be derived by the methods of Chapter 4, which are applicable generally. In the present instance, the redundants consist of six actions all applied at one end of the member. The first step is to derive expressions for the internal actions at any point Q (Fig. 6.2) in terms of these end actions. The six internal actions at Q can be represented by a column matrix M, and the six end actions can be represented by a column matrix p. We note that, irrespective of the shape of the member, the actions M are linear functions of p provided that the deformation of the member has no appreciable effect upon M. We can therefore express the relationship in the form

$$M = mp \qquad (6.1)$$

This defines a square matrix, m, of order (6×6), the characteristics of which will be found to depend upon the nature of the cross-section of the member, and upon whether the actions p are applied at the left-hand end or the right-hand end of the member.

In this case the actions will be applied at the right-hand end B (Fig. 6.2). It will be assumed that the shear center at Q coincides with the centroid of the section. In such a case the twisting moment at Q is obtained by taking moments of p around the centroidal axis at Q. Later, we shall consider the case when the shear center is not at the centroid of the section.

The member axes at Q are denoted by $\bar{x}$, $\bar{y}$, $\bar{z}$, whose directions are such that they have direction cosines $(\lambda_1, \mu_1, \nu_1)$, $(\lambda_2, \mu_2, \nu_2)$ and $(\lambda_3, \mu_3, \nu_3)$, respectively, relative to the axes at B. The elements of the matrix m are found by applying successively unit values of the redundants p and finding the resulting internal actions at Q.

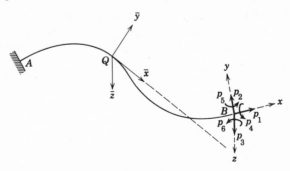

Fig. 6.2

We apply first a unit force at B in the x direction. By resolving this unit force in the direction $\bar{x}$ at Q we obtain

$$n_1^x = \lambda_1$$

In a similar way the two shears are obtained by resolving the unit force parallel to $\bar{y}$ and $\bar{z}$.

$$n_1^y = \lambda_2 \quad \text{and} \quad n_1^z = \lambda_3$$

The twisting moment at Q is obtained by taking the moment of the unit force around the axis $\bar{x}$. We note that if a unit force acts along any line $(X_0, Y_0, Z_0)(\lambda_0, \mu_0, \nu_0)$, its moment around any other line (X, Y, Z) (λ, μ, ν) is given by the expression

$$M = \begin{vmatrix} (X - X_0) & \lambda & \lambda_0 \\ (Y - Y_0) & \mu & \mu_0 \\ (Z - Z_0) & \nu & \nu_0 \end{vmatrix} \tag{6.2}$$

where the function enclosed by the vertical lines is a determinant and the expression $(X, Y, Z)(\lambda, \mu, \nu)$ signifies a line through the point (X, Y, Z) having direction cosines (λ, μ, ν). In the case under consideration the unit force acts along the line $(0, 0, 0)(1, 0, 0)$ and its moment is required about the line $(X, Y, Z)(\lambda_1, \mu_1, \nu_1)$. Equation 6.2 therefore leads to

$$m_1^x = \begin{vmatrix} X & \lambda_1 & 1 \\ Y & \mu_1 & 0 \\ Z & \nu_1 & 0 \end{vmatrix} = \begin{vmatrix} Y & \mu_1 \\ Z & \nu_1 \end{vmatrix} = (Y\nu_1 - Z\mu_1)$$

The moments about the two axes $\bar{y}$ and $\bar{z}$ are obtained in a similar way, merely by substituting the values $(\lambda_2, \mu_2, \nu_2)$ or $(\lambda_3, \mu_3, \nu_3)$ for the values $(\lambda_1, \mu_1, \nu_1)$ above. Hence

$$m_1^y = (Y\nu_2 - Z\mu_2) \quad \text{and} \quad m_1^z = (Y\nu_3 - Z\mu_3)$$

A similar process leads to the internal actions at Q resulting from unit values of p_2 and p_3. The expressions are given in equation 6.3 below.

The unit couple p_4, acting around the x axis at B, will induce no axial force or shears at Q. Thus

$$n_4^x = n_4^y = n_4^z = 0$$

It will, however, produce couples round $\bar{x}$, $\bar{y}$ and $\bar{z}$, given by

$$m_4^x = \lambda_1 \qquad m_4^y = \lambda_2 \qquad m_4^z = \lambda_3$$

Similarly, unit value of p_5 will cause $m_5^x = \mu_1$, $m_5^y = \mu_2$ and $m_5^z = \mu_3$, and unit value of p_6 will cause $m_6^x = \nu_1$, $m_6^y = \nu_2$ and $m_6^z = \nu_3$.

These values can be summarized in the form of a square matrix m_{QB}, where

$$m_{QB} = \begin{bmatrix} \lambda_1 & \mu_1 & \nu_1 & 0 & 0 & 0 \\ \lambda_2 & \mu_2 & \nu_2 & 0 & 0 & 0 \\ \lambda_3 & \mu_3 & \nu_3 & 0 & 0 & 0 \\ (Y\nu_1 - Z\mu_1) & (Z\lambda_1 - X\nu_1) & (X\mu_1 - Y\lambda_1) & \lambda_1 & \mu_1 & \nu_1 \\ (Y\nu_2 - Z\mu_2) & (Z\lambda_2 - X\nu_2) & (X\mu_2 - Y\lambda_2) & \lambda_2 & \mu_2 & \nu_2 \\ (Y\nu_3 - Z\mu_3) & (Z\lambda_3 - X\nu_3) & (X\mu_3 - Y\lambda_3) & \lambda_3 & \mu_3 & \nu_3 \end{bmatrix} \quad (6.3)$$

The first column of this matrix contains the internal actions at Q caused by unit p_1 at B. The second column contains the actions at Q caused by unit p_2 at B, and so on. Expressions for the various flexibility coefficients can now be found. For example, coefficient f_{23} is found from the elements of columns 2 and 3 together with the known values of the section properties. Thus

$$f_{23} = \int_A^B \frac{n_2^x n_3^x}{EA^x}\, dx + \int_A^B \frac{n_2^y n_3^y}{GA^y}\, dx + \int_A^B \frac{n_2^z n_3^z}{GA^z}\, dx$$

$$+ \int_A^B \frac{m_2^x m_3^x}{GI^x}\, dx + \int_A^B \frac{m_2^y m_3^y}{EI^y}\, dx + \int_A^B \frac{m_2^z m_3^z}{EI^z}\, dx$$

$$= \int_A^B \left[\frac{\mu_1 \nu_1}{EA^x} + \frac{\mu_2 \nu_2}{GA^y} + \frac{\mu_3 \nu_3}{GA^z} + \frac{(Z\lambda_1 - X\nu_1)(X\mu_1 - Y\lambda_1)}{GI^x} \right.$$

$$\left. + \frac{(Z\lambda_2 - X\nu_2)(X\mu_2 - Y\lambda_2)}{EI^y} + \frac{(Z\lambda_3 - X\nu_3)(X\mu_3 - Y\lambda_3)}{EI^z} \right] dx \quad (6.4)$$

This process can be described in matrix form if we define a rigidity matrix (EI) as

$$(EI) = \begin{bmatrix} EA^x & & & & & \\ & GA^y & & & & \\ & & GA^z & & & \\ & & & GI^x & & \\ & & & & EI^y & \\ & & & & & EI^z \end{bmatrix}$$

This is a diagonal matrix whose elements are the section properties at any particular point. $(EI)^{-1}$ is then a diagonal matrix having as elements the reciprocals $1/EA^x$, $1/GA^y$ ... $1/EI^z$.

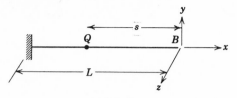

Fig. 6.3

The product $m^T(EI)^{-1}m$ is a (6×6) matrix each of whose elements yields, upon integration, the corresponding element of the flexibility matrix f_{BB}. We can write

$$f_{BB} = \int_A^B m_{QB}^T (EI)^{-1} m_{QB}\, dx \tag{6.5}$$

This matrix form should be compared with the simple case where a single flexibility coefficient is to be found and only bending distortions are considered. The coefficient is then obtained by integrating m^2/EI. The form of equation 6.5 is convenient when the calculation is to be carried out on a computer, since it allows the programming to be carried out using the same concepts as would apply to the simple case.

The flexibility of the left-hand end, f_{AA}, can be found by considering the member as cantilevered from B and applying the end forces at A. Alternatively, a flexibility transformation (see Section 9.2) can be used.

The method will be illustrated by means of a simple problem in Example 6.1. A more general problem is examined in Example 6.3.

Example 6.1 It is required to find the end flexibility coefficients for the prismatic member of Fig. 6.3.

Solution. The directions of the axes are the same for all sections. $\lambda_1 = \mu_2 = \nu_3 = 1$ and all other direction cosines are zero. For a typical point Q, which is at a distance s from the end B, the co-ordinates are $X = -s$, $Y = 0$, $Z = 0$. The matrix m is therefore

$$m_{QB} = \begin{bmatrix} 1 & 0 & 0 & 0 & 0 & 0 \\ 0 & 1 & 0 & 0 & 0 & 0 \\ 0 & 0 & 1 & 0 & 0 & 0 \\ 0 & 0 & 0 & 1 & 0 & 0 \\ 0 & 0 & -s & 0 & 1 & 0 \\ 0 & +s & 0 & 0 & 0 & 1 \end{bmatrix}$$

The matrix $(EI)^{-1}$ contains constant elements in this case. We have

$$m^T(EI)^{-1} =$$

$$
\begin{bmatrix}
1 & 0 & 0 & 0 & 0 & 0 \\
0 & 1 & 0 & 0 & 0 & +s \\
0 & 0 & 1 & 0 & -s & 0 \\
0 & 0 & 0 & 1 & 0 & 0 \\
0 & 0 & 0 & 0 & 1 & 0 \\
0 & 0 & 0 & 0 & 0 & 1
\end{bmatrix}
\begin{bmatrix}
1/EA^x & 0 & 0 & 0 & 0 & 0 \\
0 & 1/GA^y & 0 & 0 & 0 & 0 \\
0 & 0 & 1/GA^z & 0 & 0 & 0 \\
0 & 0 & 0 & 1/GI^x & 0 & 0 \\
0 & 0 & 0 & 0 & 1/EI^y & 0 \\
0 & 0 & 0 & 0 & 0 & 1/EI^z
\end{bmatrix}
$$

$$
=
\begin{bmatrix}
1/EA^x & 0 & 0 & 0 & 0 & 0 \\
0 & 1/GA^y & 0 & 0 & 0 & +s/EI^z \\
0 & 0 & 1/GA^z & 0 & -s/EI^y & 0 \\
0 & 0 & 0 & 1/GI^x & 0 & 0 \\
0 & 0 & 0 & 0 & 1/EI^y & 0 \\
0 & 0 & 0 & 0 & 0 & 1/EI^z
\end{bmatrix}
$$

It will be seen that the effect of postmultiplication by $(EI)^{-1}$ upon the matrix m^T is to multiply the elements of the first column of m^T by the first element of $(EI)^{-1}$, the elements of the second column by the second element of $(EI)^{-1}$ and so on. Postmultiplying $m^T(EI)^{-1}$ by m we obtain

$$m^T(EI)^{-1}m =$$

$$
\begin{bmatrix}
1/EA^x & 0 & 0 & 0 & 0 & 0 \\
0 & \left(\dfrac{1}{GA^y}+\dfrac{s^2}{EI^z}\right) & 0 & 0 & 0 & +s/EI^z \\
0 & 0 & \left(\dfrac{1}{GA^z}+\dfrac{s^2}{EI^y}\right) & 0 & -s/EI^y & 0 \\
0 & 0 & 0 & 1/GI^x & 0 & 0 \\
0 & 0 & -s/EI^y & 0 & 1/EI^y & 0 \\
0 & +s/EI^z & 0 & 0 & 0 & 1/EI^z
\end{bmatrix}
$$

Each of these elements is now integrated with respect to s from B to A, that is, from $s = 0$ to $s = L$.   This gives

$$f_{BB} =$$

$$\begin{bmatrix} L/EA^x & 0 & 0 & 0 & 0 & 0 \\ 0 & \left(\dfrac{L}{GA^y} + \dfrac{L^3}{3EI^z}\right) & 0 & 0 & 0 & L^2/2EI^z \\ 0 & 0 & \left(\dfrac{L}{GA^z} + \dfrac{L^3}{3EI^y}\right) & 0 & -L^2/2EI^y & 0 \\ 0 & 0 & 0 & L/GI^x & 0 & 0 \\ 0 & 0 & -L^2/2EI^y & 0 & L/EI^y & 0 \\ 0 & L^2/2EI^z & 0 & 0 & 0 & L/EI^z \end{bmatrix}$$

$$(6.6)$$

Most of these values are well known from elementary theory.   The element f_{11} ($= L/EA^x$) gives the axial extension due to unit axial force. The element f_{22} $\left(= \dfrac{L}{GA^y} + \dfrac{L^3}{3EI^z}\right)$ gives the vertical deflection of the cantilever under unit vertical force, shear distortions being included. The element f_{26} ($= L^2/2EI^z$) gives the vertical deflection due to a unit end couple in the vertical plane.

Example 6.2 The bow girder AB of Fig. 6.4 has a constant section and forms the arc of a circle subtending an angle of $120°$.   Find the end flexibility matrix.

Solution.   At a typical point Q, the co-ordinates are

$$X = -R \sin \theta \qquad Y = 0 \qquad Z = -R(1 - \cos \theta)$$

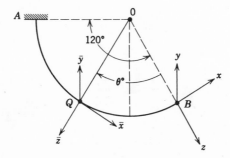

Fig. 6.4

$$
f_{BB} =
\begin{bmatrix}
\dfrac{0.831R}{EA^x} + \dfrac{1.264R}{GA^z} + 1.193\dfrac{R^3}{EI^y} & 0 & +0.375\left(\dfrac{R}{EA^x} - \dfrac{R}{GA^z}\right) - 1.125\dfrac{R^3}{EI^y} & 0 & 1.228\dfrac{R^2}{EI^y} & 0 \\[4mm]
0 & \dfrac{2.094R}{GA^y} + 1.193\dfrac{R^3}{GI^x} + 1.264\dfrac{R^3}{EI^z} & 0 & 0.035\dfrac{R^2}{GI^x} - 1.264\dfrac{R^2}{EI^z} & 0 & 1.125\dfrac{R^2}{GI^x} + 0.375\dfrac{R^2}{EI^z} \\[4mm]
+0.375\left(\dfrac{R}{EA^x} - \dfrac{R}{GA^z}\right) - 1.125\dfrac{R^3}{EI^y} & 0 & \dfrac{1.264R}{EA^x} + \dfrac{0.831R}{GA^z} + 1.264\dfrac{R^3}{EI^y} & 0 & -1.500\dfrac{R^2}{EI^y} & 0 \\[4mm]
0 & 0.035\dfrac{R^2}{GI^x} - 1.264\dfrac{R^2}{EI^z} & 0 & 0.831\dfrac{R}{GI^x} + 1.264\dfrac{R}{EI^z} & 0 & 0.375\dfrac{R}{GI^x} - 0.375\dfrac{R}{EI^z} \\[4mm]
1.228\dfrac{R^2}{EI^y} & 0 & -1.500\dfrac{R^2}{EI^y} & 0 & \dfrac{2.094R}{EI^y} & 0 \\[4mm]
0 & 1.125\dfrac{R^2}{GI^x} + 0.375\dfrac{R^2}{EI^z} & 0 & 0.375\dfrac{R}{GI^x} - 0.375\dfrac{R}{EI^z} & 0 & \dfrac{1.264R}{GI^x} + 0.831\dfrac{R}{EI^z}
\end{bmatrix}
\tag{6.7}
$$

The direction cosines of the axes at Q are

$$\begin{bmatrix} \lambda_1 & \mu_1 & \nu_1 \\ \lambda_2 & \mu_2 & \nu_2 \\ \lambda_3 & \mu_3 & \nu_3 \end{bmatrix} = \begin{bmatrix} \cos\theta & 0 & \sin\theta \\ 0 & 1 & 0 \\ -\sin\theta & 0 & \cos\theta \end{bmatrix}$$

When these values are used the matrix m_{QB} becomes

$$m_{QB} = \begin{bmatrix} \cos\theta & 0 & \sin\theta & 0 & 0 & 0 \\ 0 & 1 & 0 & 0 & 0 & 0 \\ -\sin\theta & 0 & \cos\theta & 0 & 0 & 0 \\ 0 & R(1-\cos\theta) & 0 & \cos\theta & 0 & \sin\theta \\ R(1-\cos\theta) & 0 & -R\sin\theta & 0 & 1 & 0 \\ 0 & R\sin\theta & 0 & -\sin\theta & 0 & \cos\theta \end{bmatrix}$$

This matrix is now transposed, and the successive columns are then multiplied by $1/EA^x$, $1/GA^y$ .... The resulting matrix is then post-multiplied by m_{QB} to produce the product $m^T(EI)^{-1}m$. For reasons of space this product is not shown here. Each term of this (6×6) matrix is now integrated with respect to x (where $dx = R\,d\theta$), from $\theta = 0°$ to $\theta = 120°$. This results in the flexibility matrix (6.7) shown on page 92.

6.2 INTERNAL ACTIONS

By definition of the matrix m (see equation 6.1), the internal actions at Q can readily be expressed in terms of the end actions at B.

$$M_Q = m_{QB}p_B \qquad (6.8)$$

where M_Q is a column matrix of the internal actions at Q, and p_B is a column matrix of the six end actions applied at B.

The form of the matrix m_{QB} can be more quickly derived by use of the change of axis method of the last chapter. Figure 6.5 shows a member which is cut through at the section Q. The portion BQ is in equilibrium under the influence of a system of forces p_B applied at the end B and a system of forces applied to the end Q by the part AQ. These two systems therefore equilibrate one another. But at Q, the actions applied to the part AQ are equal and opposite to the actions applied to the part BQ. Hence the actions applied at section Q to the part AQ are statically equivalent to the actions p_B applied at B, and are thus equal to the actions p_B "transferred" to the axes $\overline{xyz}$. They may be expressed as $A_{QB}p_B$ (see

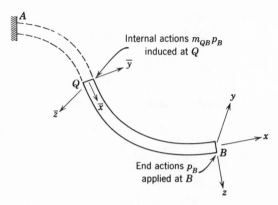

Internal actions $m_{QB}p_B$ induced at Q

End actions p_B applied at B

Fig. 6.5

equation 5.15). Moreover, since these actions at Q are applied to the left-hand side of the cut, they are by definition equal to the internal actions at Q. Hence we may write

$$M_Q = A_{QB}p_B \tag{6.9}$$

The axis transformation matrix A is the product, RT, of the rotation matrix R (equation 5.9) and the translation matrix T (equation 5.1). If this multiplication is carried out, the product is found to be identical with m (equation 6.3). It is convenient to express the product by means of the submatrices as indicated in equation 5.16, namely,

$$A = \begin{bmatrix} \lambda & 0 \\ \hline \lambda X & \lambda \end{bmatrix}$$

Similar reasoning could be applied to a member cantilevered from its right-hand end B and having forces p_A applied at the left-hand end. Then at any section Q the actions applied to the part QB are again the actions p_A "transferred" to Q, and are equal to $A_{QA}p_A$. In this case, however, since these actions are applied to the right-hand side of the cut they are equal to the internal actions with the sign changed. Therefore we have

$$M_Q = -A_{QA}p_A \tag{6.10}$$

Since the expression $M = mp$ holds for actions applied at either end of a member, the matrix m is seen to be a signed value of the axis transformation matrix A,

$$m_{QA} = -A_{QA}$$

or $$m_{QB} = +A_{QB}$$

The foregoing derivations are based on the assumption that the shear center of the cross-section at Q coincides with the centroid. When this assumption is not correct, the twisting moment is not the moment of the force system around the centroidal axis but the moment about a parallel axis through the shear center. Although it would not be difficult to take moments about this axis directly, it is easier to transform the actions p_B to an equivalent set $\bar{p}$ at Q and afterwards to take moments of these actions about the axis through the shear center. We have

$$\bar{p} = A_{QB}p_B \tag{6.11}$$

Now let the co-ordinates of the shear center, S, relative to the principal axes of the cross-section, be (y_1, z_1). It will be seen from Fig. 6.6 that the moment of the actions $\bar{p}$ about the axis through S parallel to $\bar{x}$ is equal to $z_1\bar{p}_2 - y_1\bar{p}_3 + \bar{p}_4$. This is therefore the twisting moment M_Q^x. The other internal actions at Q are equal to the relevant elements of $\bar{p}$. We therefore have

$$\begin{bmatrix} N^x \\ N^y \\ N^z \\ M^x \\ M^y \\ M^z \end{bmatrix} = \begin{bmatrix} 1 & \cdot & \cdot & \cdot & \cdot & \cdot \\ \cdot & 1 & \cdot & \cdot & \cdot & \cdot \\ \cdot & \cdot & 1 & \cdot & \cdot & \cdot \\ \cdot & +z_1 & -y_1 & 1 & \cdot & \cdot \\ \cdot & \cdot & \cdot & \cdot & 1 & \cdot \\ \cdot & \cdot & \cdot & \cdot & \cdot & 1 \end{bmatrix} \begin{bmatrix} \bar{p}_1 \\ \bar{p}_2 \\ \bar{p}_3 \\ \bar{p}_4 \\ \bar{p}_5 \\ \bar{p}_6 \end{bmatrix} \tag{6.12}$$

or

$$M_Q = S\bar{p}_Q \tag{6.13}$$

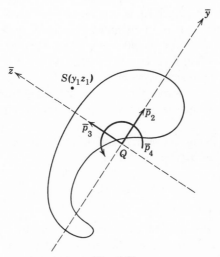

Fig. 6.6

and by substitution from equation 6.11 we have

$$M_Q = SA_{QB}P_B \tag{6.14}$$

From this we see that, in this case,

$$m_{QB} = SA_{QB} \tag{6.15}$$

The expression for the end flexibility, as stated in equation 6.5, still applies to the present case, but the matrix m_{QB} takes the form given in equation 6.15. This latter form is the more general one. If the shear center coincides with the centroid of the cross-section, then $y_1 = z_1 = 0$, and the matrix S becomes a unit matrix.

The matrix m is, by definition, the matrix by means of which the internal actions at any point are expressed in terms of actions applied at the end of the member. It is equal to $\pm SA$, the sign depending upon whether the actions are applied at the right-hand end or the left-hand end, and the form of S depending upon the location of the shear center at the cross-section under consideration.

6.3 PARTICULAR SOLUTION

For the particular solution we have to calculate in the first place the internal actions at various sections of a cantilever due to externally applied loads. At a section Q, the six internal actions will be denoted by the column matrix M_{Q0}. There is no difficulty in computing the elements of M_{Q0} by using the principles of statics. If the work is to be done by means of a computer, it is an advantage to use a process similar to that employed for the flexibility coefficients. The member is assumed to be acted upon by isolated forces and couples. When distributed forces are encountered, an equivalent system of isolated forces is substituted. At any point L the member can therefore be subjected to a system of loads W_L whose components are expressed in the member axes at that point (Fig. 6.7).

At a point Q_1 lying between L and B, these loads produce no effect. At a point Q_2 lying between L and A, the loads produce internal actions given by

$$M_{Q0} = A_{QL} \cdot W_L \tag{6.16}$$

as shown by equation 6.9.

In an evaluation of the axis transformation matrix A_{QL} the position of Q and the orientation of the member at Q must be expressed in terms of the axes at L. Since these details are not likely to be known in advance,

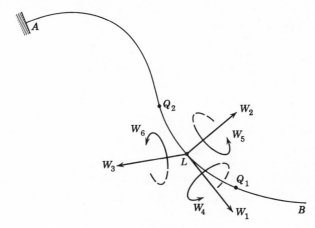

Fig. 6.7

it will often be easier to effect the transformation in two stages, "transferring" the loads at L first into equivalent loads at B and then to Q, thus:

$$W_B = A_{BL}W_L$$

and

$$M_{Q0} = A_{QB}W_B$$

$$= A_{QB}A_{BL}W_L \qquad (6.17)$$

or, if an adjustment is to be made for the shear center position at Q,

$$M_{Q0} = m_{QB}A_{BL}W_L \qquad (6.18)$$

Since $A_{BL} = A_{LB}^{-1}$ (see equation 5.24), the matrices A_{QB} and A_{BL} ($= A_{LB}^{-1}$) of equation 6.17 can both be written directly from co-ordinate data expressed in terms of the axes at B. Where this intermediate stage of "transfer" to B is employed, it must be remembered that the loads at the point L still produce no internal actions at points between L and the end of the cantilever. The method permits a similar process to be employed for all the computations, provided that the product $A_{QB}A_{BL}$ is ignored when Q is between B and L.

Once the internal actions M_{Q0} have been computed, the end displacements of the cantilever can be found by the usual process. Using matrix methods we can say that the six deformations of the element at Q are given by $(EI)^{-1}M_{Q0}$. Then since m_{QB} will transfer forces from B to Q, the matrix m_{QB}^T will transfer displacements from Q to B. Hence the deformations of element Q will cause end displacements given by

$m_{QB}^T \cdot (EI)^{-1} M_{Q0}$. If the deformation of all elements is considered, the total end displacements are therefore

$$u_{B0} = \int_A^B m_{QB}^T (EI)^{-1} M_{Q0} \, dx \qquad (6.19)$$

The matrix expressions for the flexibility (equation 6.5) and release displacements (equation 6.19) bear a close resemblance to the tabular layout adopted in Chapter 4. For the present case a similar table would contain six rows (six integrals) and seven columns. The first column would contain the elements of matrix M_0, and the remaining six the elements of m_{QB}. The rigidity values previously given in an eighth column become in the present instance the diagonal matrix (EI).

6.4 COMPLETE SOLUTION

The foregoing expressions may be used to solve fixed-ended beams of general shape. We may then regard the member, when cantilevered from the left-hand end, as a primary frame, while the free end displacements will be the release displacements.

When f and u_0 have been calculated the redundants p_B are found in the usual way

$$u_{B0} + f_{BB} p_B = 0$$

giving $\qquad\qquad p_B = f_{BB}^{-1}(-u_{B0}) = -f_{BB}^{-1} u_{B0}$

By the use of equation 6.8, the final actions at a typical point Q can be expressed in the form

$$M_Q = M_{Q0} + m_{QB} p_B \qquad (6.20)$$

Example 6.3 Figure 6.8 shows a horizontal girder curved in the form of a quadrant of an ellipse and completely fixed at both ends. Its cross-sectional dimensions vary linearly from 10 inches × 5 inches at B to 20 inches × 10 inches at A. The section turns from the vertical position at B to the horizontal position at A, the angle of twist varying linearly along the axis of the beam. G is taken as 1.0 and E as 2.5. (kip, foot units).

Two vertical loads, each of 5 kips, are situated in positions which subtend angles of 30° at the center of the ellipse.

Solution. A numerical procedure will be used. That is to say, the various matrices will be evaluated at discrete points along the beam, and integration will be performed by using Simpson's rule. The operations will be described in detail for one section only.

The member is divided into six equal intervals by points 7(B), 6, 5, 4, 3, 2

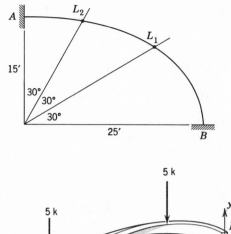

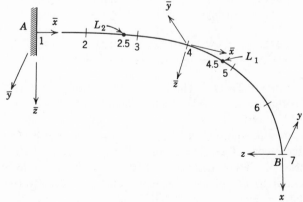

Fig. 6.8

and 1(A) (Fig. 6.9). The load points L_1 and L_2 fall in the segments
4-5 and 2-3 respectively. L_1 is numbered 4.5, not because it lies midway
between 4 and 5, but in order to show that the load at L_1 produces no M_0
values at 5 but does give values at 4. L_2 is numbered 2.5 for a similar
purpose.

Fig. 6.9

The calculations relating to point 4 are given below. The units are kips and feet.

(i) SECTION PROPERTIES:

$$A^x = 0.78125 \qquad A^y = 0.78125 \qquad A^z = 0.78125$$

$$I^x = 0.06978 \qquad I^y = 0.02543 \qquad I^z = 0.10173$$

Since $G = 1.0$ and $E = 2.5$ we have

$$(EI) = \begin{bmatrix} 1.95312 \\ & 0.78125 \\ & & 0.78125 \\ & & & 0.06978 \\ & & & & 0.06358 \\ & & & & & 0.25431 \end{bmatrix} \quad \text{and} \quad (EI)^{-1} = \begin{bmatrix} 0.51200 \\ & 1.28000 \\ & & 1.28000 \\ & & & 14.33075 \\ & & & & 15.72822 \\ & & & & & 3.93221 \end{bmatrix}$$

Table 6.1 contains the rigidity values for all points along the beam.

Table 6.1

Rigidity Values

Point	EA^x	GA^y	GA^z	GI^x	EI^y	EI^z
7	0.868	0.347	0.347	0.014	0.013	0.050
6	1.182	0.473	0.473	0.026	0.023	0.093
5	1.543	0.617	0.617	0.044	0.040	0.159
4	1.953	0.781	0.781	0.070	0.064	0.254
3	2.411	0.965	0.965	0.106	0.097	0.388
2	2.918	1.167	1.167	0.156	0.142	0.567
1	3.472	1.389	1.389	0.221	0.201	0.804

(ii) CO-ORDINATE DATA. The axes of the member at B (point 7) are taken as the basic axes (Fig. 6.9). The co-ordinates of point 4 are $X = -11.77$, $Y = 0$, $Z = +9.50$.

The axis transformation from x, y, z at B to $\bar{x}, \bar{y}, \bar{z}$ at 4 is best carried out in three steps. First the origin is changed from B to 4, without rotation of axes. Then the axes are rotated about y so as to bring the x axis tangential to the ellipse, i.e., x becomes $\bar{x}$. Finally the axes are rotated about $\bar{x}$ by an amount determined by the twist of the section between B and 4.

The translation of axes requires the matrix

$$T = \begin{bmatrix} I & 0 \\ X & I \end{bmatrix} \quad \text{where} \quad X = \begin{bmatrix} 0 & z & 0 \\ -z & 0 & x \\ 0 & -x & 0 \end{bmatrix}$$

Thus, for point 4,

$$X = \begin{bmatrix} 0 & 9.50 & 0 \\ -9.50 & 0 & -11.77 \\ 0 & 11.77 & 0 \end{bmatrix}$$

The axes are now rotated about the y axis by an angle θ_y, which is the angle between the x axis at B and the $\bar{x}$ axis at the point concerned. This requires the matrix

$$R_y = \begin{bmatrix} \lambda_y & 0 \\ 0 & \lambda_y \end{bmatrix} \quad \text{where} \quad \lambda_y = \begin{bmatrix} \cos\theta_y & 0 & \sin\theta_y \\ 0 & 1 & 0 \\ -\sin\theta_y & 0 & \cos\theta_y \end{bmatrix}$$

Thus, for point 4,

$$\lambda_y = \begin{bmatrix} 0.4284 & 0 & 0.9036 \\ 0 & 1 & 0 \\ -0.9036 & 0 & 0.4284 \end{bmatrix}$$

Finally, the axes are rotated about the new $\bar{x}$ axis by an angle θ_x. This is merely the twist of the beam, and for point 4 (the midpoint) θ_x is $\frac{1}{2} \times 90°$.

$$R_x = \begin{bmatrix} \lambda_x & 0 \\ 0 & \lambda_x \end{bmatrix} \quad \text{where} \quad \lambda_x = \begin{bmatrix} 1 & 0 & 0 \\ 0 & \cos\theta_x & \sin\theta_x \\ 0 & -\sin\theta_x & \cos\theta_x \end{bmatrix}$$

Thus, for point 4,

$$\lambda_x = \begin{bmatrix} 1 & 0 & 0 \\ 0 & 0.7071 & 0.7071 \\ 0 & -0.7071 & 0.7071 \end{bmatrix}$$

Hence we have, finally, for any point,

$$m = R_x R_y T$$

For each point we therefore require x, z, $\sin\theta_y$, $\cos\theta_y$, $\sin\theta_x$ and $\cos\theta_x$. This information is tabulated in Table 6.2.

Table 6.2

Co-ordinate Data

Point	x	z	$\sin \theta_y$	$\cos \theta_y$	$\sin \theta_x$	$\cos \theta_x$
L_1	-10.40	$+6.99$	0.8486	0.5291	0.5994	0.8006
L_2	-14.17	$+16.82$	0.9791	0.2035	0.9185	0.3954
$7(B)$	0	0	0	$+1.0$	0	$+1.0$
6	-5.06	$+1.47$	0.5128	0.8585	0.2588	0.9659
5	-9.00	$+5.00$	0.7809	0.6247	0.5000	0.8660
4	-11.77	$+9.50$	0.9036	0.4284	0.7071	0.7071
3	-13.61	$+14.49$	0.9635	0.2678	0.8660	0.5000
2	-14.66	$+19.69$	0.9916	0.1293	0.9659	0.2588
$1(A)$	-15.00	$+25.00$	$+1.0$	0	$+1.0$	0

At the load points L_1 and L_2, arbitrary axes are chosen in which to express the external loads. Since these merely consist of vertical loads in this problem, axes parallel to the basic axes at B are as good as any. Hence we put $\theta_x = \theta_y = 0$ for points L_1 and L_2.

(iii) APPLIED LOADS. The description of the external loads will depend upon the arbitrarily chosen axes at the load points. With those chosen above, each load will be a 5-kip force acting in the negative direction of y. The loading is described by Table 6.3, in which W_1, W_2 and W_3 are forces along the xyz axes and W_4, W_5 and W_6 are couples round the axes.

(iv) FLEXIBILITY AT B. This is calculated by the expression in equation (6.5). For each point, $(EI)^{-1}$ and m are evaluated as described above. The product $m^T(EI)^{-1}m$ can now be computed for this point.

Each element is multiplied by the Simpson's factor appropriate to the point, that is, 1 for the first point, 4 for the second, 2 for the third, 4 for the fourth and so on. Thus each element of the matrix $m^T(EI)^{-1}m$ for point 4 is multiplied by 4.

When this process has been carried out for each point the resulting matrices are added. The length of the interval along the beam from one point to the next is 5.318 feet, one-third of which is 1.7727 feet.

Table 6.3

Applied Loads

Point	W_1	W_2	W_3	W_4	W_5	W_6
L_1	0	-5	0	0	0	0
L_2	0	-5	0	0	0	0

Accordingly, each element of the summation matrix is multiplied by 1.7727 as required by Simpson's rule, and this yields the flexibility coefficients

$$
f_{BB} = \begin{bmatrix}
19317.2313 & -14205.5362 & 21528.6122 & -864.0293 & -2031.7258 & -402.6785 \\
-14205.5362 & 72725.1638 & -16456.3384 & 2165.1912 & 1547.2649 & 3310.7853 \\
21528.6122 & -16456.3384 & 29659.0996 & -1088.8530 & -3408.8225 & -683.2356 \\
-864.0293 & 2165.1912 & -1088.8530 & 574.7193 & 110.4763 & -115.6055 \\
-2031.7258 & 1547.2649 & -3408.8225 & 110.4763 & 606.0416 & 89.4837 \\
-402.6785 & 3310.7853 & -683.2356 & -115.6055 & 89.4837 & 423.0267
\end{bmatrix}
$$

(v) PARTICULAR SOLUTION. The particular solution requires the determination of the internal actions at each point due to the external loads. The actions can be determined by the method of equation 6.18, "transferring" the loads first to the end of the cantilever. Since in this problem the matrix m is the same as the axis transformation matrix A, we have for the point 4

$$M_{40} = A_{4B}A_{BL}W_L$$

$$= A_{4B}A_{LB}^{-1}W_L$$

The matrix A_{4B} has been determined above. For the point L_1 the matrix A_{L_1B} is found in exactly the same way, by using the values of the first row of Table 6.2. Its inverse is also found. From the first row of Table 6.3 the matrix W_{L_1} is read as

$$
W_{L_1} = \begin{bmatrix}
0 \\
-5 \\
0 \\
0 \\
0 \\
0
\end{bmatrix}
$$

The internal actions M_{40} at point 4 are now found by matrix multiplication, giving a (6×1) matrix.

$$
M_{40} = \begin{bmatrix}
0 \\
-3.5355 \\
3.5355 \\
0.7963 \\
-10.1053 \\
-10.1053
\end{bmatrix}
$$

Since L_2 is further from B than point 4, no internal actions are induced at this point by the loads at L_2.

The displacements at B are found in a similar manner to that adopted for the flexibility coefficients, but equation 6.19 is used. In this way we find that

$$u_0 = \begin{bmatrix} 27457.8973 \\ -158213.2047 \\ 24604.5968 \\ -6831.5593 \\ -1830.7467 \\ -2313.2509 \end{bmatrix}$$

The units in which these displacements are expressed are basically feet and radians. It must be remembered that a scale factor is involved because E has been taken as 2.5.

(vi) REDUNDANT ACTIONS. The compatibility equations are

$$u_0 + f_{BB}p_B = 0$$

and solution of these gives

$$p_B = \begin{bmatrix} -0.3568 \\ 3.3701 \\ 0.9074 \\ -4.3855 \\ 2.2934 \\ -21.4651 \end{bmatrix}$$

Table 6.4
Internal Actions

Point	N^x	N^y	N^z	M^x	M^y	M^z
7	−0.357	3.370	0.907	−4.386	2.293	−21.465
6	−0.772	3.410	−0.296	2.738	−2.622	−2.926
5	−0.931	3.063	−1.435	0.864	4.094	15.271
4	−0.973	−1.106	1.199	−3.810	9.528	16.594
3	−0.970	−0.902	1.361	−6.195	5.273	8.687
2	−0.946	−1.944	6.343	−6.250	−15.747	−0.097
1	−0.907	−0.357	6.630	−1.958	−51.121	2.397

(vii) COMPLETE SOLUTION. At each section along the beam the six internal actions are given by equation 6.20,

$$M = M_0 + mp_B$$

M_0 and m are known for each point, and p_B has been determined. The values of the internal actions are given in Table 6.4.

The values for the end points 7 and 1 are generally known as fixed-end actions.

PROBLEMS

6.1. The beam CD of Fig. P6.1 has a straight axis, and the dimensions of the cross-section at D are one-third of those at C. Find the flexibility matrix f_{DD} assuming that St. Venant torsion is applicable. Take $G = 10^7$ psi and $E = 2.5G$.

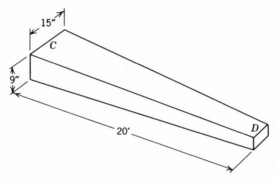

Fig. P6.1

6.2. PQ is a straight tapered beam of rectangular section and is 25 ft. long. The depth decreases from 20 inches at P to 10 inches at Q. The width is constant at 10 inches. Find the flexibility matrix f_{QQ} using a suitable approximation for the torsion term and assuming that shear deformations are negligible. Assume that $E = 2.3G$ and state the flexibility in terms of G.

6.3. A beam AB is 16 feet long and has a rectangular cross-section. It has a constant width of 1.2 feet and the axis may be assumed to be straight. The depth varies and is given by the following table:

x (ft)	0	2	4	6	8	10	12	14	16
d (ft)	2.00	1.66	1.35	1.07	0.80	0.60	0.50	0.55	0.70

where x is the distance from A.

(a) Use numerical integration and a computer to obtain the flexibility matrix f_{BB} (6 × 6). Take $E = 2.5G$.

(b) If the member is to be used in a plane frame problem with the variable depth being in the plane of loading, and if the axial deformation is assumed to be negligible, write the (2 × 2) flexibility matrix which would be required for this problem.   Use area-moment methods to provide a rough check on the computer values.

(c) In the plane problem, three loads each of 25 kips are placed 4 feet, 8 feet and 12 feet from A.   If the member is cantilevered from A, find the two end displacements at B due to these loads.   Hence find the fixed end reactions at A and B if the loads were applied to the fixed-ended beam AB.

6.4. A member AB is curved so that its centroidal axis forms part of a helix. In plan it forms a semicircle of 8-foot radius.   The upper end B is 8 feet higher than its lower end A, the axis of the helix being vertical.

The member is made of homogeneous isotropic material and has a square cross-section at all points.   The cross-section is 12 inches square at A and 8 inches square at B, the width varying linearly along the axis.

Find the flexibility matrix for the end B, assuming the end A to be completely fixed.   Express the values in inch units.   Take $G = 1$ and $E = 2.5$.

6.5. The beam of Problem 6.4 carries a uniformly distributed load of 1 kip per foot length of the member axis.   The load acts vertically at a line 9 inches outside the axis of the member (i.e., 9 inches further from the helix axis).

If the member is cantilevered from A, find the displacements of the end B due to this load.   Use inch units.

CHAPTER 7

Transformations
for a Single Member

7.1 CHANGE OF AXES

In Chapter 6 an expression was developed for the flexibility matrix relating actions and displacements at the free end of a cantilever. All of the actions and displacements were expressed in the natural axes of the member at its free end. It is frequently necessary to use axes other than these, and in this chapter we shall consider the technique of deriving the flexibility matrix in any arbitrary axes.

We may suppose that the cantilever AB (Fig. 7.1) is deformed by actions, p_C, applied at C in axes $\bar{x}, \bar{y}, \bar{z}$. They are transmitted to B by a rigid arm which itself undergoes no deformation.

If actions p_B are applied at B, this point undergoes displacements u_B, which are given by

$$u_B = f_{BB}p_B$$

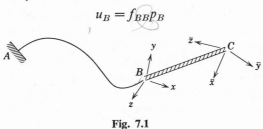

Fig. 7.1

107

where f_{BB} is a known flexibility matrix. It is required now to apply actions at C and to compute the resulting displacements of C by means of a relationship

$$u_C = f_{CC}p_C \qquad (7.1)$$

where f_{CC} is the flexibility of the cantilever AB expressed in the axes $\bar{x}, \bar{y}, \bar{z}$. The displacements at C are due entirely to the deformations of the elements between A and B.

Let actions p_C be applied at C. The equivalent actions at B are

$$p_B = A_{BC}p_C$$

where A_{BC} is the matrix which transforms the actions from C to B.

The actions p_B cause displacements u_B, which are given by

$$u_B = f_{BB}p_B$$

$$= f_{BB}A_{BC}p_C$$

The equivalent displacements at C are then

$$u_C = A_{BC}^T u_B$$

$$= A_{BC}^T f_{BB}A_{BC}p_C \qquad (7.2)$$

This equation is in the form of equation 7.1, and by comparison we see that

$$f_{CC} = A_{BC}^T f_{BB}A_{BC} \qquad (7.3)$$

The matrix A_{BC} has the form indicated by equation 5.16. The position of B and the direction of the axes x, y, z are expressed in terms of the axes at C. In some problems it may be more convenient to take the axes at B as basic and to express in terms of them the position and direction of the axes at C. This selection of axes would permit the matrix A_{CB} (which is A_{BC}^{-1}) to be written. In such a case we could write

$$f_{CC} = (A_{CB}^{-1})^T f_{BB}A_{CB}^{-1} \qquad (7.4)$$

Whether equation 7.3 or 7.4 is used depends upon the data of the problem. It should be noted (equation 5.17) that inversion of A_{CB} merely involves the transposition of the submatrices. In the following work the form of equation 7.3 will be used. The transformation indicated in equation 7.3 is known as a congruent transformation and preserves the symmetrical form of the flexibility matrix. It should be remembered that f_{BB} expresses a relationship between actions applied at B (the second

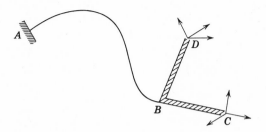

Fig. 7.2

subscript) and the resulting displacements at B (the first subscript). It will be seen from the derivation of equation 7.3 that the A_{BC}^T in front of f_{BB} results from the change of location of the displacements, while the A_{BC} after f_{BB} arises from the change of location of the actions. Hence the premultiplying matrix, A_{BC}^T, can be regarded as changing the first subscript from B to C, and the postmultiplying matrix A_{BC} as changing the second subscript. There is no need for the actions and displacements to be similarly transformed. It may be required to find the displacements at C (Fig. 7.2) caused by actions applied at D, the displacements being due to deformation of elements from A to B only. If the flexibility f_{BB} is known, the required flexibility is given by

$$f_{CD} = A_{BC}^T f_{BB} A_{BD} \qquad (7.5)$$

The proof would follow the same lines as the proof of equation 7.3.

Example 7.1 In Example 6.1 the flexibility of a prismatic cantilever was found in terms of the axes of the member at B (Fig. 7.3). It is required to express the flexibility matrix in terms of axes which are rotated 60° anticlockwise about the z axis from their previous position.

Solution. In this example the transformation involves rotation only to new axes, which will be denoted collectively by $\bar{B}$. The direction

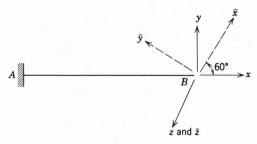

Fig. 7.3

$$f_{BB} = \begin{bmatrix}
\left(\dfrac{L}{4EA^x}+\dfrac{3L}{4GA^y}+\dfrac{L^3}{4EI^z}\right) & \left(\dfrac{-\sqrt{3}L}{4EA^x}+\dfrac{\sqrt{3}L}{4GA^y}\right)+\dfrac{\sqrt{3}L^3}{12EI^z} & 0 & 0 & 0 & \left(\dfrac{\sqrt{3}L^2}{4EI^z}\right) \\[2ex]
\left(\dfrac{-\sqrt{3}L}{4EA^x}+\dfrac{\sqrt{3}L}{4GA^y}\right)+\dfrac{\sqrt{3}L^3}{12EI^z} & \left(\dfrac{3L}{4EA^x}+\dfrac{L}{4GA^y}\right)+\dfrac{L^3}{12EI^z} & 0 & 0 & 0 & \left(\dfrac{L^2}{4EI^z}\right) \\[2ex]
0 & 0 & \left(\dfrac{L}{GA^z}+\dfrac{L^3}{3EI^y}\right) & \left(\dfrac{-\sqrt{3}L^2}{4EI^y}\right) & \left(\dfrac{-L^2}{4EI^y}\right) & 0 \\[2ex]
0 & 0 & \left(\dfrac{-\sqrt{3}L^2}{4EI^y}\right) & \left(\dfrac{L}{4GI^x}+\dfrac{3L}{4EI^y}\right) & \left(\dfrac{-\sqrt{3}L}{4GI^x}+\dfrac{\sqrt{3}L}{4EI^y}\right) & 0 \\[2ex]
0 & 0 & \left(\dfrac{-L^2}{4EI^y}\right) & \left(\dfrac{-\sqrt{3}L}{4GI^x}+\dfrac{\sqrt{3}L}{4EI^y}\right) & \left(\dfrac{3L}{4GI^x}+\dfrac{L}{4EI^y}\right) & 0 \\[2ex]
\left(\dfrac{\sqrt{3}L^2}{4EI^z}\right) & \left(\dfrac{L^2}{4EI^z}\right) & 0 & 0 & 0 & \left(\dfrac{L}{EI^z}\right)
\end{bmatrix}$$

cosines of $\bar{x}$, $\bar{y}$ and $\bar{z}$ with respect to axes x, y, z are respectively (cos 60°, sin 60°, 0); ($-$sin 60°, cos 60°, 0) and (0, 0, 1).

The transformation matrix is therefore

$$A_{BB} = R = \begin{bmatrix} \cos 60° & \sin 60° & 0 & 0 & 0 & 0 \\ -\sin 60° & \cos 60° & 0 & 0 & 0 & 0 \\ 0 & 0 & 1 & 0 & 0 & 0 \\ 0 & 0 & 0 & \cos 60° & \sin 60° & 0 \\ 0 & 0 & 0 & -\sin 60° & \cos 60° & 0 \\ 0 & 0 & 0 & 0 & 0 & 1 \end{bmatrix}$$

Matrix A_{BB}, which is A_{BB}^{-1}, is obtained in this case by merely transposing the foregoing matrix. We therefore have

$$f_{BB} = A_{BB}^{T} f_{BB} A_{BB}$$
$$= A_{BB} f_{BB} A_{BB}^{T}$$

Carrying out this transformation on f_{BB}, which is given in equation 6.6, results in the flexibility matrix shown on page 110.

The terms of the first column indicate the displacements produced by a unit force in the direction $\bar{x}$. According to the top term, f_{11}, it will cause a translation in the $\bar{x}$ direction equal to

$$\frac{L}{4EA^x} + \frac{3L}{4GA^y} + \frac{L^3}{4EI^z}$$

According to the term f_{61} it will cause a rotation about the axis $\bar{z}$ equal to ($\sqrt{3}L^2/4EI^z$).

Example 7.2   In Example 6.2 an expression for the end flexibility of a bow girder (Fig. 7.4) was obtained. If a member of exactly the same dimensions is to be used in the form of an arch, it might be required to express the flexibility in terms of axes $\bar{x}\bar{y}\bar{z}$ (Fig. 7.5). This flexibility matrix can be obtained by transformation from the one derived previously.

   Solution.   It is convenient to express the axes at B in terms of those at

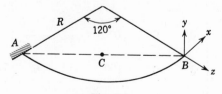

Fig. 7.4

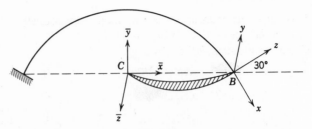

Fig. 7.5

C so that the matrix A_{BC} can be written directly without the necessity of inversion.

Relative to axes $\bar{x}\bar{y}\bar{z}$ the co-ordinates of B are $\left(R\dfrac{\sqrt{3}}{2}, 0, 0\right)$. The translation matrix is therefore

$$
T = \left[\begin{array}{ccc:ccc}
1 & 0 & 0 & 0 & 0 & 0 \\
0 & 1 & 0 & 0 & 0 & 0 \\
0 & 0 & 1 & 0 & 0 & 0 \\ \hdashline
0 & 0 & 0 & 1 & 0 & 0 \\
0 & 0 & R\dfrac{\sqrt{3}}{2} & 0 & 1 & 0 \\
0 & -R\dfrac{\sqrt{3}}{2} & 0 & 0 & 0 & 1
\end{array}\right]
$$

The direction cosines of x, y and z with respect to axes $\bar{x}$, $\bar{y}$, $\bar{z}$ are respectively $(\cos 60°, -\cos 30°, 0)$; $(0, 0, -1)$; $(\cos 30°, \cos 60°, 0)$. The rotation matrix is

$$
R = \left[\begin{array}{ccc:ccc}
\tfrac{1}{2} & -\dfrac{\sqrt{3}}{2} & 0 & 0 & 0 & 0 \\
0 & 0 & -1 & 0 & 0 & 0 \\
\dfrac{\sqrt{3}}{2} & \tfrac{1}{2} & 0 & 0 & 0 & 0 \\ \hdashline
0 & 0 & 0 & \tfrac{1}{2} & -\dfrac{\sqrt{3}}{2} & 0 \\
0 & 0 & 0 & 0 & 0 & -1 \\
0 & 0 & 0 & \dfrac{\sqrt{3}}{2} & \tfrac{1}{2} & 0
\end{array}\right]
$$

Then

$$
A_{BC} = RT =
\begin{bmatrix}
\frac{1}{2} & -\frac{\sqrt{3}}{2} & 0 & 0 & 0 & 0 \\[2mm]
0 & 0 & -1 & 0 & 0 & 0 \\[2mm]
\frac{\sqrt{3}}{2} & \frac{1}{2} & 0 & 0 & 0 & 0 \\[2mm]
\hline
0 & 0 & -\frac{3}{4}R & \frac{1}{2} & -\frac{\sqrt{3}}{2} & 0 \\[2mm]
0 & \frac{\sqrt{3}}{2}R & 0 & 0 & 0 & -1 \\[2mm]
0 & 0 & \frac{\sqrt{3}}{4}R & \frac{\sqrt{3}}{2} & \frac{1}{2} & 0
\end{bmatrix}
$$

It is then necessary to perform the multiplication $A_{BC}^{T} f_{BB} A_{BC}$ to obtain f_{CC}, where f_{BB} is given in equation 6.7. The multiplication is extensive with the matrices in algebraic form, but in a given problem, where the matrices can be expressed numerically, it presents no difficulty.

7.2 THE ELASTIC CENTER

It is possible to reduce any flexibility matrix to a diagonal form by a transformation of the type indicated in equation 7.4. The set of simultaneous equations for the unknown redundants then becomes a set of independent equations.

In the case of a general flexibility matrix, the physical significance of the transformation is difficult, though not impossible, to visualize. Furthermore, the work involved in determining the transformation matrix may be prohibitive.

In certain practical cases, however, the reduction can be effected by an axis change which is easily found from the nature of the problem. The elastic center method is essentially a special case of the change of axes described in Section 7.1, as will be shown.

Where the results of the last section are applied to a two-dimensional case, only three actions p_1, p_2 and p_6 are relevant (Fig. 7.6), and the flexibility matrix reduces to one of order (3×3). If, in addition, deformations due only to bending are taken into account, the flexibility coefficients are represented by a single integral

$$
f_{rs} = \int \frac{m_r^z m_s^z}{EI^z}\, dx
$$

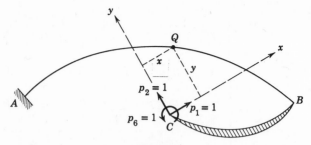

Fig. 7.6

It will be seen from Fig. 7.6 that if unit values of p_1, p_2 and p_6 are applied at an arbitrary point C the respective bending moments produced at any point Q are $m_1^z = y$, $m_2^z = -x$ and $m_6^z = 1$.   The flexibility coefficients can then be expressed explicitly in the form

$$
f_{CC} = \begin{bmatrix} \left(\int \dfrac{y^2}{EI^z}\, dx \right) & \left(-\int \dfrac{yx}{EI^z}\, dx \right) & \left(\int \dfrac{y}{EI^z}\, dx \right) \\[2.5ex] \left(-\int \dfrac{xy}{EI^z}\, dx \right) & \left(\int \dfrac{x^2}{EI^z}\, dx \right) & \left(-\int \dfrac{x}{EI^z}\, dx \right) \\[2.5ex] \left(\int \dfrac{y}{EI^z}\, dx \right) & \left(-\int \dfrac{x}{EI^z}\, dx \right) & \left(\int \dfrac{1}{EI^z}\, dx \right) \end{bmatrix} \quad (7.6)
$$

The integrals occurring here are similar to those in the calculation of areas and moments of area of plane figures.   If a graph of the function $1/EI$ is plotted using the member axis as base line, a plane figure is obtained whose geometrical properties correspond to the foregoing integrals.   It is assumed that although the width of the figure varies as $1/EI$, yet the width is at all times small compared with the dimensions of the member.   Thus in finding the second moment of an element of area about the x axis, the element is supposed to coincide with the member axis

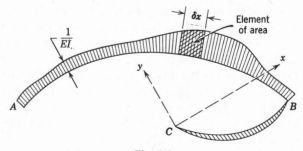

Fig. 7.7

and the second moment about its own axis is neglected. The figure plotted in this way is called the *elastic diagram*. It has the following properties:

$$\int \frac{1}{EI}\, dx = A \qquad \int \frac{1}{EI}\, x^2\, dx = I_{yy}$$

$$\int \frac{1}{EI}\, x\, dx = Q_y \qquad \int \frac{1}{EI}\, y^2\, dx = I_{xx}$$

$$\int \frac{1}{EI}\, y\, dx = Q_x \qquad \int \frac{1}{EI}\, xy\, dx = I_{xy}$$

where A is the area of the figure, Q_x and Q_y are the first moments about the x and y axes, $I_{xx}I_{yy}$ are the second moments about the x and y axes and I_{xy} is the product of inertia about the x and y axes. The flexibility matrix may now be written

$$f_{CC} = \begin{bmatrix} I_{xx} & -I_{xy} & Q_x \\ -I_{xy} & I_{yy} & -Q_y \\ Q_x & -Q_y & A \end{bmatrix} \tag{7.7}$$

The terms Q_x and Q_y will be zero if C coincides with the centroid of the elastic diagram, which is called the elastic center of the member. The terms I_{xy} will also be zero if the x and y axes coincide with the principal axes of the elastic diagram. If the member AB possesses an axis of symmetry, the position of the elastic center can readily be found and the principal axes will be known. In such a case the use of the elastic center saves considerable computation. On the other hand, when the member possesses no symmetry, the determination of the elastic center and the principal axes requires the evaluation of Q_x, Q_y and I_{xy} about some other axes, and the use of the elastic center is then unnecessary.

If a fixed-ended member AB (Fig. 7.6) is to be solved for a given system of applied loads, by applying the redundants at the elastic center the compatibility equations become

$$\int \frac{M_0 y}{EI^z}\, dx + I_{xx} p_1 = 0$$

$$-\int \frac{M_0 x}{EI^z}\, dx + I_{yy} p_2 = 0 \tag{7.8}$$

$$\int \frac{M_0}{EI^z}\, dx + A p_6 = 0$$

where I_{xx}, I_{yy} and A are properties of the elastic diagram defined above.

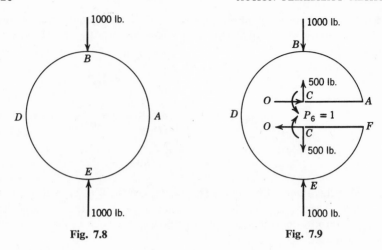

Fig. 7.8   Fig. 7.9

Example 7.3 A closed circular ring of constant cross-section is loaded as shown in Fig. 7.8. The mean diameter is 24 inches. Find the bending moment at the four cardinal points.

Solution. The elastic center is at the center of the circle, and any axes can be taken as principal axes in this case. Since EI^z is constant it may be given a value of unity. Three releases are made at A, and the three redundants are applied at the elastic center. By inspection it is clear that the axial force at A is 500-pound compression, and the shear force is zero. These will transfer unchanged to the elastic center. Since they are known they can be incorporated into the particular solution, leaving only one unknown redundant, p_6, to be found by the third equation of 7.8. The bending moments M_0 are given by the sum of the two diagrams of Fig. 7.10 (in which only half of the structure is shown).

The integral of the first is evidently zero, and for the second

$$\int \frac{M_0}{EI^z}\, dx = -2000r^2$$

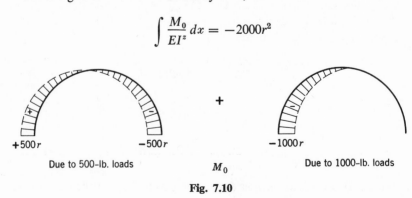

+

Due to 500-lb. loads   Due to 1000-lb. loads

M_0

Fig. 7.10

The area of the elastic diagram is $2\pi r$, so that

$$-2000r^2 + (2\pi r)p_6 = 0$$

and $p_6 = 3820$ lb-in.

The final bending moment at A is

$$M_A = +3820 - 500 \times 12 = -2180 \text{ lb-in.}$$

The final bending moment at B is

$$M_B = +3820 - 500 \times 0 = +3820 \text{ lb-in.}$$

In applying the method to bents having one or more hinges, each hinge is regarded as being a point where the member has zero depth and consequently an infinite value of $1/EI^z$. The properties of the elastic diagram are brought into line with this concept. If the diagram is imagined as having an infinite concentration of area at the hinge point, the required properties then follow. If there is one hinge, the elastic center coincides with it, the area of the diagram is infinite and p_6 is zero. If there are two hinges, the elastic center is midway between them, and the line joining the hinges is one of the principal axes, $\bar{x}\bar{x}$. Now both A and $I_{\overline{yy}}$ are infinite and $p_6 = p_2 = 0$. We have then a two-hinged arch in which the only redundant is p_1, the horizontal thrust.

It is clear that this procedure is a special instance of axis transformation. The elastic center concept assists by suggesting the most advantageous shift of axes. It also helps to reduce arithmetical errors since the flexibility coefficients which remain to be calculated have a physical analogy which in a qualitative way provides a check on the results.

The use of the principal axes of the elastic diagram results in a flexibility matrix with only diagonal elements. Unless the member, or bent, possesses symmetry, the location of these axes may require considerable calculation. However, it is often possible to choose, by inspection, axes which approximate to the principal axes. These axes can have the advantage of simplifying the calculations and at the same time producing a flexibility matrix which is better-conditioned, even though it is not in a diagonal form.

7.3 THE COLUMN ANALOGY

The column analogy goes a stage further than the elastic center method and provides a physical analogy for the u_0 terms in the compatibility equations as well as for the flexibility coefficients.

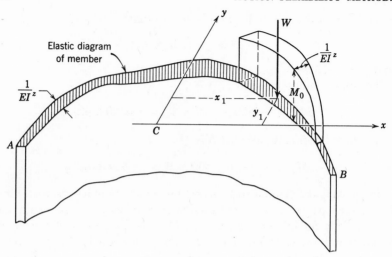

Fig. 7.11

A short column is pictured whose cross-section has the same shape as the elastic diagram of the member under consideration (Fig. 7.11). Thus in plan the column is narrow and curved (if the member is curved), and has a width at every point equal to $1/EI^z$. The top of the column is subjected to a pressure of varying intensity which is everywhere equal to M_0, the bending moment of the particular solution. Since the width of the pressure block is $1/EI^z$, the load per unit length along the top of the column is M_0/EI^z. The resultant column load, W, acts at a point (x_1, y_1) with respect to the principal axes of the elastic diagram. The total load and its moments about the x and y axes are therefore given by

$$W = \int \frac{M_0}{EI^z}\, dx$$

$$Wx_1 = \int \frac{M_0 x}{EI^z}\, dx \tag{7.9}$$

$$Wy_1 = \int \frac{M_0 y}{EI^z}\, dx$$

The compatibility equations 7.8 can now be written

$$Wy_1 + I_{xx}p_1 = 0$$

$$-Wx_1 + I_{vv}p_2 = 0 \tag{7.10}$$

$$W + Ap_3 = 0$$

leading to the explicit solution

$$p_1 = -\frac{Wy_1}{I_{xx}}$$

$$p_2 = +\frac{Wx_1}{I_{yy}} \tag{7.11}$$

$$p_6 = -\frac{W}{A}$$

The final bending moment in the member at any point Q having co-ordinates (x, y) is

$$M_Q^z = M_0^z + (p_1 m_1^z + p_2 m_2^z + p_6 m_6^z)$$

But it has been noted that $m_1^z = y$, $m_2^z = -x$ and $m_6^z = 1$, so that using the results of equation 7.11

$$M_Q = M_0^z - \left(\frac{Wy_1}{I_{xx}}y + \frac{Wx_1}{I_{yy}}x + \frac{W}{A}\right) \tag{7.12}$$

In the analogous problem, the column is subjected to a load W having eccentricities $x_1 y_1$ from the principal axes of the cross-section. This load is equivalent to a central load W together with bending moments (Wy_1) and (Wx_1) about axes x and y respectively. Owing to this loading, the compressive stress at a point (x, y) on the cross-section is

$$\frac{W}{A} + \frac{(Wy_1)}{I_{xx}}y + \frac{(Wx_1)}{I_{yy}}x.$$

Comparison with equation 7.12 shows that this is the negative of the frame moment caused by the redundants. The total frame moment at any point Q can therefore be expressed as

$$M_Q = \text{(statical moment)} - \text{(compressive stress in the analogous column at } Q) \tag{7.13}$$

The statical moments, or particular solution, M_0, referred to in equation 7.13, can be obtained by applying the given loads to any suitable primary frame. Although the flexibility coefficients have been determined on the basis of cutting the member at B and applying the redundants at the elastic center, it is not necessary for the same primary frame to be used for the particular solution.

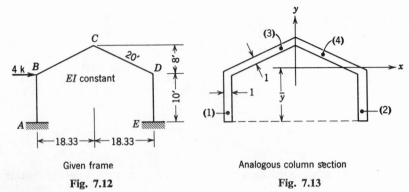

Given frame   Analogous column section

Fig. 7.12   **Fig. 7.13**

Example 7.4   Re-solve Example 4.1 by column analogy.

Solution.   The properties of the column section are found in the usual way. In the tabulation y' is the distance from the base.

Column Section Properties

Element	A	y'	Ay'	y	x	I_{xx}	I_{yy}
AB	10	5	50	−6	−18.33	443.33	3360
DE	10	5	50	−6	+18.33	443.33	3360
BC	20	14	280	+3	−9.16	286.67	2240
CD	20	14	280	+3	+9.16	286.67	2240
Sum	60		660			1460.00	11200

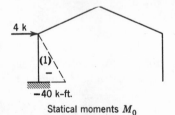

Statical moments M_0

Fig. 7.14

$$\bar{y} = \frac{660}{60} = 11.0'$$

The foregoing calculation corresponds to the calculation of the f coefficients, since A, I_{xx} and I_{yy} represent f_{33}, f_{11} and f_{22} respectively.

The resultant column load is now computed together with its moment about the x and y axes. This computation corresponds to the calculation of the u_0 coefficients.

Column Loading

Element	W	x_1	y_1	Wx_1	Wy_1
AB	−200	−18.33	−7.67	+3666	+1533

Final bending moment at any point $= M_0 - \left\{\dfrac{W}{A} + \dfrac{Wx_1}{I_{yy}}\,x + \dfrac{Wy_1}{I_{xx}}\,y\right\}$

$$= M_0 - \{-3.333 + 0.327x + 1.050y\}$$

By substitution of the co-ordinates of A, B, C, D, E in turn the final bending-moment diagram is obtained.

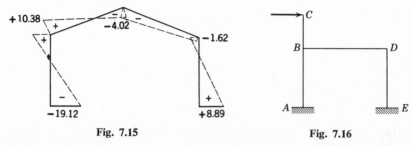

Fig. 7.15   Fig. 7.16

The column analogy is particularly convenient for dealing with single cell bents with discontinuities such as might be occasioned by the stepping of columns.

Further applications of the method are discussed in works devoted more particularly to this part of the subject.

When using any analogy method we should bear its limits of application in mind. For this method these are the same as the limits of the elastic center method, of which column analogy is an extension. Perhaps a special note should be made of the fact that the method applies only to single members. Hence in the frame of Fig. 7.16 the column section should follow only the single path $ABDE$. To introduce the branch member BC would invalidate the construction. That this is so will be quite clear if reference is made to the fundamental flexibility method, from which the column analogy is derived.

PROBLEMS

7.1. A member AB is part of a plane frame. The axial flexibility is to be neglected and the flexibility matrix of the end B in the (x, y) axes (Fig. P7.1) has been determined as

$$f_{BB} = \begin{bmatrix} 23.571 & 12.207 \\ 12.207 & 84.621 \end{bmatrix} \text{ inch, kip units (scaled).}$$

(a) Express the flexibility in the axes $(\bar{x}\ \bar{y})$ of Fig. P7.1a.
(b) Express the flexibility f_{CC} in terms of the axes $(\bar{x}\ \bar{y})$ of Fig. P7.1b. The co-ordinates of C are $(7, -2)$ inches in the (x, y) axes.

$T_d[t, \sigma)$

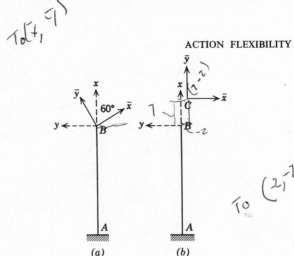

Fig. P7.1

7.2. The flexibility f_{DD} of one end of the member CD has been determined (in inch units) as

$$f_{DD} = \begin{bmatrix} 802.5 & -15.1 & +503.1 & 0 & -62.1 & -13.2 \\ & 1432.2 & +338.2 & +63.3 & -9.2 & +74.1 \\ & & 591.2 & +18.1 & -62.3 & +6.5 \\ & & & 10.8 & 0 & -0.6 \\ & \text{(symmetrical)} & & & 9.0 & -0.5 \\ & & & & & 10.4 \end{bmatrix}$$

Express this flexibility as f_{EE} in the axes at E (Fig. P7.2) where $x_E = y_D$, $y_E = x_D$ and $z_E = -z_D$. The co-ordinates of E in the axes at D are $(0, +3, -9)$ inches.

Fig. P7.2

7.3. A circular arch AB of constant section has a radius of 90 feet and subtends an angle of 120° at the center. Neglecting deformation due to shear and axial force, write down the (3×3) flexibility matrix f_{BB} (Fig. P7.3). $E = 10^6$ ksf and $I^y = 15$ ft.[4].

Transform this flexibility to f_{CC} where C coincides with the fixed support A, and the axes $(x_C \, y_C)$ coincide with the member axes at A.

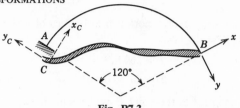

Fig. P7.3

7.4. Figure P7.4 shows a member $ACDB$ with 90° bends at C and D. Write explicitly a transformation matrix A_{AB} which will transform a system of forces from the axes shown at B to those shown at A.

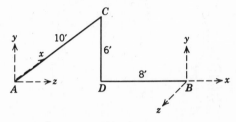

Fig. P7.4

If the member is cantilevered from A, the flexibility of the end B is expressed by the matrix f_{BB}. Assume that this matrix has been determined. In terms of f_{BB} and the transformation matrix A_{AB} write an expression for the flexibility f_{AA}.

7.5. Solve the frame shown in Fig. P7.5 by means of the column analogy.

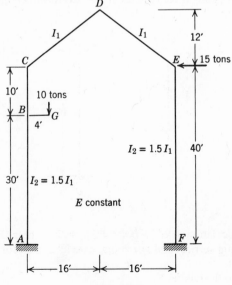

Fig. P7.5

7.6. Figure P7.6 shows a gabled portal, the columns of which are stepped at mid-height and fixed at the base.

$$I = 200 \text{ in.}^4$$

$$E = 30 \times 10^6 \text{ psi}$$

Find the bending moment at the point E by the column analogy.

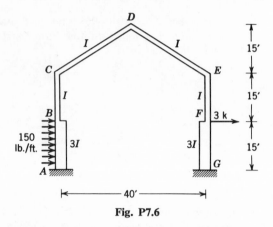

Fig. P7.6

Only deformations due to bending are to be taken into account (note that E and I are given in inch and pound units).

7.7. For the portal frame shown in Fig. P7.7, find the flexibility of the primary frame obtained by making three releases at D. Consider bending deformations

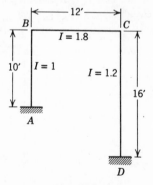

Fig. P7.7

only. Without calculation select a point E somewhere near the elastic center of the frame. Using vertical and horizontal axes at E, transform the flexibility f_{DD} to f_{EE}.

Compare the two flexibilities.

CHAPTER 8

Flexibility of a Frame in Terms of Unassembled Members

8.1 FRAME FLEXIBILITY

When a stable structure is subjected to loads it deforms only because its individual components deform. It is possible to express the total frame deformation in terms of the deformations of the components. Consequently, the flexibility of each component contributes to the flexibility of the frame as a whole.

In Chapter 6 an expression was developed for the flexibility of a member in terms of the properties of an elemental length dx. If we assumed that only a single element of length dx could deform, all other elements remaining rigid, we found that the corresponding member flexibility could be expressed as

$$df = m^T(EI)^{-1} dx\, m \tag{8.1}$$

$(EI)^{-1} dx$ can be regarded as the flexibility of the elemental length, and df is its contribution to the member flexibility. By summation, the flexibility of the whole member is obtained as

$$f = \int_A^B (m^T(EI)^{-1} dx\, m) = \int_A^B m^T(EI)^{-1}m\, dx \tag{8.2}$$

125

An analogous procedure can be used to find an expression for the flexibility of the frame. It is assumed that the flexibility of each member is known. For the structures considered in this book, each member is connected to other members only at the ends. By member flexibility we imply the relationship between forces and displacements at one end of the member when the other end is fixed.

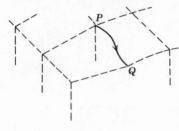

The size of the member flexibility matrix to be used depends on the nature of both the member and the frame. For a general frame with rigid joints, the matrix will be of order (6×6). However, if we are analyzing a plane frame it will only be necessary to use a submatrix of size (3×3). If axial deformations are neglected, we can

Fig. 8.1

further reduce this to (2×2). For a pin-jointed frame, axial force and deformation are the only relevant quantities and the matrix will be of order (1×1).

For a given frame, there are a number of ways of choosing the statically determinate primary frame. The primary frame chosen will be denoted by α. The releases can be called α_1, $\alpha_2 \ldots \alpha_n$ and the flexibility of the primary, $F_{\alpha\alpha}$. The distinguishing symbol α will not be needed unless the problem is to be solved more than once with different release systems.

Figure 8.1 shows a portion of the primary frame. We suppose that for the time being only a typical member PQ can deform, all others (shown dashed) being quite rigid. The flexibility of PQ is known at the end Q and is denoted by f_Q. Now a unit value of a given redundant, at the release αs for example, will give rise to certain values of the forces p_Q at Q. These can be expressed as a column matrix m_{Qs}. The size of m_{Qs} is governed by the size of the flexibility matrix for the particular member PQ; i.e., for a general member m_{Qs} will be of order (6×1). These forces will produce member deformations $f_Q \cdot m_{Qs}$ which are actually displacements of Q relative to P.

In turn the deformations of PQ produce release displacements, the displacement at release αr being $m_{Qr}^T f_Q m_{Qs}$. Thus the influence of the member flexibility f_Q on the frame flexibility coefficient f_{rs} is

$$\underset{(1 \times 1)}{\Delta_{Jrs}} = \underset{(1 \times 6)(6 \times 6)(6 \times 1)}{m_{Qr}^T \, f_Q \, m_{Qs}} \tag{8.3}$$

(The size of f_Q has been taken as (6×6), which assumes that all the end force components are relevant to the problem. This will be assumed throughout the chapter, but in most practical problems the size of f_Q will be less than this.)

The influence of PQ on all the coefficients of the frame flexibility matrix $F_{\alpha\alpha}$ can be generated by the matrix product

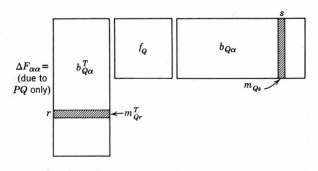

or
$$\Delta F_{\alpha\alpha} = b_{Q\alpha}^T \, f_Q \, b_{Q\alpha} \tag{8.4}$$
$$\underset{(n\times n)}{} \quad \underset{(n\times 6)(6\times 6)(6\times n)}{}$$

The matrix $b_{Q\alpha}$ is called a "transfer matrix." It serves to "transfer" forces from the n releases, α, to the member end Q. Each column of $b_{Q\alpha}$ contains the member end actions at Q due to one particular unit redundant. The end actions must be those for which the flexibility f_Q is known, and they must be expressed in the same axes, which will normally be the member axes of PQ. The number of columns in $b_{Q\alpha}$ is equal to the number of redundants, while the number of rows in $b_{Q\alpha}$ is governed by the size of f_Q.

The complete flexibility of the primary frame is obtained by summing expressions such as those of equation 8.4 for all members of the frame:

$$F_{\alpha\alpha} = \sum_{Q=0}^{Q=m} b_{Q\alpha}^T f_Q b_{Q\alpha} \tag{8.5}$$

The similarity between equations 8.5 and 8.2 is clear. The $\sum$ of 8.5 replaces the integral because the number of members in the frame is finite. A similar correspondence is seen between equations 8.4 and 8.1.

It is possible to express equation 8.5 by a single matrix product. The individual transfer matrices b_α are stacked in a single large matrix b_α, while the member flexibilities f_Q are set out as submatrices along the diagonal of f.

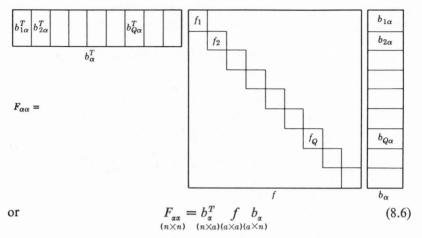

or
$$F_{\alpha\alpha} = b_\alpha^T \quad f \quad b_\alpha \qquad (8.6)$$
$$\underset{(n \times n)}{} \quad \underset{(n \times a)(a \times a)(a \times n)}{}$$

where a is 6 times the number of members.

The square matrix, f, is the matrix of unassembled member flexibilities. It is easily seen that the product $b_\alpha^T f b_\alpha$ is the same as the expression $\sum_{Q=0}^{m} b_{Q\alpha}^T f_Q b_{Q\alpha}$. Although the matrices of equation 8.6 are convenient for the purpose of reference, the form of equation 8.5 is usually more suitable for computation purposes.

A numerical example will be given after the particular solution has been considered.

8.2 PARTICULAR SOLUTION

The procedure for finding the release displacements, u_0, due to applied loads differs very little from that of Section 8.1. The applied loads are "transferred" to the ends of the various members. The member deformations are computed and the corresponding displacements "transferred" to the release locations.

For the time being we suppose that loads are applied only at joints so that each member is loaded only at its ends. The actions at the end Q of the typical member PQ due to applied loads can be represented by a matrix B_{Q0}. The number of rows in B_{Q0} is equal to the number of columns in the matrix f_Q, and the number of columns depends on the number of systems of loading to be considered, which we can denote by l. The matrix B_{Q0} is similar to $b_{Q\alpha}$ except that it refers to applied loads instead of unit redundants.

The deformation of PQ is then given by $f_Q \cdot B_{Q0}$. These displacements of point Q are transferred as before to the releases by the matrix $b_{Q\alpha}^T$. Due to the deformation of PQ alone we thus obtain

$$\underset{(n\times l)}{u_{\alpha 0}} = \underset{(n\times 6)}{b_{Q\alpha}^T} \underset{(6\times 6)}{f_Q} \underset{(6\times l)}{B_{Q0}}$$

where $u_{\alpha 0}$ are the release displacements of this particular primary frame α.

Summing expressions such as this for all members, we obtain

$$U_{\alpha 0} = \sum b_{Q\alpha}^T f_Q B_{Q0} \tag{8.7}$$

The symbol U is used since the total release displacements are the *summation* of the displacements caused by the various members individually.

As before, this equation can be expressed by a single matrix product

$$\underset{(n\times l)}{U_{\alpha 0}} = \underset{(n\times a)}{b_{\alpha}^T} \underset{(a\times a)}{f} \underset{(a\times l)}{B_0} \tag{8.8}$$

where B_0 consists of the B_0 matrices for the individual members stacked one below the other.

8.3 COMPLETE SOLUTION

The redundant actions can now be found in the usual way by solution of the compatibility equations $U_{\alpha 0} + F_{\alpha\alpha}p_\alpha = 0$.

Thus

$$\underset{(n\times l)}{p_\alpha} = -\underset{(n\times n)(n\times l)}{F_{\alpha\alpha}^{-1} U_{\alpha 0}} \tag{8.9}$$

Reverting to the typical member PQ, we see that the member end actions due to the redundants p_α are given by $b_{Q\alpha}p_\alpha$. Hence the total member end actions at Q are

$$\underset{(6\times l)}{p_Q} = \underset{(6\times l)}{B_{Q0}} + \underset{(6\times n)(n\times l)}{b_{Q\alpha} p_\alpha} \tag{8.10}$$

In this way the actions at the end of any member can be calculated. Actions at any other position along the member can then be found by statics.

Deflections of the frame at any points $D_1, D_2, D_3 \ldots$ can easily be determined. The total end action on the typical member is given by equation 8.10. Hence the total deformation of the member is given by

$$\underset{(6\times l)}{u_Q} = \underset{(6\times 6)}{f_Q} (\underset{(6\times l)}{B_{Q0}} + \underset{(6\times n)(n\times l)}{b_{Q\alpha} p_\alpha}) \tag{8.11}$$

It is now necessary to transfer the displacement u_Q to the stations D_1, $D_2 \ldots$. The required transfer matrix is obtained by finding the end actions at Q due to unit loads at each of the points $D_1, D_2 \ldots$ separately.

We thus obtain a matrix b_{QD} with one column for each of the points $D_1, D_2 \ldots$. Since b_{QD} transfers forces from the D points to Q, the matrix b_{QD}^T will transfer displacements from Q to the D points. Thus the deflections at $D_1, D_2 \ldots$ due to the deformation of PQ are given by

$$u_D = b_{QD}^T f_Q (B_{Q0} + b_{Q\alpha} p_\alpha)$$

The total deflections are then

$$U_D = \sum b_{QD}^T f_Q (B_{Q0} + b_{Q\alpha} p_\alpha) \qquad (8.12)$$

For clarity it will be assumed for the time being that the points at which deflections are required are not the same as the points at which the frame is loaded. When this is the case, the load matrix, B_0, and the deflection matrix, b_D, can be regarded as independent.

Example 8.1 It is required to solve the gabled portal of Example 4.1 (see Fig. 8.2a). The horizontal deflection at D and the vertical deflection at C are required. The primary frame is obtained by making three releases at E.

Solution. (i) MEMBER FLEXIBILITIES. Axes are arbitrarily chosen for each member. The choice of x direction for a given member automatically determines the end at which the flexibility is to be expressed. For member BC, for instance, the flexibility will be determined at C (Fig. 8.2b). Since axial deformations are to be neglected, the only relevant end displacements are transverse deflection and rotation. These will be denoted *in that order* by u_2 and u_6 (Fig. 8.2). The member flexibility matrix is thus of size (2×2).

Using the relevant terms from the complete matrix of equation 6.6 and neglecting shear we obtain the member flexibility as

$$f = \begin{bmatrix} L^3/3EI & L^2/2EI \\ L^2/2EI & L/EI \end{bmatrix} \qquad (8.13)$$

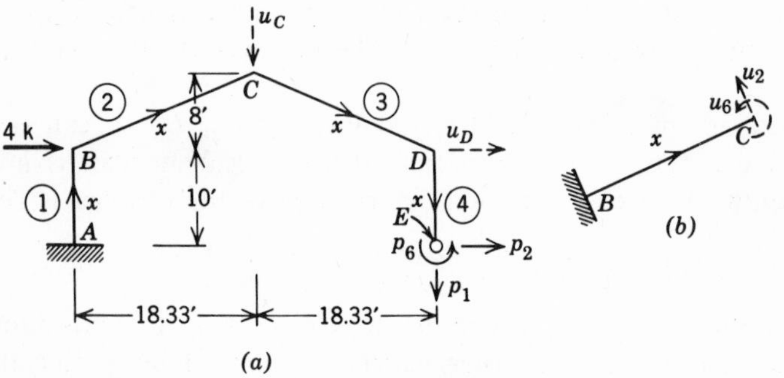

(a)

(b)

Fig. 8.2

If the members are labeled 1, 2, 3 and 4 as shown (Fig. 8.2a), their flexibilities (with $EI = 1$) are given by

$$f_1 = f_4 = \begin{bmatrix} 333.3 & 50 \\ 50 & 10 \end{bmatrix} \quad \text{and} \quad f_2 = f_3 = \begin{bmatrix} 2666.7 & 200 \\ 200 & 20 \end{bmatrix}$$

(ii) TRANSFER FROM RELEASES TO MEMBER ENDS. To find the first column, for instance, of the b_α matrices, we apply unit value of redundant p_1 and write down the end shear and moment, *in that order*, for each member. The sign of the end actions must correspond to the flexibility axes (see Fig. 8.2).

$$b_Q = \begin{array}{|ccc|l}
\hline
0 & -1 & 0 & \\
-36.66 & +10 & +1 & \leftarrow b_{1\alpha} \\
\hline
-0.9165 & -0.4 & 0 & \\
-18.33 & +18 & +1 & \leftarrow b_{2\alpha} \\
\hline
-0.9165 & +0.4 & 0 & \\
0 & +10 & +1 & \leftarrow b_{3\alpha} \\
\hline
0 & +1 & 0 & \\
0 & 0 & +1 & \leftarrow b_{4\alpha} \\
\hline
\end{array}$$

(iii) PRIMARY FRAME FLEXIBILITY. The submatrices $b_{1\alpha}, b_{2\alpha}, b_{3\alpha}, b_{4\alpha}$ are the transfer matrices to the ends of members, 1, 2, 3 and 4. Each member contributes to the frame flexibility as follows:

$$\Delta_1 F_{\alpha\alpha} = \begin{bmatrix} 0 & -36.66 \\ -1 & +10 \\ 0 & +1 \end{bmatrix} \begin{bmatrix} 333.3 & 50 \\ 50 & 10 \end{bmatrix} \begin{bmatrix} 0 & -1 & 0 \\ -36.66 & +10 & +1 \end{bmatrix}$$

$$= \begin{bmatrix} 13439.5 & -1833.0 & -366.6 \\ -1833.0 & 333.3 & 50 \\ -366.6 & 50 & 10 \end{bmatrix}^*$$

$$\Delta_2 F_{\alpha\alpha} = \begin{bmatrix} -0.9165 & -18.33 \\ -0.4000 & +18 \\ 0 & +1 \end{bmatrix} \begin{bmatrix} 2666.7 & 200 \\ 200 & 20 \end{bmatrix} \begin{bmatrix} -0.9165 & -0.4000 & 0 \\ -18.33 & +18 & +1 \end{bmatrix}$$

$$= \begin{bmatrix} 15679.5 & -7454.2 & -549.9 \\ -7454.2 & 4026.7 & 280.0 \\ -549.9 & 280.0 & 20.0 \end{bmatrix} *$$

$$\Delta_3 F_{\alpha\alpha} = \begin{bmatrix} -0.9165 & 0 \\ +0.4000 & +10 \\ 0 & +1 \end{bmatrix} \begin{bmatrix} 2666.7 & 200 \\ 200 & 20 \end{bmatrix} \begin{bmatrix} -0.9165 & +0.4000 & 0 \\ 0 & +10 & +1 \end{bmatrix}$$

$$= \begin{bmatrix} 2240.0 & -2810.6 & -183.3 \\ -2810.6 & 4026.7 & 280.0 \\ -183.3 & 280.0 & 20.0 \end{bmatrix} *$$

$$\Delta_4 F_{\alpha\alpha} = \begin{bmatrix} 0 & 0 \\ +1 & 0 \\ 0 & +1 \end{bmatrix} \begin{bmatrix} 333.3 & 50 \\ 50 & 10 \end{bmatrix} \begin{bmatrix} 0 & +1 & 0 \\ 0 & 0 & +1 \end{bmatrix} = \begin{bmatrix} 0 & 0 & 0 \\ 0 & +333.3 & 50 \\ 0 & 50 & 10 \end{bmatrix} *$$

Then by summation

$$F_{\alpha\alpha} = \begin{bmatrix} 31359.0 & -12097.8 & -1099.8 \\ -12097.8 & 8720.0 & 660 \\ -1099.8 & 660 & 60 \end{bmatrix}$$

The significance of this method is shown by comparing the starred matrices with the values in Table 4.3, where the figures on any one row give the contribution of a particular member to the total flexibility. The results are seen to agree.

Instead of evaluating $\Delta_1 F_{\alpha\alpha}, \Delta_2 F_{\alpha\alpha} \ldots$ separately, the same result could be obtained by the product $b_\alpha^T f b_\alpha$.

(iv) TRANSFER FROM LOAD AND DEFLECTION POINTS TO MEMBER ENDS. For the matrix B_0 we apply the given load system and write down the end shear and moment for each member (since there is only one system of loading in this problem, B_0 contains only one column). For the b_D matrix we apply a unit load corresponding to each required deflection in turn, and again write down the end shear and moment for each member.

$$B_0 = \begin{bmatrix} -4 \\ 0 \\ \hline 0 \\ 0 \\ \hline 0 \\ 0 \\ \hline 0 \\ 0 \end{bmatrix} \begin{matrix} \leftarrow B_{10} \\ \\ \leftarrow B_{20} \\ \\ \leftarrow B_{30} \\ \\ \leftarrow B_{40} \end{matrix} \qquad b_D = \begin{bmatrix} -1 & 0 \\ 0 & -18.33 \\ \hline -0.4 & -0.9165 \\ +8 & 0 \\ \hline +0.4 & 0 \\ 0 & 0 \\ \hline 0 & 0 \\ 0 & 0 \end{bmatrix} \begin{matrix} \leftarrow b_{1D} \\ \\ \leftarrow b_{2D} \\ \\ \leftarrow b_{3D} \\ \\ \leftarrow b_{4D} \end{matrix}$$

(v) COMPLETE SOLUTION. When the external load is applied to the primary frame, the resulting release displacements are given by

$$U_{\alpha 0} = \sum b_{Q\alpha}^T f_Q B_{Q0}$$

The contribution from member 1 is, for instance,

$$\Delta_1 U_{\alpha 0} = \begin{bmatrix} 0 & -36.66 \\ 1 & +10 \\ 0 & +1 \end{bmatrix} \begin{bmatrix} 333.3 & 50 \\ 50 & 10 \end{bmatrix} \begin{bmatrix} -4 \\ 0 \end{bmatrix} = \begin{bmatrix} +7332 \\ -667 \\ -200 \end{bmatrix}$$

(Compare again with Table 4.3.)

The contributions from other members are zero in this problem; hence, upon summation, we obtain

$$U_{\alpha 0} = \begin{bmatrix} +7332 \\ -667 \\ -200 \end{bmatrix}$$

The redundants are now given by

$$p_\alpha = -F_{\alpha\alpha}^{-1} U_{\alpha 0} = \begin{bmatrix} -0.327 \\ -1.050 \\ +8.878 \end{bmatrix}$$

Taking member 1 as a typical member, we can now write:

$$\text{Total end actions on member } 1 = p_1 = B_{10} + b_{1\alpha}p_\alpha = \begin{bmatrix} -2.950 \\ +10.366 \end{bmatrix}$$

$$\text{Total deformation of member } 1 = u_1 = f_1 p_1 = \begin{bmatrix} -465 \\ -44 \end{bmatrix}$$

(These values represent the lateral displacement and rotation, respectively, of point B relative to A.)

The consequent displacement of points D and C (in the given directions) due to the deformation of member 1 are

$$U_{D1} = b_{1D}^T u_1 = \begin{bmatrix} +465 \\ +804 \end{bmatrix}$$

Information regarding the other members is obtained in a similar way. By summation we obtain the total deflection at points D and C as

$$U_D = \begin{bmatrix} U_D \\ U_C \end{bmatrix} = \begin{bmatrix} +268 \\ -217 \end{bmatrix}$$

It must be remembered that EI has been taken as 1.0 (in kip, foot units). The positive directions of U_D and U_C are governed by the choice of unit load in compiling the b_D matrix.

In the above problem, the releases were all made at the end of a member. Frequently a release is made at some intermediate point between the ends of a member. The procedure is not modified in any way in such a case. The product of member end actions and (complete) member flexibility still represents the deformation of the member. In the final solution this product represents, as before, the displacement of one end relative to the other, since the value of the redundants have been chosen so as to eliminate any discontinuity along the length of the member

To illustrate the method, we examine the above frame using a different system of releases.

Example 8.2 Determine the release flexibility of the primary frame of Fig. 8.3.

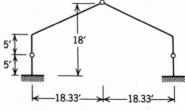

Fig. 8.3

Solution. The primary frame will be called β to distinguish it from the previous one, which we called α. Irrespective of the hinges at the midpoints of AB and DE, the flexibilities of the complete members are used in the analysis. Thus, as before,

$$f_1 = f_4 = \begin{bmatrix} 333.3 & 50 \\ 50 & 10 \end{bmatrix} \quad \text{and} \quad f_2 = f_3 = \begin{bmatrix} 2666.7 & 200 \\ 200 & 20 \end{bmatrix}$$

To find the first column of the b_β matrices, unit value of the first redundant is applied and the shear and moment at the *end* of each member is determined.

$$b_\beta = \begin{array}{|ccc|l}
\hline
+0.0385 & -0.0769 & 0.0385 & \\
+0.8077 & +0.3846 & 0.1923 & \leftarrow b_{1\beta} \\
\hline
+0.0404 & -0.0308 & -0.0096 & \\
0 & +1.0000 & 0 & \leftarrow b_{2\beta} \\
\hline
+0.0096 & +0.0308 & -0.0404 & \\
-0.1923 & +0.3846 & +0.8077 & \leftarrow b_{3\beta} \\
\hline
-0.0385 & +0.0769 & -0.0385 & \\
+0.1923 & -0.3846 & +1.1923 & \leftarrow b_{4\beta} \\
\hline
\end{array}$$

We then calculate the frame flexibility from

$$F_{\beta\beta} = \sum b_\beta^T f b_\beta$$

This gives

$$F_{\beta\beta} = \begin{bmatrix} +14.8503 & +3.1327 & -1.8234 \\ +3.1327 & +21.4213 & +3.1367 \\ -1.8234 & +3.1367 & +6.3210 \end{bmatrix}$$

The shear and moment at the end of each member are now computed for the external 4-kip load and for unit loads at each of the deflection points.

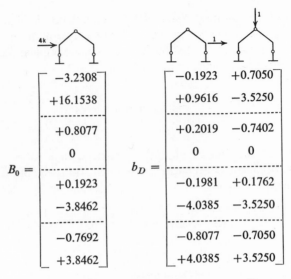

$$B_0 = \begin{bmatrix} -3.2308 \\ +16.1538 \\ \hline +0.8077 \\ 0 \\ \hline +0.1923 \\ -3.8462 \\ \hline -0.7692 \\ +3.8462 \end{bmatrix} \qquad b_D = \begin{bmatrix} -0.1923 & +0.7050 \\ +0.9616 & -3.5250 \\ \hline +0.2019 & -0.7402 \\ 0 & 0 \\ \hline -0.1981 & +0.1762 \\ -4.0385 & -3.5250 \\ \hline -0.8077 & -0.7050 \\ +4.0385 & +3.5250 \end{bmatrix}$$

In the same manner as before we can now compute $U_{\beta 0}$.

$$U_{\beta 0} = \sum b_\beta f B_0 = \begin{bmatrix} +84.0557 \\ +88.2771 \\ -49.2773 \end{bmatrix}$$

It should be noted that these values represent angular discontinuities at the release hinges β_1, β_2 and β_3.

The redundants are

$$p_\beta = -F_{\beta\beta}^{-1} U_{\beta 0} = \begin{bmatrix} -4.3672 \\ -4.0144 \\ +3.6334 \end{bmatrix}$$

Considering the same typical member as before, namely member 1, we can now find the total end actions and deformations.

$$\text{Total end actions on member } 1 = p_1 = B_{10} + b_{1\beta}p_\beta = \begin{bmatrix} -2.95 \\ +10.38 \end{bmatrix}$$

$$\text{Total deformation of member } 1 = u_1 = f_1 p_1 = \begin{bmatrix} -465 \\ -44 \end{bmatrix}$$

The forces p_1 are the final actions at the end B of member 1, and the displacements u_1 are the final deformations of member 1, i.e., the displacements of end B relative to end A. These values should therefore be the same as those obtained in the previous solution, when primary frame α was used.   It will be seen that the values do agree.

The displacements u_1 are now transferred to the deflection points C and D by the matrix b_{1D}^T (as obtained from the frame β).   The deformation of members 2, 3 and 4 are transferred in a similar way, and upon summation we obtain

$$U_D = \begin{bmatrix} U_D \\ U_C \end{bmatrix} = \begin{bmatrix} +268 \\ -217 \end{bmatrix}$$

It should be noted that while the contributions of the individual member deformations to U_D are different in the present solution from what they were in the previous solution, the final or summation values of U_D are nevertheless the same as before.

8.4   MEMBERS WITH INTERMEDIATE LOADING

In Section 8.2 the assumption was made that loads were applied to the frame only at the joints.   When this is so, each member receives load only at its ends.   The deformation of a member PQ can thus be expressed entirely in terms of its end forces p_Q and the end flexibility f_Q.

If the member receives loads at some points intermediate between the ends, such loads will cause deformation not accounted for by the product $f_Q p_Q$.   Such loads can be included in the analysis by separately computing the member end deformation due to such intermediate loads and adding this term to the deformation due to end forces.   This is not the only method of dealing with the problem.

As a typical illustration, suppose that the deformation of a member PQ is expressed by the displacements $\{u_2 \quad u_6\}$ of end Q (Fig. 8.4) relative to P.   The end flexibility matrix is (2×2).   If in addition to end actions the member carries a uniformly distributed load w, we compute the end displacements due to w and denote these by a separate term u_*.

$$u_* = \begin{bmatrix} u_2 \\ u_6 \end{bmatrix}_* = \begin{bmatrix} -wL^4/8EI \\ -wL^3/6EI \end{bmatrix} \tag{8.14}$$

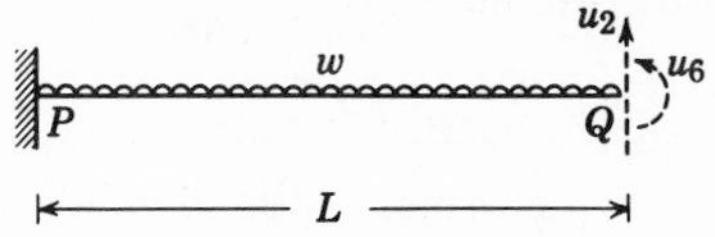

Fig. 8.4

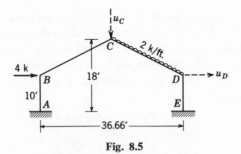

Fig. 8.5

The total member deformation, as defined, is then given by

$$u_Q = u_{Q*} + f_Q P_Q \tag{8.15}$$

Example 8.3 Suppose that the frame of Example 8.1 carries a distributed load normal to the member CD (Fig. 8.5). Solve the frame for the 4-kip load and the distributed load separately.

Solution. The member flexibilities, the b_α matrix and the frame flexibility $F_{\alpha\alpha}$ remain the same as before since they are independent of the loading. The load transfer matrix now has two columns since there are two separate load systems.

$$
B_0 =
\begin{array}{cc}
\begin{array}{|cc|}
\hline
-4 & +16 \\
0 & -944 \\
\hline
0 & -27.2 \\
0 & -400 \\
\hline
0 & 0 \\
0 & 0 \\
\hline
0 & 0 \\
0 & 0 \\
\hline
\end{array}
&
\begin{array}{l}
B_{10} \\ \\
B_{20} \\ \\
B_{30} \\ \\
B_{40}
\end{array}
\end{array}
$$

For members 1, 2 and 4 the release displacements due to loading, $U_{\alpha 0}$, are computed as before, namely

$$\Delta U_{\alpha 0} = b_\alpha^T f B_0$$

Member 3, however, is deformed both by end loads and by the distributed load.

Due to end loads, the member deformation is

$$u_3 = \begin{bmatrix} 2666.7 & 200 \\ 200 & 20 \end{bmatrix} \begin{bmatrix} 0 & 0 & 0 \\ 0 & 0 & 0 \end{bmatrix} = \begin{bmatrix} 0 & 0 \\ 0 & 0 \end{bmatrix}$$

$$\qquad\qquad\; f_3 \qquad\quad B_{30}$$

Due to the distributed load we have from equation 8.14

$$u_{3*} = \begin{bmatrix} 0 & -40000 \\ 0 & -2667 \end{bmatrix}$$

The first column refers to the first load system, which contains no intermediate loads.

Hence the deformation of member 3 due to loading is

$$u_{30} = u_{3*} + f_3 B_{30} = \begin{bmatrix} 0 & -40000 \\ 0 & -2667 \end{bmatrix}$$

The resulting release displacements are

$$\Delta_3 U_{\alpha 0} = b_{3\alpha}^T (u_{3*} + f_3 B_{30}) = \begin{bmatrix} 0 & +36660 \\ 0 & -42670 \\ 0 & -2667 \end{bmatrix}$$

The total release displacement due to loading is then

$$U_{\alpha 0} = \begin{bmatrix} 7332 & 675815 \\ -667 & -205388 \\ -200 & -24547 \end{bmatrix}$$

The redundants are

$$p_\alpha = -F_{\alpha\alpha}^{-1} U_{\alpha 0} = \begin{bmatrix} -0.327 & -20.087 \\ -1.050 & -44.396 \\ +8.878 & +526.023 \end{bmatrix}$$

The total member end actions are now found.

$$p_1 = B_{10} + b_{1\alpha} p_\alpha = \begin{bmatrix} -4 & +16 \\ 0 & -944 \end{bmatrix} + \begin{bmatrix} 1.050 & 44.396 \\ 10.366 & 548.452 \end{bmatrix}$$

$$\qquad\quad = \begin{bmatrix} -2.950 & +60.396 \\ +10.366 & -395.548 \end{bmatrix}$$

$$p_2 = B_{20} + b_{2\alpha}p_\alpha = \begin{bmatrix} 0 & 0 \\ 0 & 0 \end{bmatrix} + \begin{bmatrix} +0.720 & +36.168 \\ -4.028 & -174.910 \end{bmatrix}$$

$$= \begin{bmatrix} +0.720 & +36.168 \\ -4.028 & -174.910 \end{bmatrix}$$

$$p_3 = B_{30} + b_{3\alpha}p_\alpha = \begin{bmatrix} 0 & 0 \\ 0 & 0 \end{bmatrix} + \begin{bmatrix} -0.120 & +0.651 \\ -1.622 & -187.937 \end{bmatrix}$$

$$= \begin{bmatrix} -0.120 & +0.651 \\ -1.622 & -187.937 \end{bmatrix}$$

$$p_4 = B_{40} + b_{4\alpha}p_\alpha = \begin{bmatrix} 0 & 0 \\ 0 & 0 \end{bmatrix} + \begin{bmatrix} -1.050 & -44.396 \\ +8.878 & +256.023 \end{bmatrix}$$

$$= \begin{bmatrix} -1.050 & -44.396 \\ +8.878 & +256.023 \end{bmatrix}$$

As far as internal actions are concerned, each member can now be analyzed individually by statics. In the case of member 3, the distributed load must be taken into account as well as the end loading. In all the u and p matrices, the two columns refer to the two separate load systems.

To find the displacements of D and C, we first find the *total* member deformations and then transfer these to the deflection points. The member deformations are given by

$u_1 = f_1 p_1$	$=$	$\begin{array}{rr} -464.935 & +352.587 \\ -43.840 & -935.680 \end{array}$
$u_2 = f_2 p_2$	$=$	$\begin{array}{rr} -613.576 & -25335.994 \\ +63.440 & +3735.400 \end{array}$
$u_3 = u_{3*} + f_3 p_3$	$=$	$\begin{array}{rr} -356.404 & -77413.778 \\ -56.440 & -6295.540 \end{array}$
$u_4 = f_4 p_4$	$=$	$\begin{array}{rr} +93.935 & -1996.037 \\ +36.280 & +340.430 \end{array}$

These displacements are transferred by the b_D matrices (see p. 130). If the displacements of D and C are denoted collectively by U_D, then

$$U_D = \sum_{Q=1}^{4} b_{QD}^T U_Q = \begin{bmatrix} +1075 \\ +40371 \end{bmatrix}$$

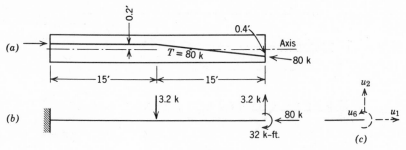

Fig. 8.6

When a member of the frame is deformed only by end actions, the deformation can be expressed as fp. If additional deformation occurs for any reason whatsoever, this can be accounted for by a u_* term which merely gives the value of the member end displacements due to the cause in question. Temperature variation can be dealt with by this procedure.

Another cause of deformation is prestressing. Suppose that we have to analyze a concrete frame for the effect of prestressing alone. Our basic problem is to calculate the deformation of any individual member due to prestress.

The member shown in Fig. 8.6a is stressed by a cable having a tension of 80 kips. Essentially, the forces acting on the concrete member consist of a compressive force at each end of 80 kips in the direction of the prestressing cable and a force of 3.2 kips at the center point due to the change of direction of the cable. Strictly speaking, this force bisects the angle formed by the cable and therefore has a small horizontal component, but this has been neglected. Moreover, the horizontal component of the 80-kip force has been taken as 80 kips.

If we regard the member as being cantilevered from the left-hand end, the forces causing deformation can be summarized as shown in Fig. 8.6b. The end forces are the forces at the centroid equivalent to the inclined 80-kip force. The deformation due to the end forces can be computed by means of the flexibility matrix in the usual way. The deformation caused by the central force can be represented by a u_* term.

Assume that axial deformation is relevant in this case and that the end displacements are as defined in Fig. 8.6c. Then, due to the central load, we shall have

$$
u_* = \begin{bmatrix} 0 \\[2ex] -\dfrac{5}{48}\dfrac{WL^3}{EI} \\[2ex] -\dfrac{1}{8}\dfrac{WL^2}{EI} \end{bmatrix} = \frac{1}{EI} \begin{bmatrix} 0 \\[2ex] -9000 \\[2ex] -360 \end{bmatrix}
$$

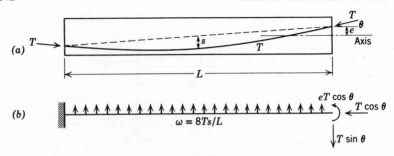

Fig. 8.7

Another illustration is shown in Fig. 8.7a, where the prestressing cable is parabolic. The forces exerted by the cable on the concrete consist of inclined end compressive forces and a uniformly distributed upward load caused by the parabolic draping. The forces can be represented by the system of Fig. 8.7b. The distributed load gives rise to a u_* term the elements of which are as given in equation 8.14. Since axial deformation will be relevant in this case we shall have

$$u_* = \begin{bmatrix} 0 \\ -wL^4/8EI \\ -wL^3/6EI \end{bmatrix} \qquad (8.16)$$

In addition to the individual member flexibilities, the basic data for the present method of analysis consist of the matrices b_α, B_0 and b_D. These matrices transfer forces to the member ends from the releases α, from the load positions and from the deflection positions respectively. Naturally, the transposes of these matrices also serve to transfer displacements in the reverse direction.

Although the matrices b_α, B_0 and b_D have been regarded as quite distinct in the foregoing explanation, this is not essential. In the above, the matrix B_0 gave member end actions due to the *whole* of the applied loading. We could construct a matrix b_0 on the basis of *unit* values of the applied load and then multiply by a further vector W containing the magnitudes of the various loads. We should then have

$$B_0 = b_0 W \qquad (8.17)$$

Matrices b_0 and b_D could then be regarded as submatrices of a general matrix b. If the deflection of some of the load points is required, some columns of b would be common to both b_0 and b_D. Such a procedure is also convenient if the structure is to be analyzed for several load conditions where the magnitude, but not the location, of the loading is changed from one load condition to another.

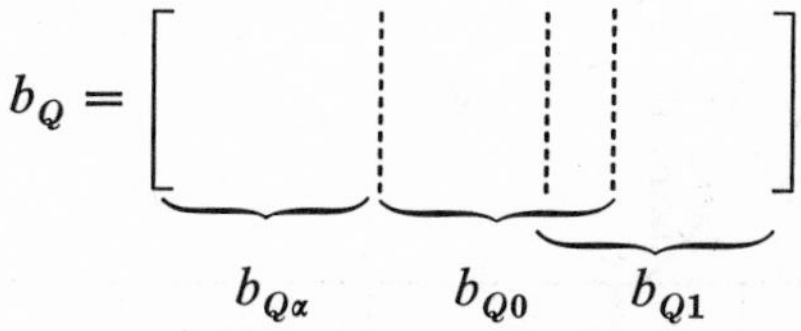

$$b_Q = \left[\quad \vdots \quad \vdots \quad \vdots \quad \right] \tag{8.18}$$

$$\underbrace{}_{b_{Q\alpha}} \quad \underbrace{}_{b_{Q0}} \quad \underbrace{}_{b_{Q1}}$$

The submatrix b_Q of b, which refers to the member Q, can be represented as shown in equation 8.18. The columns of the submatrix $b_{Q\alpha}$ give the member end forces due to unit redundants. The columns of submatrix b_{Q0} give member end forces due to *unit* values of the external loads. The columns of the submatrix b_{QD} give member end forces due to unit loads at the locations where frame displacements are to be calculated. As indicated, there is no need for the submatrices of b_Q to be mutually exclusive.

Example 8.4 The braced portal of Fig. 8.8 is subjected to four loading cases as indicated in the accompanying table. The relative rigidities of the bracing members (EA) and the bending members (EI) are given by

$$\frac{EA}{EI} = \frac{1}{20}$$

The axial deformation of the bending members is neglected.

Determine the support reactions, the axial forces in the bracing members, the vertical displacements at E and F and the horizontal displacement at G for each of the four loading cases shown in the table. (see p. 146).

Solution. By the introduction of a node at E, the number of different components in the frame can be reduced to two. The basic member flexibilities are (with $EA = 1$ and $EI = 20$),

$$f_1 = \begin{bmatrix} 16.67 & 7.5 \\ 7.5 & 0.5 \end{bmatrix} \qquad \text{for the bending members}$$

and

$$f_2 = [14.14] \qquad \text{for the braces}$$

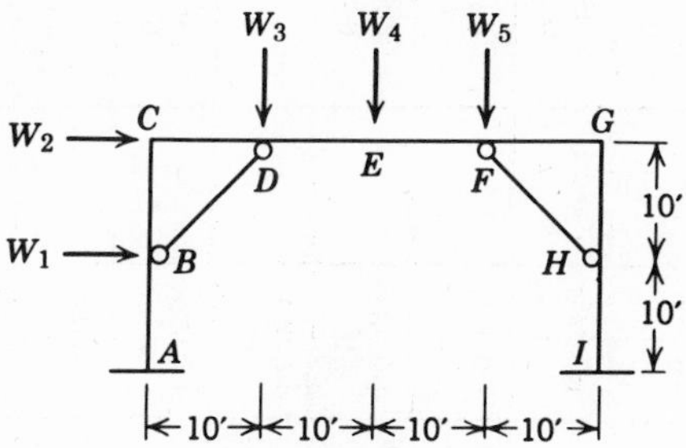

Fig. 8.8

$$(8.19)$$

$b =$

	A $p_1=1$	C $p_2=1$	E $p_3=1$	G $p_4=1$	I $p_5=1$	$H_B=1$	$H_C=1$	$V_D=1$	$V_E=1$	$V_F=1$	$H_G=1$	
	1	2	3	4	5	6	7	8	9	10	11	
	-0.025 / $+1$	0 / 0	-0.05 / 0		-0.025 / 0	-0.75 / 0	-0.5 / 0	$+0.25$ / 0	$+0.5$ / 0	$+0.25$ / 0	-0.5 / 0	← Member 1
	-0.075 / 0	-0.1 / $+1$	$+0.05$ / 0		$+0.025$ / 0	$+0.75$ / 0	$+0.5$ / 0	-0.25 / 0	-0.5 / 0	-0.25 / 0	$+0.5$ / 0	← Member 2
	$+0.025$ / 0	$+0.1$ / -1	-0.1 / 0		-0.025 / 0	-0.25 / 0	-0.5 / 0	-0.25 / 0	$+0.5$ / 0	$+0.25$ / 0	-0.5 / 0	Shear ⎫
	-0.025 / 0		0 / $+1$		$+0.025$ / 0	$+0.25$ / 0	$+0.5$ / 0	$+0.25$ / 0	-0.5 / 0	-0.25 / 0	$+0.5$ / 0	moment ⎬
	$+0.025$ / 0		$+0.05$ / 0		$+0.025$ / -1	-0.25 / 0	-0.5 / 0	-0.25 / 0	-0.5 / 0	-0.25 / 0	-0.5 / 0	
	-0.025 / 0		-0.05 / 0	$+0.1$ / -1	$+0.075$ / 0	$+0.25$ / 0	$+0.5$ / 0	$+0.25$ / 0	$+0.5$ / 0	$+0.25$ / 0	$+0.5$ / 0	
	$+0.025$ / 0		$+0.1$ / 0	-0.1 / $+1$	-0.025 / 0	-0.25 / 0	-0.5 / 0	-0.25 / 0	-0.5 / 0	$+0.25$ / 0	-0.5 / 0	
	-0.025 / 0		0 / -1		$+0.025$ / 0	$+0.25$ / 0	$+0.5$ / 0	$+0.25$ / 0	$+0.5$ / 0	-0.25 / 0	$+0.5$ / 0	
	-0.0707	-0.1414	$+0.1414$		$+0.0707$	$+0.707$	$+1.414$	-0.707	-1.414	-0.707	$+1.414$	
	$+0.0707$		$+0.1414$	-0.1414	-0.0707	-0.707	-1.414	-0.707	-1.414	-0.707	-1.414	← Member 10
	$\underbrace{\qquad\qquad}_{b_\alpha}$				$\underbrace{\qquad}_{b_0}$			$\underbrace{\qquad}_{b_0}$		$\underbrace{\qquad}_{b_D}$		

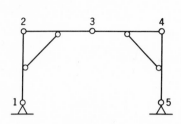

Fig. 8.9

Fig. 8.10

The primary frame chosen is shown in Fig. 8.9. It is obtained by making hinge releases at A, C, E, G and I since the braced portal is fivefold statically indeterminate. The incidence of the various members (direction of the x axis) is shown in Fig. 8.10. By locating the positive end of each member at a hinge, the number of end forces to be calculated is minimized.

The releases, and the component members, can be numbered in any order. The numbering adopted for the releases is shown in Fig. 8.9. It is chosen so that the frame flexibility will possess double symmetry. The numbering of the members is shown in Fig. 8.10.

The transfer matrix b (equation 8.19) is prepared for a unit value of each redundant and a unit force at each load position and each deflection position.

The elements in a given column of b will represent the relevant member end forces produced in the primary frame by the loading indicated at the top of the matrix column in question. The relevant forces will be the shear and moment for members 1–8 and the axial force for members 9 and 10. The elements of the third column are produced by the application of a pair of couples at hinge E. This produces external reactions as shown in Fig. 8.11a, and member end forces as shown in Fig. 8.11b.

The b_α matrix comprises the first 5 columns of b. From these and from

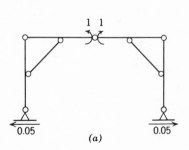

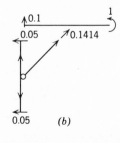

Fig. 8.11

the member flexibilities, the frame flexibility is found as in previous examples.

$$F_{\alpha\alpha} = b_\alpha^T f b_\alpha = \begin{bmatrix} +0.542 & +0.083 & +0.125 & -0.042 & -0.208 \\ +0.083 & +0.616 & -0.441 & +0.283 & -0.042 \\ +0.125 & -0.441 & +2.631 & -0.441 & +0.125 \\ -0.042 & +0.283 & -0.441 & +0.616 & +0.083 \\ -0.208 & -0.042 & +0.125 & +0.083 & +0.542 \end{bmatrix}$$

The matrix B_0 is required for the calculation of release displacements due to applied loads. This matrix can be formed by selecting from b columns 6–10 (forming a submatrix which can be called b_0) and multiplying by a loading matrix W which gives the required load combinations.

$$W = \begin{bmatrix} 22 & \cdot & \cdot & 22 \\ 11 & \cdot & \cdot & 11 \\ \cdot & 17 & 25 & 25 \\ \cdot & 17 & 30 & 30 \\ \cdot & 17 & 25 & 25 \end{bmatrix}$$

Then,

$$u_0 = b_\alpha^T f B_0 = b_\alpha^T f b_0 W = \begin{bmatrix} -100.8 & +42.5 & +68.7 & -32.1 \\ -27.5 & -171.0 & -275.6 & -303.1 \\ -18.3 & +512.1 & +838.8 & +820.4 \\ +18.3 & -171.0 & -275.6 & -257.3 \\ +73.3 & +42.5 & +68.7 & +142.1 \end{bmatrix}$$

The redundants p_α can then be evaluated.

$$p_\alpha = -F_{\alpha\alpha}^{-1} u_0 = \begin{bmatrix} +150.2 & -88.6 & -140.7 & +9.5 \\ +32.8 & +123.4 & -195.6 & +228.4 \\ +5.3 & -144.9 & -239.9 & -234.7 \\ -21.0 & +123.4 & +195.6 & +174.6 \\ -73.1 & -88.6 & -140.7 & -213.8 \end{bmatrix}$$

The member end actions, p, are given by

$$p = b_0 W + b_\alpha p_\alpha$$

The matrix p is (18×4), there being two rows each for members 1–8 and one row each for members 9 and 10. The four columns correspond to the four loading conditions. For reasons of space the first two rows (the end forces for member 1) only are shown

$$
p = \left[
\begin{array}{cccc}
-23.6622 & +14.1836 & +22.5381 & -1.1241 \\
+150.1684 & -88.5734 & -140.7034 & +9.4650 \\
\hdashline
& & &
\end{array}
\right.
\begin{array}{l}
\text{shear} \\
\text{moment}
\end{array}\left.\raisebox{1ex}{}\right\} p_1
$$

The deformation of each member is given by $u = fp$. Thus for member 1, for example, we have

$$
u_1 = \begin{bmatrix} 16.67 & 7.5 \\ 7.5 & 0.5 \end{bmatrix} p_1 = \begin{bmatrix} 3735.18 & -427.86 & -679.57 & 52.25 \\ -102.35 & 62.09 & 98.68 & -3.70 \end{bmatrix}
$$

The member deformations are transferred to the deflection points E, F and G by the matrix b_D^T where b_D comprises the last three columns of the transfer matrix b. Thus for member 1 the matrix b_{1D} (submatrix of b_D for member 1) is

$$
b_{1D} = \begin{bmatrix} +0.5 & +0.25 & -0.5 \\ 0 & 0 & 0 \end{bmatrix}
$$

and

$$
b_{1D}^T \cdot u_1 = \begin{bmatrix} 1867.59 & -213.93 & -339.78 & 26.12 \\ 933.79 & -106.96 & -169.89 & 13.06 \\ -1867.59 & 213.93 & 339.78 & -26.12 \end{bmatrix}
$$

The rows correspond to displacement of E, F and G respectively. The displacements caused by the deformation of each member are computed in turn. Summation of the results gives

$$
U = \begin{bmatrix} U_E \downarrow \\ U_F \downarrow \\ U_G \rightarrow \end{bmatrix} = \begin{bmatrix} -53 & +796 & +1303 & +1250 \\ -119 & +506 & +818 & +699 \\ +218 & 0 & 0 & +218 \end{bmatrix}
$$

The true values of displacement could be obtained by dividing through by EA, the rigidity of the diagonal bracing members.

PROBLEMS

8.1. The pin-jointed frame of Fig. P8.1 is twofold redundant. The cross-sectional area is 2 in.^{2} for members 1, 2, 3 and 4, 4 in.^{2} for members 5, 6, 7 and 8 and 3 in.^{2} for the remaining members.

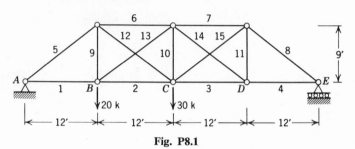

Fig. P8.1

Select two suitable releases. Calculate the values of the redundants and the vertical deflection at point D when the frame is loaded as shown. Take $E = 30 \times 10^3$ ksi. Use the methods of Chapter 8.

8.2. The plane frames of Fig. P8.2 are constructed from three members. For members 1 and 3, $L = 10$ feet and $I = 1.0$. For member 2, $L = 20$ feet and $I = 2.0$. Frame (a) is a fixed-ended portal. Frames (b) and (c) are both fixed at A, C and D before the releases are made.

Determine the flexibilities of the individual basic members, neglecting shear and axial deformations. Hence determine the flexibility of each of the primary

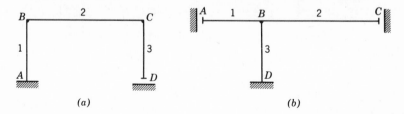

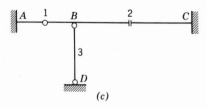

Fig. P8.2

frames shown in terms of E.   Explain the physical significance of the singular matrices which you obtain for (b) and (c).

8.3. The space frames of Fig. P8.3 are constructed from three members with properties as follows:

Member	1, 3	2
L	10 feet	20 feet
I^x	0.2	0.4
I^y	3.0	6.0
I^z	1.0	2.0

Frame (a) is initially fixed at A, C and D.   The three members are mutually perpendicular and are rigidly connected at B.

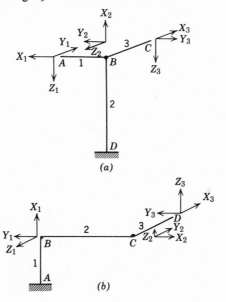

(a)

(b)

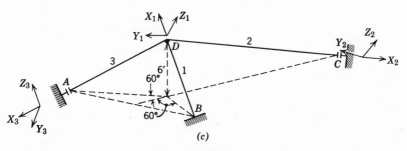

(c)

Fig. P8.3

Frame (b) is initially fixed at A and D. The three members are mutually perpendicular and joints B and C are rigid.

Frame (c) is initially fixed at A, B and C. The three members are rigidly connected to D, which is 6 feet above the horizontal plane ABC.

Find the flexibilities of the primary frames shown in terms of G. Take $E = 2.5G$. Neglect deformations due to axial force and shear force.

8.4. In the frame of Fig. P8.4, the members ABC and DEF are each continuous, and are rigidly connected to the member CD. All these members have a section of 1 foot square. The horizontal member BE is pinned at each end, and the area of its cross section is 1 in.².

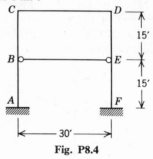

Fig. P8.4

Find the release flexibility of the primary frame formed by completely cutting the horizontal members at the center. Neglect axial deformations in all members except BE. Use feet units.

8.5. Figure P8.5 shows a frame composed of eight members, each of which is identical to the member PQ. They are arranged so that the centroidal axes of the columns are vertical, and the centroidal axes of the beams are horizontal. The joints at B, D, F and H are cubes of side 2 feet, and the joint at J is a cube of side 1 foot. These cubes are assumed to be completely rigid.

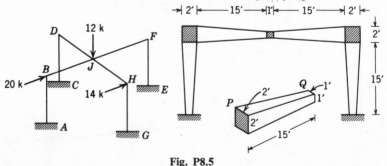

Fig. P8.5

Find the end flexibility f_{QQ}^P $(=f)$ of the member PQ, assuming that $G = 1$ and $E = 2.5$. Choose a suitable primary frame and find its flexibility by means of f. Calculate the redundants, and find the internal actions at the center of each horizontal member. Also find the *two components* of horizontal displacement at F. Use feet and kip units.

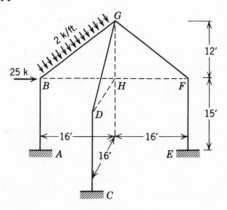

Fig. P8.6

8.6. Figure P8.6 shows a frame comprising six members. Joints *ABGFE* lie in one vertical plane, and joints *CDG* lie in a vertical plane perpendicular to the first. Each member has a rectangular cross-section 1.0 foot × 0.4 foot. The 1.0-foot dimension in each member lies in the plane containing the member and the point *H*. The elastic moduli are $E = 10^5$ ksf and $G = 0.4 \times 10^5$ ksf.

Two systems of loading are applied separately to the frame: (*a*) a uniformly distributed load of 2 kips/foot along the member *BG*, and (*b*) a horizontal load of 25 kips in the plane *ABG*.

For each load, calculate the end actions at one end of each member and the vertical deflection of the point *G*.

8.7. The concrete frame of Fig. P8.7 is to be prestressed with steel cables having the profile shown. The cable profile in the two horizontal members is the same

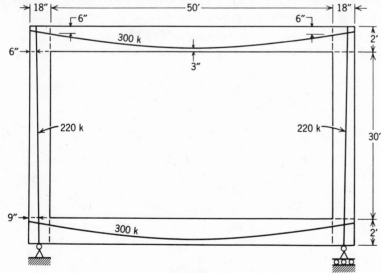

Fig. P8.7

and is parabolic in each case. The cables in the vertical members are straight. Cable forces are shown in the figure.

The members are all of rectangular section, and are 12 inches wide. Assuming a value of 5×10^3 ksi for E for the concrete, calculate the axial force and bending moment at the center of each horizontal member due to prestressing alone. The weight of the structure itself is to be neglected.

8.8. In the plane frame of Fig. P8.8 each curved member is in the form of a circular arc subtending an angle of 120° at the center of the circle. The vertical members are prismatic. All members have a rectangular section 12 inches × 6 inches, the larger dimension being in the plane of the frame. Take $E = 10^4$ ksi.

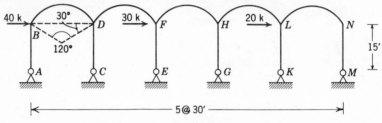

Fig. P8.8

Three loading conditions are to be considered:

(a) the load at B alone
(b) loads at B and F
(c) loads at B, F and L

For each case of loading it is required to calculate the horizontal deflection at the top of each column, and the stress resultants at the right-hand end of each curved member. Use unit loads throughout as described in Example 8.4. (N.B.: the flexibility matrix for each type of member is derived in Chapter 6).

8.9. The frame shown in Fig. P8.9 consists of a horizontal grid of beams supported on fixed-base columns at each of the outer joints. There are no supports

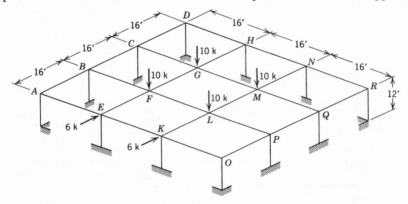

Fig. P8.9

at the interior joints F, G, L and M. The section of every member is a square of side 1 foot. All joints are to be assumed rigid.

The horizontal loads are either both present or both absent. The four vertical loads may, however, be applied one at a time or in any combination.

It is desired to investigate the stress resultants in the members for all possible load combinations. In the first instance it is required to list the six stress resultants at the top of every column and the vertical deflection at F, G, L and M for each combination of loading.

Full use should be made of the symmetry of the structure in order to reduce the number of load conditions to be investigated. Axial deformation of the members may be neglected.

CHAPTER 9

Frame Flexibility Transformations

9.1 PRINCIPLE OF CONTRAGREDIENCE

In Section 4.1 the most elementary aspect of this principle was discussed. It was shown that, for a statically determinate frame, if a force p_A at A gives rise to a force p_B at B, and a displacement u_B gives rise to a displacement u_A, then these quantities are related in a contragredient manner. That is, if

$$p_B = h_{BA} p_A \qquad (9.1a)$$

then
$$u_A = h_{BA} u_B \qquad (9.1b)$$

The necessary senses of the various quantities were stated in Section 4.1 and will be assumed in what follows.

The application of the principle will now be extended to statically indeterminate frames. For such a frame, a statically determinate primary can be employed. The force p_B, caused by p_A at A, can then be expressed as the sum of two parts—a particular solution and a complementary solution.

Let the force p_A be applied to the statically determinate primary frame. It causes at B a force p_{B0} given by $p_{B0} = h_0 p_A$. It also causes release

154

displacements $u_{10} = j_1 p_A$, $u_{20} = j_2 p_A$, etc.

$$
\begin{bmatrix} u_{10} \\ u_{20} \\ \cdot \\ \cdot \\ \cdot \\ u_{n0} \end{bmatrix} = \begin{bmatrix} j_1 \\ j_2 \\ \cdot \\ \cdot \\ \cdot \\ j_n \end{bmatrix} p_A
$$

or
$$[u_0] = [j]p_A$$

These displacements are removed by suitable redundants $\{p_1 \;\; \cdots \;\; p_n\}$ such that

$$u_0 + fp = 0$$

or
$$p = -f^{-1}u_0 = -[f]^{-1}[j]p_A$$

These redundants produce further forces at B given by $p_{B1} = h_1 p_1$, $p_{B2} = h_2 p_2$, etc. If $[h]$ is a column matrix $\{h_1 \;\; h_2 \;\; \cdots \;\; h_n\}$, then

$$p_{Bn} = h^T p$$
$$= -h^T f^{-1} j p_A$$

The total force at B is thus

$$p_B = p_{B0} + p_{Bn}$$
$$= h_0 p_A - h^T f^{-1} j p_A$$
$$= (h_0 - h^T f^{-1} j) p_A \tag{9.2}$$
$$= h_{BA} p_A \tag{9.3}$$

It should be noted that since h^T is a row matrix and j is a column matrix, the product $h^T f^{-1} j$ is a scalar quantity. This must be so if subtraction from h_0, a scalar, is to be compatible.

Using the same primary frame, we now make a displacement u_B at B. From equations 4.2 we know that this causes a displacement at A equal to $h_0 u_B (= u_{A0})$ as well as release displacements $u'_{10} = h_1 u_B$, $u'_{20} = h_2 u_B$, etc., or

$$[u'_0] = [h]u_B$$

These release displacements are removed by redundants $\{p'_1 \;\; \cdots \;\; p'_n\}$ such that

$$[p'] = -[f]^{-1}[u'_0] = -[f]^{-1}[h]u_B$$

By Maxwell's reciprocal theorem we know that the displacements at A due to unit value of the redundants are $j_1, j_2 \;\; \cdots \;\; j_n$ respectively.

Thus the displacement at A due to the complementary solution is

$$u_{An} = j^T p'$$
$$= -j^T f^{-1} h u_B$$

The total displacement at A is thus

$$u_A = u_{A0} + u_{An}$$
$$= h_0 u_B - j^T f^{-1} h u_B$$
$$= (h_0 - j^T f^{-1} h) u_B \qquad (9.4)$$

At first sight the second term (complementary solution) in the bracket of equation 9.4 looks different from the second term of equation 9.2. However, since f^{-1} is a symmetrical matrix, $j^T f^{-1} h$ is the transpose of $h^T f^{-1} j$. Recalling that each of these products is a scalar quantity, we see that transposition leaves them unchanged, so that they are in fact equal.

Hence

$$u_A = h_{BA} u_B$$

and the contragredience law applies to statically indeterminate frames.

In Section 5.3 it was shown that this relationship could be extended to the situation where p_A and p_B represent systems of forces. This extension evidently applies to statically indeterminate as well as statically determinate frames.

We may thus restate the general principle of contragredient transformation of forces and displacements. This states that if

$$p_B = H_{BA} p_A \qquad (9.5a)$$

then

$$u_A = H_{BA}^T u_B \qquad (9.5b)$$

where p_A and p_B represent systems of forces, and h_{BA} is a transformation matrix not necessarily square.

9.2 CHANGE OF RELEASES

For any frame, a statically determinate primary frame can be chosen in a number of different ways. Each choice will require n releases, where n is the number of redundancies in the original frame. Each primary frame will have its own flexibility matrix, but these matrices are, nevertheless, related to one another. The relationship is readily derived from the contragredience principle.

We denote the first primary frame by α and let the releases be $\alpha 1$, $\alpha 2, \ldots \alpha n$. Similarly, the second primary frame, β, is obtained by making releases $\beta_1, \beta_2, \ldots \beta n$. Suppose that the flexibility of frame α is known and is denoted by $F_{\alpha\alpha}$. This means that the relationship between forces p_α, applied at the release α, and the corresponding displacements, is known in the form

$$u_\alpha = F_{\alpha\alpha} p_\alpha \qquad (9.6)$$

It is required to find the flexibility of the frame β. Therefore we commence by applying a set of forces p_β at the releases of this frame. These forces will give rise to forces, p_α, at the locations $\alpha 1 \ldots \alpha n$ where the releases for frame α were previously made. The forces p_α can be calculated, and we let the result be represented by the equation

$$p_\alpha = H_{\alpha\beta} p_\beta \qquad (9.7)$$

The relation between forces p_α and displacements u_α is known (equation 9.6). Hence

$$u_\alpha = F_{\alpha\alpha} p_\alpha = F_{\alpha\alpha} H_{\alpha\beta} p_\beta$$

Furthermore, the relation between u_α and u_β is known, since

$$u_\beta = H_{\alpha\beta}^T u_\alpha$$

Hence

$$u_\beta = H_{\alpha\beta}^T F_{\alpha\alpha} H_{\alpha\beta} p_\beta \qquad (9.8)$$

The relationship between u_β and p_β is the flexibility, $F_{\beta\beta}$, of the frame β. Thus from equation 9.8 we see that

$$F_{\beta\beta} = H_{\alpha\beta}^T F_{\alpha\alpha} H_{\alpha\beta} \qquad (9.9)$$

The matrix $H_{\alpha\beta}$ can be obtained directly by applying unit forces at β as described above and computing the forces at releases α. Alternatively we can determine a matrix $H_{\beta\alpha}$ by applying unit forces at α if this is more convenient. Then $H_{\alpha\beta}$ is obtained by inversion of $H_{\beta\alpha}$. This is possible since $H_{\alpha\beta}$ is a square matrix of order $(n \times n)$.

Example 9.1 Figure 9.1a shows a three-span beam. Treated as a plane frame this is twofold redundant. Primary frame α is obtained by regarding the two interior supports as redundants (Fig. 9.1b). Primary frame β is obtained by inserting hinges at K and L, the midpoints of spans QR and RS (Fig. 9.1c). Obtain the matrices relating the redundants p_α with those p_β, and hence transform $f_{\alpha\alpha}$ to $f_{\beta\beta}$.

Solution. Initially the matrix $H_{\beta\alpha}$ will be determined. Unit value of $p_{\alpha 1}$ is applied to frame α (Fig. 9.2), and the bending moments are calculated

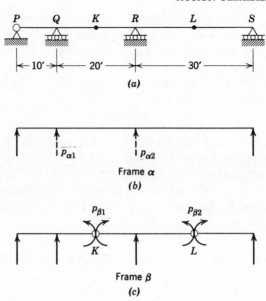

Fig. 9.1

at the points K and L. These bending moments correspond to the releases $\beta1$ and $\beta2$ of frame β:

$$p_{\beta1} = -6.67 \qquad p_{\beta2} = -2.50$$

These two values constitute the first *column* of $H_{\beta\alpha}$.

Unit value of $p_{\alpha2}$ is then applied to frame α, and the bending moments at K and L are again evaluated:

$$p_{\beta1} = -10 \qquad p_{\beta2} = -7.5$$

These values constitute the second column of $H_{\beta\alpha}$. The values of $p_{\beta1}$ and $p_{\beta2}$ produced by any values of $p_{\alpha1}$ and $p_{\alpha2}$ applied simultaneously to frame α are then given by

$$\begin{bmatrix} p_{\beta1} \\ p_{\beta2} \end{bmatrix} = \begin{bmatrix} -6.67 & -10 \\ -2.50 & -7.5 \end{bmatrix} \begin{bmatrix} p_{\alpha1} \\ p_{\alpha2} \end{bmatrix} \tag{9.10}$$

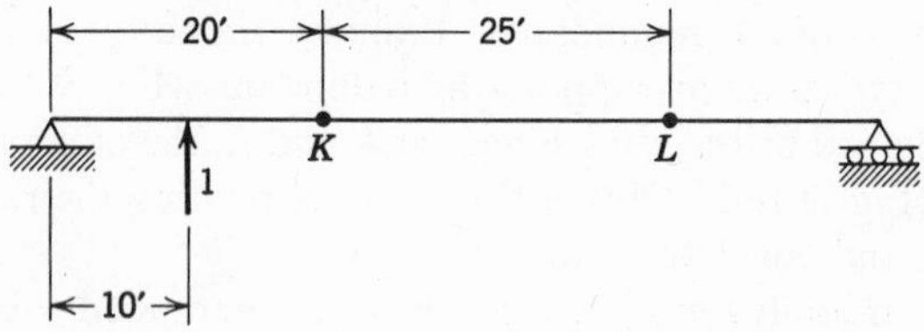

Fig. 9.2

This relationship is in the form

$$p_\beta = H_{\beta\alpha}p_\alpha$$

Alternatively the relations could be expressed in the form

$$p_\alpha = H_{\alpha\beta}p_\beta$$

To determine the matrix $H_{\alpha\beta}$ directly, unit value of $p_{\beta1}$ is applied to frame β and the reactions at Q and R are found (Fig. 9.3). This gives

$$p_{\alpha1} = -0.30 \qquad p_{\alpha2} = +0.10$$

These values constitute the first column of $H_{\alpha\beta}$. When unit value of $p_{\beta2}$ is applied to frame β, the reactions at Q and R are

$$p_{\alpha1} = 0.40 \qquad p_{\alpha2} = -0.267$$

These values constitute the second column of $H_{\alpha\beta}$. The values of $p_{\alpha1}$ and $p_{\alpha2}$ produced by any values of $p_{\beta1}$ and $p_{\beta2}$ applied simultaneously to frame β are then given by

$$\begin{bmatrix} p_{\alpha1} \\ p_{\alpha2} \end{bmatrix} = \begin{bmatrix} -0.30 & +0.40 \\ +0.10 & -0.267 \end{bmatrix} \begin{bmatrix} p_{\beta1} \\ p_{\beta2} \end{bmatrix} \qquad (9.11)$$

or

$$p_\alpha = H_{\alpha\beta}p_\beta.$$

If $H_{\alpha\beta}$ is multiplied by $H_{\beta\alpha}$ we have

$$H_{\alpha\beta}H_{\beta\alpha} = \begin{bmatrix} -0.30 & +0.40 \\ +0.10 & -0.267 \end{bmatrix} \begin{bmatrix} -6.67 & -10 \\ -2.50 & -7.5 \end{bmatrix} = \begin{bmatrix} 1 & 0 \\ 0 & 1 \end{bmatrix}$$

showing that $H_{\alpha\beta} = H_{\beta\alpha}^{-1}$.

By the methods of Chapter 4 it can be shown that the flexibility of frame α is

$$F_{\alpha\alpha} = \begin{bmatrix} 1389 & 2167 \\ 2167 & 4500 \end{bmatrix}$$

The flexibility of the frame β is therefore

$$F_{\beta\beta} = H_{\alpha\beta}^T F_{\alpha\alpha} H_{\alpha\beta} = \begin{bmatrix} -0.30 & +0.10 \\ +0.40 & -0.267 \end{bmatrix} \begin{bmatrix} 1389 & 2167 \\ 2167 & 4500 \end{bmatrix} \begin{bmatrix} -0.30 & +0.40 \\ +0.10 & -0.267 \end{bmatrix}$$

$$= \begin{bmatrix} +39.99 & -26.57 \\ -26.57 & +80.17 \end{bmatrix}$$

A further illustration of flexibility transformation is given in Example 9.2.

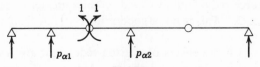

Fig. 9.3

9.3 CHOICE OF RELEASES

For any given structure, different primary frames will lead to different sets of compatibility equations, and the conditioning of some of these sets will be better than that of others. It is therefore a matter of some importance to select a satisfactory system of releases, i.e., one that will lead to equations which can be solved without undue loss of accuracy.

Sometimes the conditioning of the compatibility equations can be improved by a specific axis transformation. A case in point is the transfer of releases to the elastic center as described in Section 7.2, after which the flexibility matrix becomes a diagonal matrix. If the position of the elastic center and of the principal axes has to be computed however, the benefit is apparent rather than real, since the procedure for finding the elastic center and principal axes is the same as that for solving the original somewhat ill-conditioned equations. Precisely the same round-off errors have therefore occurred in either solution. The flexibility matrix of any primary frame can be converted to diagonal form by a congruent transformation similar to that discussed for the elastic center. The apparent improvement effected by such means always suffers from the objection just noted.

On the other hand, if the elastic center and principal axes of a single-cell structure can be located by inspection, the improvement obtained by using these axes is a real one. Similarly, in the general case a real improvement in the primary frame is one which is obtained without the aid of calculation. Only general comments can be made in regard to this choice.

We note in the first place that for the compatibility equations to be well-conditioned, we require that the flexibility matrix shall be as strongly diagonal as possible and also that the u_0 terms shall be as small as possible.

In the ith column of a flexibility matrix, the terms represent the release displacements caused by unit value of the ith redundant. The element on the diagonal is the displacement which the ith redundant causes at its own release, while the off-diagonal elements are the displacements at other releases. We require therefore that each redundant should produce a greater displacement at its own release than at any other. The frame of Fig. 9.4 is one in which this requirement is not satisfied. It will be seen that the axial force redundant at C will produce greater displacements at B and A than at C. This is not a good primary frame from this point of view.

A frame in which the effects of a given redundant are restricted to a localized region is usually a good choice. Many off-diagonal terms are

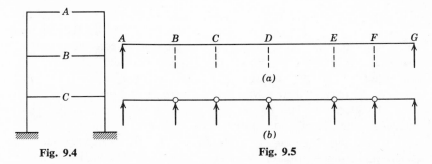

Fig. 9.4   Fig. 9.5

zero in this case and the others tend to be smaller than the diagonal term. As an example of this, consider the six-span beam of Fig. 9.5*a*. Removal of the five interior supports produces an unsatisfactory primary frame, namely the simply supported beam *AG*. The application of any one redundant will cause displacement at every release. Moreover, in some cases the off-diagonal terms will exceed the diagonal terms. For instance, a force at *B* will cause a greater displacement at *D* than at *B*. On the other hand, the introduction of a hinge over each support (Fig. 9.5*b*) provides a good primary frame. A pair of couples at any one hinge causes discontinuity at that hinge and smaller discontinuity at the adjacent hinges. At other releases the displacement is zero.

Apart from the flexibility matrix being strongly diagonal, it is also advantageous for the redundant actions to be as small as possible. The particular solution is obtained directly by statics. The complementary solution is obtained by statics after the redundants have been determined by solution of the compatibility equations. The latter is therefore more liable to computational error than the former. Now the complementary solution depends upon the redundants, *p*, which are given by the expression

$$p = -F^{-1}u_0$$

To minimize *p* we clearly require u_0 to be as small as possible. This criterion demands that the primary frame shall behave as nearly as possible like the given structure.

Consider a two-bay frame with fixed column bases. The primary frame of Fig. 9.6*a*, with three releases at *C* and *E*, is poor because the applied load will clearly produce large release displacements. In other words, the primary frame is very flexible compared to the real frame.

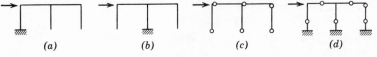

(a)   (b)   (c)   (d)

Fig. 9.6

The primary frames of Figs. 9.6*b* and 9.6*c* are successively better in this respect.   If the hinges at *A*, *C* and *E* are now moved up the columns (Fig. 9.6*d*) to positions approximating to the contraflexure points of the real frame, the primary frame is still further improved.   A hinge at a contraflexure point will result in no loss of rigidity at all.   The effect of moving the releases in this way is referred to in Problem 9.5 at the end of the chapter.   In plane frames, it will be found that the introduction of hinges is usually preferable to the complete "cutting" of members.

Since the deformation of the frame differs for different systems of external loading, a primary frame which is ideal for one load system may be somewhat unsatisfactory for another.   This deficiency can be overcome to some extent by the use of mixed systems, which will be described in the next section.

9.4   MIXED SYSTEMS

As discussed above, for any given frame there are any number of different primary frames.   Each primary frame is characterized by a particular system of releases, and consequently with a particular release flexibility matrix.

Hitherto it has been assumed that the particular solution is obtained by the application of the given external loads to the *chosen* primary frame. However, this is not mandatory.   It is permissible to compute stress resultants as if the loads were applied to some other primary frame.   This procedure may be useful either (*a*) to minimize the arithmetical work involved or (*b*) to minimize the release displacements u_0 as discussed in the previous section.   In either case an improvement is effected in the result.

It is necessary first to appreciate that a particular solution need not be associated with a special primary frame.   It must be associated with the

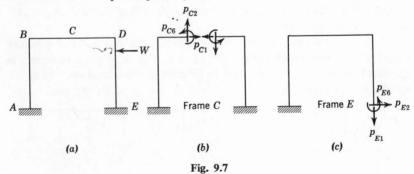

(a)   (b)   (c)

Fig. 9.7

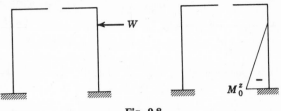

Fig. 9.8

given load system, and must be consistent therewith. But the primary frame used in the derivation of the particular solution is irrelevant.

The particular solution has so far been regarded as the solution which results from the application of the given load system to a primary frame. More generally, arbitrary values of the redundants may be applied as well as the given loads. The complementary solution will then determine the balance of the redundants necessary to ensure compatibility. If by chance the correct values of the redundants were incorporated in the particular solution, the displacements u_0 at the releases would be zero, indicating that a complementary solution is not required.

The process is analogous to the solution of a differential equation where, if certain arbitrary functions are added to the particular integral, a compensating change occurs in the complementary function. Consider the plane frame of Fig. 9.7a. Primary frame C is obtained by releasing the axial force, shear force and bending moment at C. Three similar releases at E produce primary frame E. Application of the load W alone to frame C gives the bending-moment diagram M_0^z of Fig. 9.8.

If, in addition to W, frame C is subjected to such values of p_{C1}, p_{C2} and p_{C6} as are needed to cause the three internal actions at E to be zero, the M_0^z diagram of Fig. 9.9 can be obtained. This latter diagram, however, is consistent with the external load having been applied to frame E.

In general we may suppose that frames α and β are any two primary frames corresponding to a given statically indeterminate frame. For a

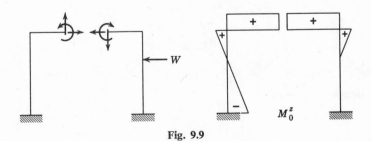

Fig. 9.9

Table 9.1

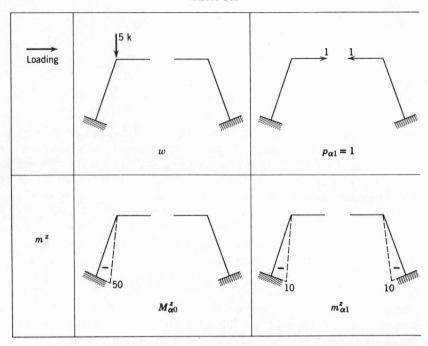

given external loading, the particular solution based on frame α can be transformed into the particular solution for frame β by including suitable values of the redundants p_α together with the external loads. This will always be possible since the number of redundants p_α is equal to the number of releases in frame β. The particular solution cannot, therefore, be identified specifically with either frame α or frame β.

It follows that when the compatibility equations are written, the particular solution can be associated with the flexibility coefficients derived from frame α, frame β or any other primary frame. When the flexibility coefficients of one primary frame are associated with the particular

Fig. 9.10

Table 9.1 (continued)

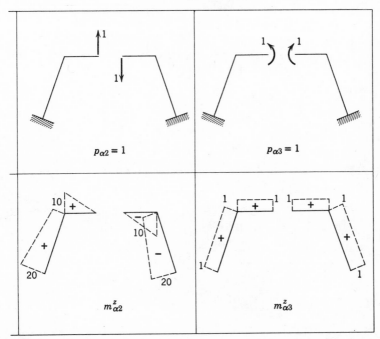

$p_{\alpha 2} = 1$

$p_{\alpha 3} = 1$

$m^z_{\alpha 2}$

$m^z_{\alpha 3}$

solution which is *apparently* based on another, it is said that a mixed system is used.

Example 9.2 The plane frame of Fig. 9.10 is to be solved in three ways: (1) by the use of primary frame α, (2) by the use of primary frame β and (3) by the use of a mixed system.

Bending distortions only will be considered. Since EI^z is constant it will be regarded as unity. For this problem the redundants of frame α will be denoted by $p_{\alpha 1}$, $p_{\alpha 2}$ and $p_{\alpha 3}$, and those of frame β by $p_{\beta 1}$, $p_{\beta 2}$ and $p_{\beta 3}$.

Solution 1. This solution employs frame α (Fig. 9.10b).

Table 9.2

Integral	Member	$u_{\alpha 1 \cdot 0}$	$u_{\alpha 2 \cdot 0}$	$u_{\alpha 3 \cdot 0}$	$f_{\alpha 1 \cdot \alpha 1}$	$f_{\alpha 1 \cdot \alpha 2} = f_{\alpha 2 \cdot \alpha 1}$	$f_{\alpha 1 \cdot \alpha 3} = f_{\alpha 3 \cdot \alpha 1}$	$f_{\alpha 2 \cdot \alpha 2}$	$f_{\alpha 2 \cdot \alpha 3} = f_{\alpha 3 \cdot \alpha 2}$	$f_{\alpha 3 \cdot \alpha 3}$
$\dfrac{1}{EI^z}\int m^z_r m^z_s\, dx$	AB	+2357.0	−5892.5	−353.6	+471.4	−1178.5	−70.7	+3299.8	+212.1	+14.1
	BC							+333.3	+50.0	+10.0
	CD							+333.3	−50.0	+10.0
	DE				+471.4	+1178.5	−70.7	+3299.8	−212.1	+14.1
Sum		+2357.0	−5892.5	−353.6	+942.8	0	−141.4	+7266.3	0	+48.3

Table 9.3

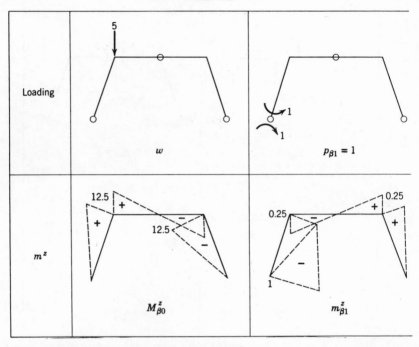

The compatibility equations are therefore

$$u_{\alpha 0} + F_{\alpha \alpha} p_{\alpha} = 0$$

$$
\begin{bmatrix} +2357.0 \\ -5892.5 \\ -353.6 \end{bmatrix}
+
\begin{bmatrix} +942.8 & 0 & -141.4 \\ 0 & +7266.3 & 0 \\ -141.4 & 0 & +48.3 \end{bmatrix}
\begin{bmatrix} p_{\alpha 1} \\ p_{\alpha 2} \\ p_{\alpha 3} \end{bmatrix}
= 0 \quad (9.12)
$$

whence

$$
\begin{bmatrix} p_{\alpha 1} \\ p_{\alpha 2} \\ p_{\alpha 3} \end{bmatrix}
=
\begin{bmatrix} -2.500 \\ +0.811 \\ 0 \end{bmatrix}
$$

The final support reactions as given by solution 1 are shown in Fig. 9.11.
Solution 2. This solution employs frame β (Fig. 9.10c).

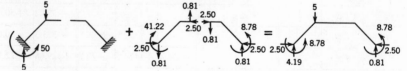

Fig. 9.11

Table 9.3 (continued)

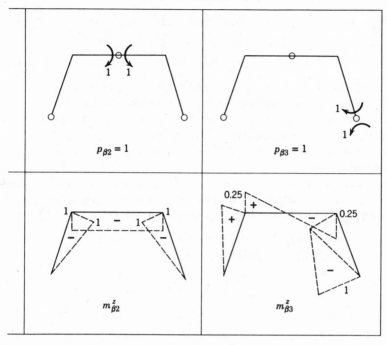

$p_{\beta2} = 1$ 　　　　 $p_{\beta3} = 1$

$m_{\beta2}^z$ 　　　　 $m_{\beta3}^z$

Table 9.4

Integral	Member	$u_{\beta1\cdot0}$	$u_{\beta2\cdot0}$	$u_{\beta3\cdot0}$	$f_{\beta1\cdot\beta1}$	$f_{\beta1\cdot\beta2} = f_{\beta2\cdot\beta1}$	$f_{\beta1\cdot\beta3} = f_{\beta3\cdot\beta1}$	$f_{\beta2\cdot\beta2}$	$f_{\beta2\cdot\beta3} = f_{\beta3\cdot\beta2}$	$f_{\beta3\cdot\beta}$
$\dfrac{1}{EI^z}\int m_r^z m_s^z\,dx$	AB	−44.19	−58.92	+14.73	+6.19	+3.54	−0.88	+4.71	−1.18	+0.2
	BC	−10.42	−62.50	+10.42	+0.21	+1.25	−0.21	+10.00	−1.25	+0.2
	CD	−10.42	+62.50	+10.42	+0.21	−1.25	−0.21	+10.00	+1.25	+0.2
	DE	−14.73	+58.92	+44.19	+0.29	−1.18	−0.88	+4.71	+3.54	+6.1
Sum		−79.76	0	+79.76	+6.90	+2.36	−2.18	+29.43	+2.36	+6.9

The compatibility equations are therefore

$$u_{\beta0} + F_{\beta\beta}p_\beta = 0$$

$$\begin{bmatrix} -79.76 \\ 0 \\ +79.76 \end{bmatrix} + \begin{bmatrix} +6.90 & +2.36 & -2.18 \\ +2.36 & +29.43 & +2.36 \\ -2.18 & +2.36 & +6.90 \end{bmatrix}\begin{bmatrix} p_{\beta1} \\ p_{\beta2} \\ p_{\beta3} \end{bmatrix} = 0 \qquad (9.13)$$

whence

$$\begin{bmatrix} p_{\beta1} \\ p_{\beta2} \\ p_{\beta3} \end{bmatrix} = \begin{bmatrix} +8.78 \\ 0 \\ -8.78 \end{bmatrix}$$

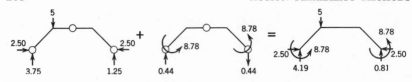

Fig. 9.12

The final support reactions as given by solution 2 are shown in Fig. 9.12.

Solution 3. This solution employs the flexibility matrix of frame α and the particular solution of frame β. The matrix $F_{\alpha\alpha}$ is more convenient than $F_{\beta\beta}$ since $F_{\alpha\alpha}$ has a number of zero elements. The single element of the second row renders the solution of the second equation independent of the other two.

The elements of the matrix $u_{\alpha \cdot \beta 0}$ for the mixed system were computed by combining the $M_{\beta 0}^z$ diagram (Table 9.3), which is apparently based on frame β, successively with $m_{\alpha 1}$, $m_{\alpha 2}$ and $m_{\alpha 3}$ from Table 9.1. This gives

$$u_{\alpha 1 \cdot \beta 0} = 0 \qquad u_{\alpha 2 \cdot \beta 0} = +3189.7 \qquad u_{\alpha 3 \cdot \beta 0} = 0$$

The compatibility equations are then

$$u_{\alpha \cdot \beta 0} + F_{\alpha\alpha} p_\alpha = 0$$

$$\begin{bmatrix} 0 \\ +3189.7 \\ 0 \end{bmatrix} + \begin{bmatrix} +942.8 & 0 & -141.4 \\ 0 & +7266.3 & 0 \\ -141.4 & 0 & +48.3 \end{bmatrix} \begin{bmatrix} p_{\alpha 1} \\ p_{\alpha 2} \\ p_{\alpha 3} \end{bmatrix} = 0 \quad (9.14)$$

whence

$$\begin{bmatrix} p_{\alpha 1} \\ p_{\alpha 2} \\ p_{\alpha 3} \end{bmatrix} = \begin{bmatrix} 0 \\ -0.439 \\ 0 \end{bmatrix}$$

It will be observed that equations 9.14, which are based on the mixed system, lead to a considerably simpler solution than either of the other two sets of equations derived in solutions 1 and 2. The final support reactions, shown in Fig. 9.13, are the same as before.

Two primary frames have been investigated in the foregoing problem, and the two flexibility matrices $F_{\alpha\alpha}$ and $F_{\beta\beta}$ will be used to illustrate the relationship

$$F_{\beta\beta} = H_{\alpha\beta}^T F_{\alpha\alpha} H_{\alpha\beta}$$

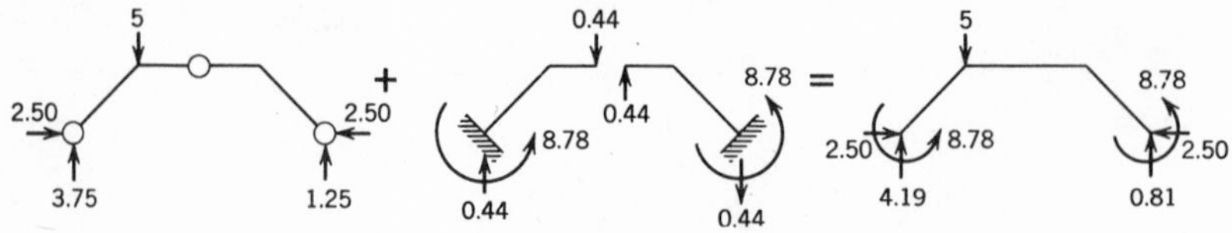

Fig. 9.13

In this instance it is easier to obtain the matrix $H_{\beta\alpha}$. With this in view, unit value of $p_{\alpha 1}$ is applied to frame α. The bending moments produced at A, C and E, which are released to form frame β, constitute the first column of $H_{\beta\alpha}$. The values, obtained directly from diagram $m^z_{\alpha 1}$ in Table 9.1 are -10, 0 and -10 respectively. Similarly, unit value of $p_{\alpha 2}$ produces bending moments $+20$, 0 and -20 (diagram $m^z_{\alpha 2}$). Unit value of $p_{\alpha 3}$ produces bending moments $+1$, $+1$ and $+1$ (diagram $m^z_{\alpha 3}$). Hence

$$H_{\beta\alpha} = \begin{bmatrix} -10 & +20 & +1 \\ 0 & 0 & +1 \\ -10 & -20 & +1 \end{bmatrix} \text{ and, by inversion } H_{\alpha\beta} = \begin{bmatrix} -\dfrac{1}{20} & +\dfrac{1}{10} & -\dfrac{1}{20} \\ +\dfrac{1}{40} & 0 & -\dfrac{1}{40} \\ 0 & 1 & 0 \end{bmatrix}$$

The matrix $H_{\alpha\beta}$ could have been determined directly by applying unit values of p_β to frame β. The required elements would then be the axial force, shear force and bending moment at cross-section C, since these are the actions released to form frame α. Although these are not given directly by Table 9.3, they are easily computed and agree with the values obtained by inversion of $H_{\beta\alpha}$.

Using the transformation matrix to obtain $F_{\beta\beta}$ from $F_{\alpha\alpha}$, we have

$$F_{\beta\beta} = H^T_{\alpha\beta} F_{\alpha\alpha} H_{\alpha\beta}$$

$$= \begin{bmatrix} -\dfrac{1}{20} & +\dfrac{1}{40} & 0 \\ +\dfrac{1}{10} & 0 & +1 \\ -\dfrac{1}{20} & -\dfrac{1}{40} & 0 \end{bmatrix} \begin{bmatrix} +942.8 & 0 & -141.4 \\ 0 & +7266.3 & 0 \\ -141.4 & 0 & +48.3 \end{bmatrix}$$

$$\times \begin{bmatrix} -\dfrac{1}{20} & +\dfrac{1}{10} & -\dfrac{1}{20} \\ +\dfrac{1}{40} & 0 & -\dfrac{1}{40} \\ 0 & +1 & 0 \end{bmatrix}$$

$$= \begin{bmatrix} +6.90 & +2.36 & -2.18 \\ +2.36 & +29.43 & +2.36 \\ -2.18 & +2.36 & +6.90 \end{bmatrix}$$

These values agree with those calculated directly in Table 9.4.

The method of using mixed systems of releases can be rendered more powerful by employing at the same time the principle of superposition. Consider the frame of Fig. 9.14 with the loading shown. Any single release system will result in bending moments, M_0, occurring throughout the primary frame. Although it is possible to choose the releases in a manner which is suitable for one of the loads, the same releases will be unsuitable for other loads.

However, the full solution can be obtained by the addition of the solutions for each load separately. Suppose, therefore, that a release system is adopted for the calculation of the frame flexibility, F. Call this system α, and let the flexibility be $F_{\alpha\alpha}$. For the first individual load we can use a primary frame β, leading to release displacements $u_{\alpha \cdot \beta 0}$ as explained in the previous example. The redundants corresponding to this load are then given by the compatibility equation

$$u_{\alpha \cdot \beta 0} + F_{\alpha\alpha}P_\alpha = 0 \qquad (9.15)$$

In a similar way, if a primary frame γ is adopted for the next load, the corresponding redundants are given by the equation

$$u_{\alpha \cdot \gamma 0} + F_{\alpha\alpha}P_\alpha = 0 \qquad (9.16)$$

and so on for the remaining loads.

The principle of superposition ensures that the summation of these separate results leads to the correct solution when the frame sustains all the loads together. By the addition of the equations 9.15, 9.16 ... we obtain

$$(u_{\alpha \cdot \beta 0} + u_{\alpha \cdot \gamma 0} + \cdots) + F_{\alpha\alpha}P_\alpha = 0 \qquad (9.17)$$

This equation indicates that we can employ a composite M_0 diagram comprising the M_0 values for the separate loads, each applied to its own primary frame. Referring to the frame of Fig. 9.14, we see that for the load on column EF, the least extensive M_0 diagram is obtained by considering the column to be cantilevered from E. A similar treatment

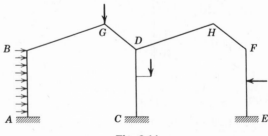

Fig. 9.14

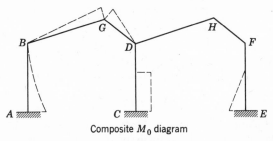

Composite M_0 diagram

Fig. 9.15

is suitable for the other two column loads. For the vertical load at G, however, a primary frame can be chosen which restricts the M_0 values to the members BG and GD. The composite diagram resulting from these different releases is shown in Fig. 9.15.

For the evaluation of a frame flexibility a system of hinges is most convenient. By the combination of the results of such a release system with the composite M_0 diagram of Fig. 9.15 a complete solution is obtained in the usual way.

PROBLEMS

9.1. Figure P9.1 shows two possible primary frames for a four-span continuous beam $ABCDE$. Determine the flexibility matrix for primary frame α and hence determine the flexibility of β by transformation.

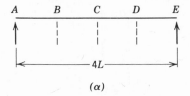

Fig. P9.1

9.2. The frame of Fig. P9.2 is pin-jointed. Given the flexibility matrix $F_{\alpha\alpha}$ of the primary frame obtained by cutting members 3 and 8, determine the necessary transformation matrices and the flexibility matrices for the primary frames obtained by cutting

(a) members 5 and 10

(b) members 6 and 11 $F_{\alpha\alpha} = \begin{bmatrix} 16.88 & 2.16 \\ 2.16 & 16.88 \end{bmatrix}$

(c) members 3 and 10

(d) members 6 and 7

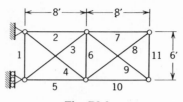

Fig. P9.2

9.3. Figure P9.3 shows two primary frames α and β for a fixed-based portal. Assuming the flexibility matrix $F_{\alpha\alpha}$ for primary frame α is known, express the flexibility matrix $F_{\beta\beta}$ for primary frame β in terms of $F_{\alpha\alpha}$. Write down the transformation matrix $H_{\alpha\beta}$.

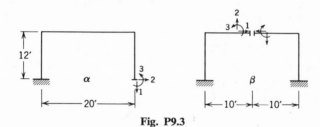

Fig. P9.3

9.4. Two primary frames for a gabled portal are shown in Fig. P9.4. The

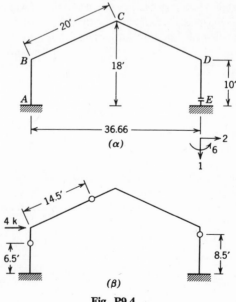

Fig. P9.4

primary flexibility matrix $F_{\alpha\alpha}$ is given as

$$F_{\alpha\alpha} = \begin{bmatrix} +31359 & -12098 & -1100 \\ -12098 & +8720 & +660 \\ -1100 & +660 & +60 \end{bmatrix}$$

(a) Using the flexibility matrix $F_{\alpha\alpha}$, determine the flexibility matrix $F_{\beta\beta}$ for the primary frame β.

(b) Suppose in a flexibility solution for the loaded gable portal the primary flexibility matrix $F_{\beta\beta}$ is used. What happens when the locations of the β releases are close to the points of inflection in the redundant structure for the given load system?

Using $F_{\beta\beta}$, find the three reactions at E when the frame is loaded by a horizontal load of 4 kips at B.

9.5. The frame of Fig. P9.5 is plane and has rigid joints at B and D and is fixed at supports A and E. The moment of inertia is constant. Assume that deformations due to shear and axial force are negligible and that E is constant.

(a) Calculate $F_{\alpha\alpha}$ for primary frame α.

(b) Hence, determine the primary frame flexibilities $F_{\beta\beta}$, $F_{\gamma\gamma}$, $F_{\delta\delta}$ and $F_{\varepsilon\varepsilon}$ by transforming $F_{\alpha\alpha}$.

Comment on the flexibility matrices so produced.

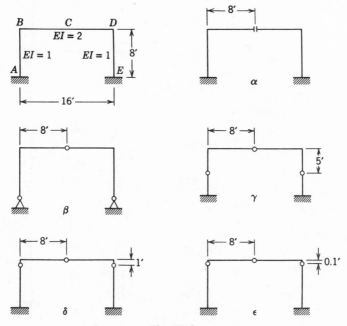

Fig. P9.5

9.6. A two-bay fixed-base portal is shown in Fig. P9.6a together with two primary frames (b) and (c). Determine the primary flexibility matrix $F_{\alpha\alpha}$ and hence find $F_{\beta\beta}$ by transformation of $F_{\alpha\alpha}$. The β primary frame releases are at P and Q, where P is the elastic center of the portal $ABDC$, and Q is the elastic center of the portal $CDFE$. Assume EI is constant for the portal.

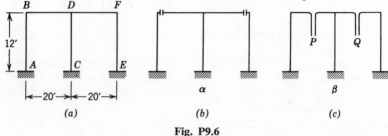

(a)   (b)   (c)

Fig. P9.6

9.7. Figure P9.7 indicates various possible primary frames for the frame of Fig. P9.7a. Comment on the suitability of these primary frames in relation to the following types of loading:

(a) horizontal wind load
(b) concentrated vertical floor loads
(c) combined loads (a) and (b).

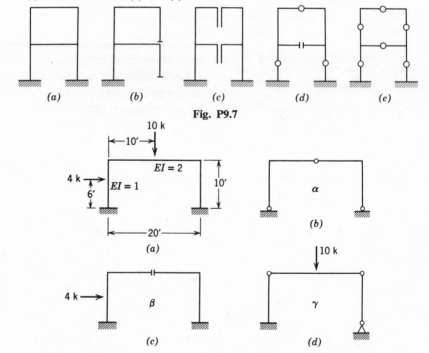

(a)   (b)   (c)   (d)   (e)

Fig. P9.7

(a)

(b)

(c)

(d)

Fig. P9.9

9.8. For the frame of Fig. P9.2 comment on the following choices for the releases:

(*a*) cuts in members 5, 10

(*b*) cuts in members 8, 9

(*c*) cuts in members 3, 8

(*d*) cuts in members 6, 11

9.9. A loaded portal frame is shown in Fig. P9.9*a* together with three possible primary frames α, β and γ. Determine the support reactions using the primary frame flexibility $F_{\alpha\alpha}$ and the principle of superposition. Assume that the horizontal load of 4 kips is applied to primary frame β, and the vertical load of 10 kips is applied to the primary frame γ.

DISPLACEMENT STIFFNESS METHODS

CHAPTER 10

Principle of Stiffness Analysis

The displacement solution of frames is so called because the joint displacements (instead of the redundant actions as in part I) appear as the unknowns in the simultaneous equations. In many respects the theorems and explanation of Part II could be deduced from the corresponding theorems and explanations employed in Part I, simply by interchanging certain terms. For instance, where the word action appeared in Part I, the word displacement will now be used, and vice versa.

Nevertheless, the displacement method will be developed ab initio, and the similarity to the previous chapters should be noted. The principle of the displacement solution is typified by the second solution of Example 2.1. In Example 2.1 the displacement method was employed for the analysis of a frame in which only one joint displacement was possible. It is intended, now, to extend this method to the analysis of frames which have more than one degree of joint freedom. Chapter 10 will be confined to a general outline of the method, similar to that given in Chapter 3 for the action method of solution.

10.1 RESTRAINTS

In the first instance, the various members of the frame are isolated from one another by temporarily inhibiting a sufficient number of joint

179

displacements. Clearly, if all six displacement components of every joint are prevented, each member becomes fixed-ended and its solution is not influenced by the behavior of neighboring members. Such complete fixity is not always necessary to avoid interaction between members, but for the present complete joint fixity will be assumed. In this approach, therefore, the primary frame is one in which every member is fixed-ended.

The physical conception of joint locking can be assisted by supposing that artificial restraining devices are available which are capable of exerting actions on a joint sufficient to inhibit movement—couples to prevent rotation and forces to prevent translation.

Complete fixity at a particular joint may require as many as six components of reaction, and these are supplied by six distinct restraints. For the time being the various restraints throughout the frame will be numbered serially 1, 2, 3 .... The action exerted by restraint n upon the relevant joint will be called the "action at restraint n" and will be denoted by P_n. Similarly, when a point is permitted to move in the direction of one of its restraints, n, the displacement will be referred to as a "displacement at restraint n," and will be denoted by u_n.

The concept of a restraint in the stiffness method is the counterpart of the concept of a release in the flexibility method. In that case, at each release an action was temporarily destroyed, whereas in the present instance at each restraint a displacement is temporarily inhibited. Just as we could previously make six separate releases at one cross-section, so we can now impose six separate restraints at one joint.

10.2 PARTICULAR SOLUTION

When the given load system is applied, it is applied to members with ends fully restrained. The solution of these members constitutes the particular solution of the frame. Basically this particular solution is not so readily obtained as it was in the action method, because the fixed-ended members are themselves statically indeterminate structures. However, in many frames the members will be of a simple type, and the fixed-ended solution can be written down directly as a standard form. As a result of the particular solution artificial restraint actions are called into play to prevent the joint displacements. In effect these restraints are merely a measure of the lack of equilibrium between the actions exerted upon the joint by the adjacent member ends. For example, the force in the x direction exerted by a restraint upon a joint is equal to the resultant of the x forces exerted by the joint upon the adjacent members. If this resultant is zero the restraint force is not required.

10.3   COMPLEMENTARY SOLUTION

Equilibrium is restored by the complementary solution which results from displacing each joint by the correct amount.   The movement of a particular joint J (Fig. 10.1) will induce forces not only upon that joint but also upon any joint such as A, B or C which is connected to it by a member.   The state of fixity imposed on these adjacent joints will prevent the effect of the movement of J from extending throughout the frame. For the purpose of expressing the forces and couples arising from the displacement of a joint it will be convenient to deal with the actions exerted *by* the joint *upon* the ends of the adjacent members.   Then if joint J is given a displacement u in the positive x direction, positive actions in the x direction will be induced thereby on the member ends at J. Forces in the y and z directions, as well as couples, may also be induced at J, but whether these will be positive or not depends upon the shape of members JA, JB, JC.   The actions induced on the members at their far ends may also be either positive or negative.   Similar remarks apply to positive displacements of J in the y and z directions and also to rotations.

The actions and displacements caused by the simultaneous imposition of the true values of all joint displacements constitute the complementary solution.

10.4   EQUILIBRIUM EQUATIONS

If n is the number of degrees of joint freedom (for the whole frame) which are to be temporarily removed, we impose n restraints of a suitable nature.

At restraint 1, the action called into play when the external loads are applied to the primary frame is denoted by P_{10}.   Displacements $u_1, u_2, u_3 \ldots$

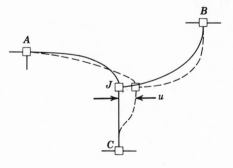

Fig. 10.1

at restraints 1, 2, 3 . . . will each induce an action at the first restraint, and these values will be denoted by P_{11}, P_{12}, P_{13} . . . . In the final state of the frame, the total value of the action at restraint 1 is therefore

$$P_1 = P_{10} + P_{11} + P_{12} \cdots + P_{1n}$$

Similarly, the total value of action at restraint 2 is

$$P_2 = P_{20} + P_{21} + P_{22} \cdots + P_{2n}$$

and so on for the other restraints.

When all the joints are in equilibrium $P_1 = P_2 = P_3 \ldots = \ldots = P_n = 0$. Joint equilibrium is therefore expressed by the equations

$$P_{10} + P_{11} + P_{12} \cdots + P_{1n} = 0$$
$$P_{20} + P_{21} + P_{22} \cdots + P_{2n} = 0$$
$$\vdots \tag{10.1}$$
$$P_{n0} + P_{n1} + P_{n2} \cdots + P_{nn} = 0$$

The load terms P_{10}, P_{20} . . . are calculated directly from the external loads. The remaining terms are re-expressed in terms of the unknown joint displacements using action-displacement relations in the form of stiffness coefficients.

10.5 STIFFNESS COEFFICIENTS

A typical stiffness coefficient is denoted by K_{rs}, where

K_{rs} = the value of the action at restraint r induced by a unit displacement at restraint s.

The value of P_{rs} induced by a displacement u_s at s is then

$$P_{rs} = K_{rs}u_s \tag{10.2}$$

As explained above, the coefficient K_{rs} will be zero unless r and s represent restraints either at the same joint or at adjacent joints.

Using relationships similar to that of equation 10.2, we can rewrite the equilibrium equations in terms of restraint displacements:

$$P_{10} + K_{11}u_1 + K_{12}u_2 \cdots + K_{1n}u_n = 0$$
$$P_{20} + K_{21}u_1 + K_{22}u_2 \cdots + K_{2n}u_n = 0$$
$$\vdots \tag{10.3}$$
$$P_{n0} + K_{n1}u_1 + K_{n2}u_2 \cdots + K_{nn}u_n = 0$$

10.6 ACTIONS AT ANY POINT

The action at any point, not necessarily a restraint position, can be found by the same procedure, provided that the necessary stiffness coefficients have been calculated for the given point. The total action will be the sum of that due to the applied loads and those due to successive joint displacements. Hence, the equations 10.3 can be extended as follows:

$$P_{10} + K_{11}u_1 \cdots + K_{1n}u_n = 0$$

$$\begin{aligned}
\cdot & \\
\cdot & \\
\cdot & \\
P_{n0} + K_{n1}u_1 \cdots + K_{nn}u_n &= 0 \\
P_{a0} + K_{a1}u_1 \cdots + K_{an}u_n &= P_a \\
P_{b0} + K_{b1}u_1 \cdots + K_{bn}u_n &= P_b
\end{aligned}$$

(10.4)

At a boundary joint, complete freedom will often not prevail. For instance, at a pinned support, the three rotations are permitted but the three translations are not. Artificial restraints will then be needed to prevent the rotations, but *real* restraints are available to resist the translations. In the solution of the frame the total rotational restraints will therefore be equated to zero, while the x, y, z reactions can be calculated by equations similar to the last two of equations 10.4.

Furthermore, it is sometimes convenient to use equations of the latter type to calculate internal actions at various positions along the members, once the end displacements are known.

10.7 EXPRESSION IN MATRIX FORM

The foregoing equations can be written in matrix form.

Let $[P_0]$ represent the restraint actions of the particular solution. These values are sometimes called the "initial values of the artificial restraints," or alternatively the "initial out of balance actions." Also let $[P_n]$ represent the actions introduced by the complementary solution. Then

$$[P_0] = \begin{bmatrix} P_{10} \\ P_{20} \\ \cdot \\ \cdot \\ \cdot \\ P_{n0} \end{bmatrix} \quad \text{and} \quad [P_n] = \begin{bmatrix} P_{11} + P_{12} \cdots + P_{1n} \\ P_{21} + P_{22} \cdots + P_{2n} \\ \cdot \\ \cdot \\ \cdot \\ P_{n1} + P_{n2} \cdots + P_{nn} \end{bmatrix}$$

The equilibrium equations 10.1 can then be written

$$[P_0] + [P_n] = 0 \tag{10.5}$$

This equation should then be compared with the corresponding equation 2.7 in the solution of the simple Example 2.1.

If $[u]$ is the column matrix of the joint displacements and $[K]$ is the stiffness matrix

$$[u] = \begin{bmatrix} u_1 \\ u_2 \\ \cdot \\ \cdot \\ \cdot \\ u_n \end{bmatrix} \quad \text{and} \quad [K] = \begin{bmatrix} K_{11} & K_{12} & \cdots & K_{1n} \\ \cdot & & & \\ \cdot & & & \\ \cdot & & & \\ K_{n1} & K_{n2} & \cdots & K_{nn} \end{bmatrix}$$

The action displacement relations are then

$$[P_n] = [K][u] \tag{10.6}$$

Substituting for $[P_n]$ in equation 10.5, we have

$$[P_0] + [K][u] = 0 \tag{10.7}$$

This is the matrix expression of equations 10.3, and at the same time it is identical in form with equation 2.8.

Equation 10.7 should be compared with the converse equation 3.7, which applies in the method of influence coefficients.

The solution of a frame by the present method commences with the determination of the initial restraint values, P_0, and the joint stiffness coefficients, which are the elements of the matrix K. The calculation of these quantities will be discussed in the following chapters.

CHAPTER 11

Stiffness Analysis
of Simple Frames

In this chapter the stiffness analysis of simple frames will be studied as a preliminary to a more general treatment in Chapter 14. Here we shall consider small plane frames with prismatic members in which only bending deformation is relevant.

11.1 MEMBER STIFFNESS

The stiffness coefficients for a particular member represent the end actions induced by unit end displacements. If axial deformations are neglected, then for a simple prismatic member only four end displacements are possible: (1) transverse displacement at each end (Fig. 11.1a and c) and (2) rotation at each end (Figs. 11.1b and d).

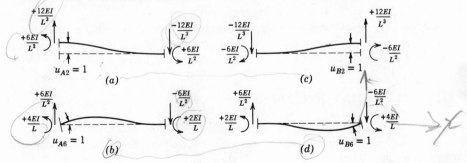

Fig. 11.1

185

There are four corresponding end actions and consequently sixteen stiffness coefficients, which are shown in Fig. 11.1. The positive directions for both actions and displacements follow the normal sense, i.e., upward for u_2 and p_2, counter-clockwise for u_6 and p_6. If the member experiences both displacements at each end, then by superposition the total end actions induced are given by the equations

$$p_{2A} = + \frac{12EI}{L^3} u_{2A} + \frac{6EI}{L^2} u_{6A} - \frac{12EI}{L^3} u_{2B} + \frac{6EI}{L^2} u_{6B}$$

$$p_{6A} = + \frac{6EI}{L^2} u_{2A} + \frac{4EI}{L} u_{6A} - \frac{6EI}{L^2} u_{2B} + \frac{2EI}{L} u_{6B}$$

$$p_{2B} = - \frac{12EI}{L^3} u_{2A} - \frac{6EI}{L^2} u_{6A} + \frac{12EI}{L^3} u_{2B} - \frac{6EI}{L^2} u_{6B}$$

$$p_{6B} = + \frac{6EI}{L^2} u_{2A} + \frac{2EI}{L} u_{6L} - \frac{6EI}{L^2} u_{2B} + \frac{4EI}{L} u_{6B}$$

(11.1)

In matrix form these equations can be written

$$
\begin{bmatrix} p_{2A} \\ p_{6A} \\ \cdots \\ p_{2B} \\ p_{6B} \end{bmatrix}
= EI
\begin{bmatrix}
+\dfrac{12}{L^3} & +\dfrac{6}{L^2} & -\dfrac{12}{L^3} & +\dfrac{6}{L^2} \\
+\dfrac{6}{L^2} & +\dfrac{4}{L} & -\dfrac{6}{L^2} & +\dfrac{2}{L} \\
\cdots & \cdots & \cdots & \cdots \\
-\dfrac{12}{L^3} & -\dfrac{6}{L^2} & +\dfrac{12}{L^3} & -\dfrac{6}{L^2} \\
+\dfrac{6}{L^2} & +\dfrac{2}{L} & -\dfrac{6}{L^2} & +\dfrac{4}{L}
\end{bmatrix}
\begin{bmatrix} u_{2A} \\ u_{6A} \\ \cdots \\ u_{2B} \\ u_{6B} \end{bmatrix}
$$

(11.2)

or

$$p = ku$$

(11.3)

The two submatrices on the diagonal are the end stiffness matrices at A and B respectively, while the off-diagonal submatrices are the cross-stiffness or carry-over stiffness matrices.

If relative transverse displacement of the member ends cannot occur, then u_{2A} and u_{2B} are known to be zero and there is no need to compute the elements of the first and third columns of the matrix k.

11.2 JOINT STIFFNESS

If a joint, or node, of the frame is given a displacement, the ends of at least some members adjacent to the joint will undergo the same displacement.

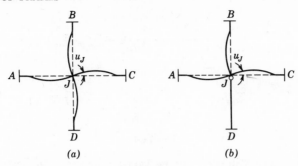

Fig. 11.2

In Fig. 11.2a the joint J is rigidly connected to the members JA, JB, JC and JD. When J rotates by u_J all four members rotate by the same amount. The rotation stiffness of the joint is therefore the sum of the rotation stiffnesses of the members.

In Fig. 11.2b the joint J is rigidly connected to JA, JB and JC only, JD being connected by a hinge. Consequently JD does not share the joint rotation. The joint stiffness (in rotation) is thus the sum of three member stiffnesses only.

11.3 SOLUTION OF A SIMPLE FRAME

The steps in the solution of a simple frame will be examined in some detail. The main purpose of Example 11.1 is to clarify the physical significance of the terms and symbols used in the solution. This applies particularly to the sense of the actions.

Example 11.1 The frame shown in Fig. 11.3 was solved in Example 4.4 by the flexibility method. It will now be re-solved by the stiffness method. Only bending deformations are taken into account.

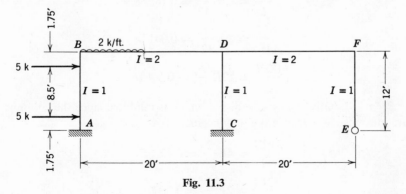

Fig. 11.3

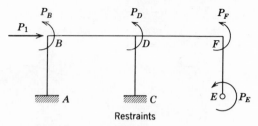

Restraints

Fig. 11.4

Solution. The solution will be set out in stages to illustrate the procedure.

(i) Restraints. To maintain joint fixity, restraints are required against rotation at *B*, *D*, *E* and *F*, and against horizontal movement at *B*, *D* and *F*. However, since the beams are assumed to be inextensible, the horizontal displacements of *B*, *D* and *F* may be equated, and the three restraints at the same time reduced to one. The restraints are named as shown in Fig. 11.4. These restraint names are employed below as subscripts in the description of stiffness coefficients, end actions and displacements.

(ii) End Stiffnesses of Members. For each member certain end stiffness coefficients are required. For brevity only those coefficients which are required for this problem will be evaluated. Since the three columns are identical, and the two beams are identical, it will be sufficient to determine the properties of one column and one beam.

Column. Each column can undergo relative transverse end displacement (sidesway); hence we require all stiffness coefficients (of equation 11.2):

$$\frac{4EI}{L} = 4E\frac{1}{12} = 0.3333E$$

$$\frac{2EI}{L} = 2E\frac{1}{12} = 0.1667E$$

$$\frac{6EI}{L^2} = 6E\frac{1}{12^2} = 0.0417E$$

$$\frac{12EI}{L^3} = 12E\frac{1}{12^3} = 0.0069E$$

Beam. Relative transverse displacement is inhibited since the columns are inextensible. Hence the only coefficients required are

$$\frac{4EI}{L} = 4E\frac{2}{20} = 0.4000E$$

$$\frac{2EI}{L} = 2E\frac{2}{20} = 0.2000E$$

Since the joints have no vertical freedom, vertical equilibrium of the joints is not considered. As a consequence beam end shears are not required.

(iii) INITIAL END ACTIONS. When the members are in the initial, fixed-ended state, the actions exerted *by* the joints *upon* the ends of the members are called initial end actions and are denoted by p_0. In this problem these initial end actions comprise only couples and transverse forces, the magnitude of which can be found by elementary beam theory. The values are shown in Fig. 11.5. Common joint axes have already been adopted. In a general problem these axes need not be the same from one joint to the next, but in this instance it is convenient to use the same axis directions for every joint. These directions are shown in Fig. 11.5. The signs specified for the initial end actions are in accordance with the joint axes.

Where the end actions at a particular joint do not form a system in equilibrium, the relevant restraints are called upon to exert equilibrating actions. For instance, joint B exerts a couple of $+45.833$ kip-feet on member BD and a couple of -7.5 kip-feet on member BA. These do not balance, and the joint must exert a couple of -38.333 kip-feet upon restraint P_B. The initial couple exerted by restraint P_B on joint B is the *sum* of the initial end actions, namely, $+38.333$ kip-feet.

In some frames, an external load may be applied directly to a joint, in which case the restraint is then called upon to *resist* such a load.

(iv) FINAL END ACTIONS. To reach a state of equilibrium the joints must suffer displacement. The displacements are associated with the restraints and are accordingly denoted by u_B, u_D, u_E, u_F and u_1. The end actions induced by each of these restraint displacements can be expressed

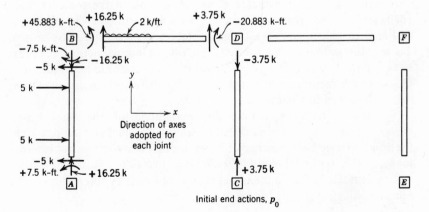

Initial end actions, p_0

Fig. 11.5

directly in terms of the stiffness coefficients computed above. These end actions are added to the initial values, p_0, to give the final end actions. These are again designated according to restraints. Thus, since restraint P_B is a rotational restraint at joint B, p_B is a *couple* exerted by *joint* B upon a member; p_B^A is the couple exerted by B on member BA, while p_B^D is the couple exerted by B on member BD. Restraint 1 acts collectively on joints B, D and F. Hence p_1^C is the horizontal force exerted by the joint D upon member DC.

End Couples

$$
\left.
\begin{aligned}
p_B^A &= -7.500 + 0.3333u_B + \quad 0u_D \quad + \quad 0u_E \quad + \quad 0u_F \quad + 0.0417u_1 \\
p_B^D &= +45.833 + 0.4000u_B + 0.2000u_D + \quad 0u_E \quad + \quad 0u_F \quad + \quad 0u_1
\end{aligned}
\right\} P_B
$$

$$
\left.
\begin{aligned}
p_D^B &= -20.833 + 0.2000u_B + 0.4000u_D + \quad 0u_E \quad + \quad 0u_F \quad + \quad 0u_1 \\
p_D^C &= \quad 0 \quad + \quad 0u_B \quad + 0.3333u_D + \quad 0u_E \quad + \quad 0u_F \quad + 0.0417u_1 \\
p_D^F &= \quad 0 \quad + \quad 0u_B \quad + 0.4000u_D + \quad 0u_E \quad + 0.2000u_F + \quad 0u_1
\end{aligned}
\right\} P_D
$$

$$
p_E^F = \quad 0 \quad + \quad 0u_B \quad + \quad 0u_D \quad + 0.3333u_E + 0.1667u_F + 0.0417u_1\} P_E \quad (11.4)
$$

$$
\left.
\begin{aligned}
p_F^D &= \quad 0 \quad + \quad 0u_B \quad + 0.2000u_D + \quad 0u_E \quad + 0.4000u_F + \quad 0u_1 \\
p_F^E &= \quad 0 \quad + \quad 0u_B \quad + \quad 0u_D \quad + 0.1667u_E + 0.3333u_F + 0.0417u_1
\end{aligned}
\right\} P_F
$$

End Horizontal Forces

$$
\left.
\begin{aligned}
p_1^A &= -5.000 + 0.0417u_B + \quad 0u_D \quad + \quad 0u_E \quad + \quad 0u_F \quad + 0.0069u_1 \\
p_1^C &= \quad 0 \quad + \quad 0u_B \quad + 0.0417u_D + \quad 0u_E \quad + \quad 0u_F \quad + 0.0069u_1 \\
p_1^E &= \quad 0 \quad + \quad 0u_B \quad + \quad 0u_D \quad + 0.0417u_E + 0.0417u_F + 0.0069u_1
\end{aligned}
\right\} P_1
$$

In equations 11.4 the factor E has been omitted from the stiffness coefficients. These can be considered as scaled values. The equations will lead to values of the restraint displacements which are also scaled. These values will not affect the determination of internal actions but must be taken into account if true displacements of the frame are required. The effect of scale factors could be determined by an analysis in the same form as that followed in Chapter 4.

(v) EQUILIBRIUM EQUATIONS. The magnitude of the final action exerted by any restraint is equal to the sum of the final end actions upon the adjacent members together with the reactions exerted against external loads, if any, applied directly to the joint in question. Restraint actions will be denoted by P, and their final values are found by summation of the relevant values of p. For example,

$$
P_B = p_B^A + p_B^D
$$

To assist the process of summation, the expressions for the individual end actions, p, have been bracketed in equations 11.4 according to the restraint to which they contribute.   For equilibrium, all the final restraint actions must be zero.   Hence we can write the equilibrium equations

$$P_B = +38.333 + 0.7333u_B + 0.2000u_D + \quad 0u_E \quad + \quad 0u_F \quad + 0.0417u_1 = 0$$

$$P_D = -20.833 + 0.2000u_B + 1.1333u_D + \quad 0u_E \quad + 0.2000u_F + 0.0417u_1 = 0$$

$$P_E = \quad 0 \quad + \quad 0u_B \quad + \quad 0u_D \quad + 0.3333u_E + 0.1667u_F + 0.0417u_1 = 0 \quad (11.5)$$

$$P_F = \quad 0 \quad + \quad 0u_B \quad + 0.2000u_D + 0.1667u_E + 0.7333u_F + 0.0417u_1 = 0$$

$$P_1 = \quad -5.000 + 0.0417u_B + 0.0417u_D + 0.0417u_E + 0.0417u_F + 0.0208u_1 = 0$$

These equations can be written

$$P_0 + Ku = 0 \tag{11.6}$$

where K is the frame stiffness matrix.

It will be seen that when the individual member equations (equations 11.4) are summed as described above, the member stiffness coefficients combine to give the joint stiffness which is an element of the frame K matrix.   For example

$$K_{BB} = k_{BB}^A + k_{BB}^D = 0.3333 + 0.4000 = 0.7333$$

In a similar way the initial end actions, p_0, combine to give the initial value of the restraint actions P_0.   Thus

$$P_{B0} = p_{B0}^A + p_{B0}^D = -7.500 + 45.833 = +38.333$$

The equilibrium equations 11.5 give the following values of the restraint displacements:

$$u_B = -87.71 \quad u_D = +18.18 \quad u_E = -55.59 \quad u_F = -22.77 \quad u_1 = +535.79$$

The signs of these displacements are interpreted in accordance with the directions of the joint axes which are specified in Fig. 11.4.

(vi) END ACTIONS. Substitution of the values of the joint displacements in equations 11.4 yields the final values of the end actions on the various members.   These are shown in Fig. 11.6.   Equations 11.4 do not give the end actions at A and C, but these are not necessary for the solution of frame.

The internal actions at every section of the frame can now be determined by statics.   The bending moment at each point is given in Fig. 11.7, where the graph is drawn on the compression side of the member.

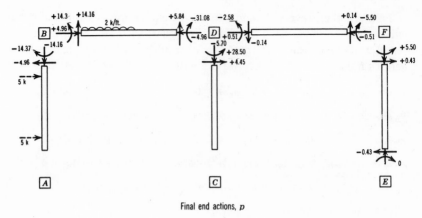

Final end actions, p

Fig. 11.6

In a frame containing members of a more complex shape, the methods discussed in Chapter 6 (see equation 6.20) could be used to determine the internal actions once the end actions are known.

The analysis set out above can be regarded as typical. The steps in the solution can be summarized as follows:

1. Specification of the necessary restraints.

2. Determination of the stiffness characteristics of each member in the frame.

3. Determination of the initial end actions on the members for the given external loading.

4. Statement of the equilibrium equations in terms of initial end actions and stiffness coefficients.

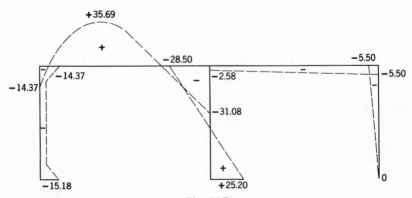

Fig. 11.7

5. Solution of the equilibrium equations to obtain the restraint displacements.

6. The use of these displacements to obtain the required end actions on the individual members.

11.4 PLANE BUILDING FRAMES

For plane frames with horizontal and vertical members only it is possible to carry out an analysis similar to that described above with very little effort.   Once the member stiffness coefficients have been determined the values in the frame stiffness matrix can readily be written down.   This will be illustrated with reference to a small building frame in which all axial deformations will be neglected.

Example 11.2   The outline of a small building frame is shown in Fig. 11.8. Numbers proportional to the moments of inertia are shown adjacent to the members.   The frame is to be solved separately for two systems of loading, namely (1) vertical loads on some beams as shown and (2) horizontal wind loads assumed to be acting at the floor levels.   Axial and shear deformations are to be neglected.

Solution.   (i) Stiffness Coefficients.   Since only bending deformations are relevant, the stiffness coefficients required for the columns are

$$\frac{2EI}{L}, \quad \frac{4EI}{L}, \quad \frac{6EI}{L^2} \quad \text{and} \quad \frac{12EI}{L^3}$$

(see equations 11.1).   For the beams only $2EI/L$ and $4EI/L$ are required since relative vertical end displacements are considered to be zero.

The values of these coefficients are computed for each member and are summarized in Fig. 11.9.   For convenience E has been taken as 100.   All beams and columns on one floor are the same in this problem.

(ii) Choice of Restraints.   Restraints are chosen which will fix every joint against all types of displacement.   A rotation restraint is required

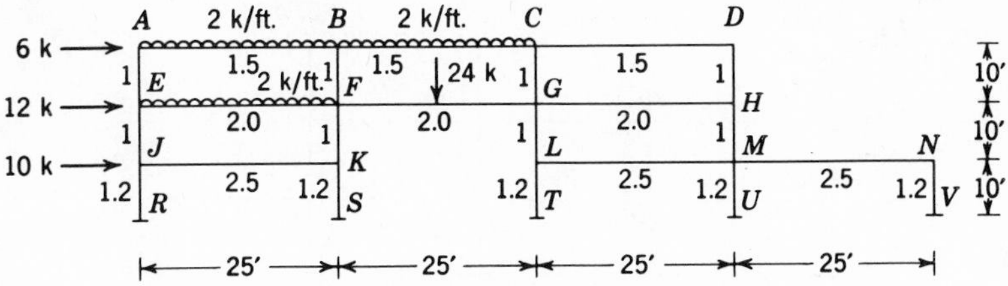

Fig. 11.8

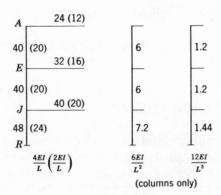

(columns only)

Fig. 11.9

at each joint and these will be denoted by P_A, P_B, P_C ... at joints A, B, C .... One horizontal restraint is required at each floor except at floor 1 where two are necessary because of the missing member KL. These have been numbered in Fig. 11.10 according to the floor at which they act; the second restraint at floor 1 is numbered 101. All vertical joint movement is inhibited by inextensible columns in this problem, but if this were not the case then vertical restraints would also be required.

(iii) FRAME STIFFNESS MATRIX. Since there are 17 restraints, the frame stiffness matrix will be (17 × 17). Terms on the diagonal will be the sum of the stiffness coefficients of all members for the clamping of which this particular restraint is responsible. The significance of the entries can be seen by giving each restraint in turn a unit displacement.

The elements in the first *column* (A) of K (Fig. 11.11) are the restraint forces called into play by unit displacement of restraint A. Thus, giving A unit rotation, we see that this calls for a couple at A equal to $4EI/L$ for AB plus $4EI/L$ for AE. Hence $K_{AA} = 24 + 40 = 64$. There are carry-over moments of $2EI/L$ ($=12$) to B and $2EI/L$ ($=20$) to E. The column shear in AE also calls for restraints of $6EI/L^2$ ($=6$) at P_3 and P_2.

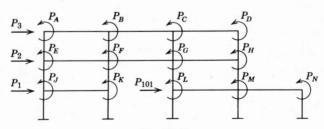

Fig. 11.10

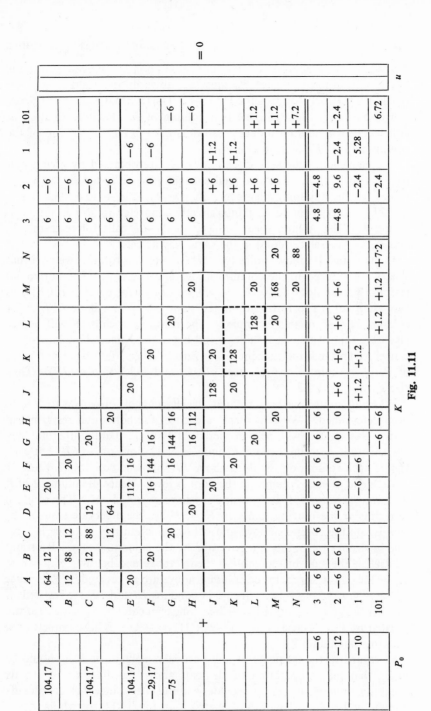

Fig. 11.11

An anticlockwise rotation of A would cause floor 3 to move towards the left if unrestrained; hence P_3 must act towards the right ($+$). For equilibrium P_2 acts towards the left ($-$). Thus we find elements $+6$ and -6 opposite P_3 and P_2 in the first column of K. Positive rotation at either end of a column induces restraints of $+6EI/L^2$ at the top of the column and $-6EI/L^2$ at the bottom.

The elements in the second column of K are obtained by giving unit rotation to joint B. The diagonal element BB is the sum of the $4EI/L$ values for the adjoining members: $K_{BB} = 24 + 24 + 40 = 88$. There is a $2EI/L$ carry-over to all joints directly connected to B, i.e., joints A, C and F. The column shear induced in the BF calls for restraints P_3 and P_2, and these are found in the same way as before.

Joints C and D follow similarly. When joint E is rotated, we note that shears are induced in the columns above and below E. The horizontal restraint on the floor above E, P_3, will be $6EI/L^2$ for column EA ($+6$ in this example). The restraint on the floor below E will be $6EI/L^2$ for column EI (-6 in this example). The restraint at floor E will be the algebraic sum of the shears above and below, and since these happen to cancel we find that the element K_{2E} is zero. When J is rotated, the value of P_1 is the sum of -6 (*bottom* of JE) and $+7.2$ (*top* of JR). Thus element K_{1J} is $+1.2$.

When all joints have been rotated, the elements of columns A to N have been determined. We now displace each of the horizontal restraints in turn. Restraint 2 will be considered as typical. Unit horizontal displacement of restraint 2 (floor E) induces end couple of $-6EI/L^2$ at each end of each column on the floor above EH, and end couples of $+6EI/L^2$ at each end of each column on the floor below. Hence in column 2 of K we have -6 in rows A, B, C, D and $+6$ in rows J, K, L, M. The rotation restraints at the moving joints E, F, G, H are the algebraic sum of the couples on the columns above and below, which in this instance is zero. The horizontal restraints are governed by the column shears. Restraint P_2 itself is the sum of the column shears above and below. $K_{22} = 8 \times 1.2 = 9.6$. The shears in the columns above are all resisted by P_3; hence $K_{32} = -4 \times 1.2 = '-4.8$. Shears in columns EJ and FK are resisted by P_1; hence $K_{12} = -2 \times 1.2 = -2.4$. Shear in columns GL and HM are resisted by P_{101}; hence $K_{101.2} = -2 \times 1.2 = -2.4$. This completes the elements in column 2.

In regard to the elements of any particular column of K it should be noted that the computation of elements above the diagonal is, strictly speaking, unnecessary, but it provides a useful check since they are already known by the symmetry of the K matrix. In Fig. 11.11, the whole matrix is divided into major sections separating the rotation restraints $A \ldots N$

from those of translation 3 ... 101. Further subdivision indicates how the individual floors influence the general form of the matrix. Thus rotations of the top floor joints $A \dots D$ induce carry-over moments to the floor below (joints $E \dots H$) which are represented by the diagonal sub-matrix $E \dots H$, but none to any floors below this. Consequently, apart from the horizontal restraints, the matrix is banded, and the width of the band is governed by the number of joints on one floor (if the joints are numbered in this manner across floors).

(iv) PARTICULAR SOLUTION. For the vertical loading, the fixed end restraints, P_0, are calculated for each loaded member (Fig. 11.12).

The total value of each restraint is the sum of the restraints exerted *upon* the adjacent members.

$$P_{A0} = +104.17$$

$$P_{B0} = +104.17 - 104.17 = 0$$

$$P_{C0} = -104.17$$

$$P_{E0} = +104.17$$

$$P_{F0} = -104.17 + 75 = -29.17$$

$$P_{G0} = -75$$

All other P_0 values are zero.

For the next load condition (horizontal loading), restraint P_3 is called upon to *resist* the load of 6 k. Hence P_{30} is -6. Similarly, $P_{20} = -12$ and $P_{10} = -10$. All other P_0 values are zero. (See Fig. 11.11).

(v) EVALUATION OF DISPLACEMENTS. The equilibrium equations are given by

$$\underset{(17\times2)}{P_0} + \underset{(17\times17)}{K} \underset{(17\times2)}{u} = \underset{(17\times2)}{0}$$

The first and second columns of P_0 contain the P_0 values for the first and second conditions of loading respectively. The two columns of u correspond to the restraint displacements for the two load conditions.

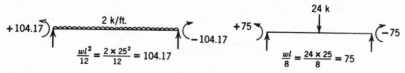

Fig. 11.12

These equations are now solved for u.

$$u = \begin{bmatrix} -1.498 & -0.245 \\ -0.092 & -0.183 \\ +1.060 & -0.157 \\ -0.329 & -0.183 \\ \hdashline -0.857 & -0.426 \\ +0.172 & -0.274 \\ +0.300 & -0.410 \\ -0.079 & -0.640 \\ \hdashline +0.123 & -0.655 \\ -0.068 & -0.683 \\ -0.078 & -0.669 \\ -0.001 & -0.411 \\ -0.037 & -0.341 \\ \hdashline +2.222 & +20.339 \\ +0.570 & +15.942 \\ -0.532 & +8.649 \\ +0.456 & +5.315 \end{bmatrix} \begin{matrix} A \\ B \\ C \\ D \\ \\ E \\ F \\ G \\ H \\ \\ J \\ K \\ L \\ M \\ N \\ \\ 3 \\ 2 \\ 1 \\ 101 \end{matrix}$$

(vi) INTERNAL ACTIONS IN MEMBERS. It will be sufficient to compute the final end forces on each member, since the actions at any other point can then be obtained by statics. The end forces are given by the equation

$$p = p_0 + ku$$

where u is the end displacement and k is the relevant stiffness.

Consider FG as a typical beam. For the beams the only end displacement is rotation (Fig. 11.13).

Fig. 11.13

For the first condition of loading,

$$p_F = p_{F0} + \frac{4EI}{L} u_F + \frac{2EI}{L} u_G$$

$$= +75 + (32 \times 0.172) + (16 \times 0.300) = 81.176 \text{ kip-feet}$$

$$p_G = p_{G0} + \frac{2EI}{L} u_F + \frac{4EI}{L} u_G$$

$$= -75 + (16 \times 0.172) + (32 \times 0.300) = -62.648 \text{ kip-feet}$$

The end shears can be found from statics (Fig. 11.14).

Consider KF as a typical column. The relative lateral displacement of the ends (top–bottom) is $(u_2 - u_1)$ see Fig. 11.15a. This produces end couples of $+(6EI/L^2)(u_2 - u_1)$. The total end couples are then

$$p_F = p_{F0} + \frac{4EI}{L} u_F + \frac{2EI}{L} u_K + \frac{6EI}{L^2} (u_2 - u_1)$$

$$= 0 + (40 \times 0.172) + (20 \times -0.068) + 6(0.570 + 0.532)$$

$$= +12.13 \text{ kip-feet}$$

$$p_K = p_{K0} + \frac{2EI}{L} u_F + \frac{4EI}{L} u_K + \frac{6EI}{L^2} (u_2 - u_1)$$

$$= 0 + (20 \times 0.172) + (40 \times -0.068) + 6(0.570 + 0.532)$$

$$= +7.33 \text{ kip-feet}$$

Where more than one displacement component occurs at each end of the member, as with the column, it may be worth while to evaluate the end forces all together by using the member stiffness matrix. Furthermore,

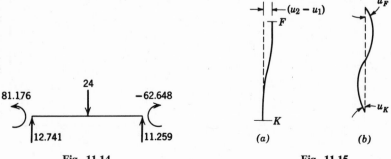

Fig. 11.14   Fig. 11.15

	3	A	B	C	D	2	E	F	G	H	1	J	K	101	L	M	N
3	4.8	6	6	6	6	-4.8	6	6	6	6							
A	6	64	12			-6	20										
B	6	12	88	12		-6		20									
C	6		12	88	12	-6			20								
D	6			12	64	-6				20							
2	-4.8	-6	-6	-6	-6	9.6	0	0	0	0	-2.4	6	6	-2.4	6	6	
E	6	20				0	112	16			-6	20					
F	6		20			0	16	144	16		-6		20				
G	6			20		0		16	144	16				-6	20		
H	6				20	0			16	112				-6		20	
1						-2.4	-6	-6			5.28	+1.2	+1.2				
J						6	20				+1.2	128	20				
K						6		20			+1.2	20	128				
101						-2.4			-6	-6				6.72	+1.2	+1.2	+7.2
L						6			20					+1.2	128	20	
M						6				20				+1.2	20	168	20
N														+7.2		20	88

Fig. 11.16

the end actions for both the load conditions can be evaluated at the same time.

$$
\begin{bmatrix} S_F \\ M_F \\ S_K \\ M_K \end{bmatrix} =
\begin{bmatrix}
\dfrac{12EI}{L^3} & \dfrac{6EI}{L^2} & -\dfrac{12EI}{L^3} & \dfrac{6EI}{L^2} \\[2mm]
\dfrac{6EI}{L^2} & \dfrac{4EI}{L} & -\dfrac{6EI}{L^2} & \dfrac{2EI}{L} \\[2mm]
\hline
-\dfrac{12EI}{L^3} & -\dfrac{6EI}{L^2} & \dfrac{12EI}{L^3} & -\dfrac{6EI}{L^2} \\[2mm]
\dfrac{6EI}{L^2} & \dfrac{2EI}{L} & -\dfrac{6EI}{L^2} & \dfrac{4EI}{L}
\end{bmatrix}
\begin{bmatrix} u_2 \\ u_F \\ u_1 \\ u_K \end{bmatrix}
$$

$$
=
\begin{bmatrix}
1.2 & 6 & -1.2 & 6 \\
6 & 40 & -6 & 20 \\
\hline
-1.2 & -6 & 1.2 & -6 \\
6 & 20 & -6 & 40
\end{bmatrix}
\begin{bmatrix}
+0.570 & +15.942 \\
+0.172 & -0.274 \\
\hline
-0.532 & +8.649 \\
-0.068 & -0.683
\end{bmatrix}
$$

which gives

$$
\begin{bmatrix} S_F \\ M_F \\ S_K \\ M_K \end{bmatrix} =
\begin{bmatrix}
1.946 & 3.010 \\
12.132 & 19.138 \\
-1.946 & -3.010 \\
7.332 & 10.958
\end{bmatrix}
$$

The first column gives the values of the end shears and moments for the first condition of loading, while the second column gives corresponding values for the other condition of loading.

The form of the frame stiffness matrix K can be modified to some extent. A very simple modification is effected by taking the restraints in a different sequence. In the above solution the rotation restraints were considered first and then the lateral restraints. Another possible arrangement is to consider all the restraints, rotation and horizontal, on the top floor first, then all those on the next floor and so on. This sequence results in the matrix of Fig. 11.16. Since the restraints of each floor are grouped together, the non-zero elements are not scattered so far from the diagonal as they are in Fig. 11.11. The submatrices indicated in Fig. 11.16 are *floor submatrices*. The central submatrix is that for floor

EFGH and the submatrices above and below are carry-overs to the floors above and below. In a more extensive frame the grouping about the diagonal is more noticeable. There will be as many submatrices on the diagonal as there are floors in the building, and a carry-over submatrix above and below each of these (except the first and last). This form of *K* matrix is often called a tri-diagonal form.

It should be noted that the numerical values in Fig. 11.16 are identical with those in Fig. 11.11. They have merely been re-arranged. The conditioning of the new equations is thus neither better nor worse than that of the previous set of equations. Where the number of equations involved is very large, however, one or other form of matrix may offer computational advantages which may result in improved accuracy. This will depend on the computational procedure adopted.

Another possible modification does produce different numerical values for the elements of *K*. The process might be referred to as a grouping of the restraints. In developing the matrix of Fig. 11.11, as each restraint was displaced in turn, all other restraints were kept fixed. Thus when restraint 2 was displaced, floor *EFGH* moved horizontally while the floors above and below remained fixed (Fig. 11.17).

On the other hand, floors *A* and *E* could be moved together (Fig. 11.18). This would be equivalent to grouping restraints 3 and 2. Such a grouping is advantageous. In the first place the coefficients are more easily determined. The columns of only one floor are deformed in Fig. 11.18, whereas the columns of two floors are deformed in Fig. 11.17. There is a consequent simplification of the work, and in addition there are less non-zero elements than before. In the second place, the conditioning of the equations may be improved. The choice of these groups is quite

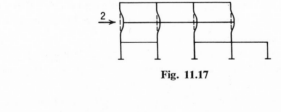

Fig. 11.17

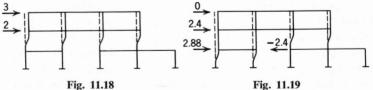

Fig. 11.18   **Fig. 11.19**

arbitrary although some groupings are more advantageous than others. The number of groups must be equal to the original number of individual restraints.

In the original solution we had 4 horizontal restraints (since the frame has 4 degrees of horizontal freedom) and it is important to ensure that we now define 4 *independent groups* of horizontal restraints. Suppose we denote these groups by $\bar{3}$, $\bar{2}$, $\bar{1}$ and $\overline{101}$. We might define, for instance,

$$\bar{3} = 3$$
$$\bar{2} = 3 + 2$$
$$\bar{1} = 3 + 2 + 1 \qquad (11.7)$$
$$\overline{101} = 3 + 2 + 1 + 101$$

Then a displacement $\bar{3}$ would merely be a displacement of the top floor as before. A unit displacement $\bar{2}$ would imply a unit displacement of both 3 and 2 (Fig. 11.18). We note that the restraint *forces* are grouped in a corresponding manner. Thus the value to be assigned to the force $\bar{2}$ is the sum of the forces 3 and 2.

A unit displacement $\bar{1}$ signifies a displacement of 3, 2 and 1 (Fig. 11.19). Note that on the bottom floor, joints J and K have moved (restraint 1) while joints L, M and N (restraint 101) have not moved. The forces induced by column shears are indicated in Fig. 11.19. The values to be ascribed to restraints $\bar{3}$, $\bar{2}$, $\bar{1}$ and $\overline{101}$ due to this particular displacement are then given by

$$\bar{3} = 0$$
$$\bar{2} = 0 + 2.4 = 2.4$$
$$\bar{1} = 0 + 2.4 + 2.88 = 5.28$$
$$\overline{101} = 0 + 2.4 + 2.88 - 2.4 = 2.88$$

These values are entered in the column $\bar{1}$ of the matrix of Fig. 11.20.

Finally, we note that the initial restraint values, P_0, must be grouped in a corresponding manner. Thus for the wind loading

$$P_{\bar{3}0} = -6$$
$$P_{\bar{2}0} = -(6 + 12) = -18$$
$$P_{\bar{1}0} = -(6 + 12 + 10) = -28$$
$$P_{\overline{101}.0} = -(6 + 12 + 10 + 0) = -28$$

	$\bar{3}$	A	B	C	D	$\bar{2}$	E	F	G	H	$\bar{1}$	J	K	$\overline{101}$	L	M	N
$\bar{3}$	4.8	6	6	6	6	0	6	6	6	6							
A	6	64	12			0	20										
B	6	12	88	12		0		20									
C	6		12	88	12	0			20								
D	6			12	64	0				20							
$\bar{2}$	0	0	0	0	0	4.8	6	6	6	6	2.4	6	6	0	6	6	
E	6	20				6	112	16			0	20					
F	6		20			6	16	144	16		0		20				
G	6			20		6		16	144	16	6				20		
H	6				20	6			16	112	6					20	
$\bar{1}$						2.4	0	0	6	6	5.28	7.2	7.2	2.88	6	6	
J						6	20				7.2	128	20	7.2			
K						6		20			7.2	20	128	7.2			
$\overline{101}$						0			0	0	2.88	7.2	7.2	7.20	7.2	7.2	7.2
L						6		20			6			7.2	128	20	
M						6			20		6			7.2	20	168	20
N														7.2		20	88

Fig. 11.20

The solution of the equations $P_0 + Ku = 0$ now yields values of u which can be regarded as "group displacements." Thus, for instance, $u_{\bar{2}} = u_3 + u_2$, i.e., $u_{\bar{2}}$ is the sum of the horizontal movements of floors 3 and 2. The individual floor displacements can be found from the group displacements by means of equations 11.7. The remainder of the solution then follows as before.

PROBLEMS

11.1. For the frames shown in Fig. P11.1, specify the necessary restraints. Find the initial values of these restraints for the given loading, and also find the values of the initial member end actions.

In frames (a) and (b) assume that the members are inextensible. In frame (c) take axial deformations into account. Consider frame (d) first on the assumption of inextensible members, and then on the assumption of extensible members.

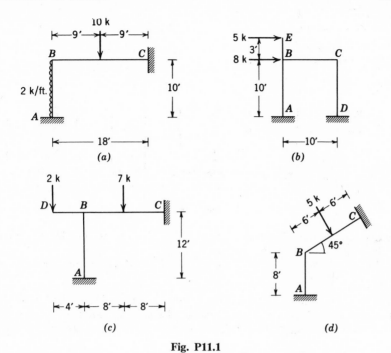

Fig. P11.1

11.2. Solve the frame of Fig. P11.2. Give a detailed solution laid out in the style of Example 11.1.

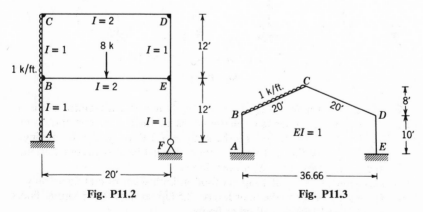

Fig. P11.2   Fig. P11.3

11.3. The gabled portal of Fig. P11.3 carries a uniformly distributed normal loading of 1 kip per foot on member *BC*. Give a detailed solution laid out in the style of Example 11.1.

11.4. For each of the plane frames of Fig. P11.4, discuss the layout of the *K*

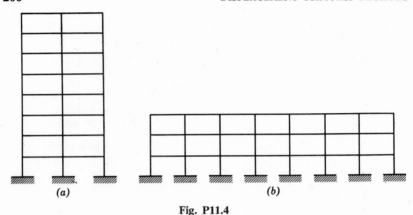

Fig. P11.4

matrix: (i) when the joints are numbered up columns and (ii) when the joints are numbered across floors.

Comment on the width of the band of non-zero elements and its relation to the size of the frame.

11.5. Write the stiffness matrix for the plane rigid-jointed frame of Fig. P11.5. Only bending deformations are to be considered. Also write the load matrix P_0 for the loading indicated. Take $E = 100$, $I = 1.0$ for all columns.

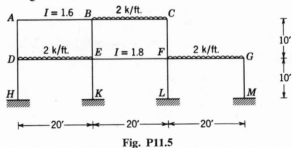

Fig. P11.5

11.6. In the plane frame of Fig. P11.6, all the beams have a moment of inertia of 2 and the column moments of inertia are as indicated. All columns on one floor are identical. The frame is to be analyzed for three systems of loading:

(a) Distributed loading of 1 kip per foot on the left-hand spans of odd floors, and the right-hand spans of even floors.

(b) Distributed loading of 1 kip per foot on both spans of odd floors only.

(c) Horizontal forces at the floor levels: 2.5 kips at floor 9, 6.5 kips at floors 4 and 5, and 5 kips at all other floors.

Solve for the three load conditions simultaneously. For condition 1, tabulate the mid-span moments in each loaded beam. For condition 2, tabulate the center support moment at each loaded floor. For condition 3, tabulate the top and bottom moments of each external column.

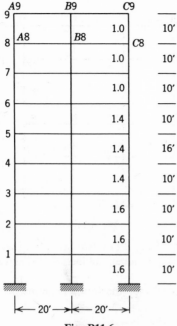

Fig. P11.6

11.7. Solve the frame shown in Fig. P11.7 for horizontal and vertical loads separately.

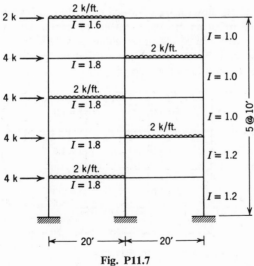

Fig. P11.7

11.8. Re-solve the frame of Fig. P11.7 when loaded by the horizontal loads only. Use grouped horizontal restraints.

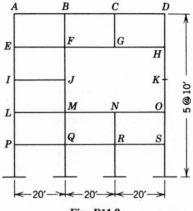

Fig. P11.9

11.9. In the plane frame of Fig. P11.9 two beams and two columns are missing as shown.   All beams have a moment of inertia of 2, and all columns a moment of inertia of 1.

Write the stiffness matrix for the frame in terms of rotational and lateral restraints considering

(*a*) Individual lateral restraints.

(*b*) Grouped lateral restraints.

(*c*) The effect of inserting (or deleting) a joint at *K* on the pattern of non-zero elements in the stiffness matrix of (*a*).

11.10. Figure P11.10 shows a frame which is partly cantilevered.   The values given against the members are the moments of inertia relative to the upper columns.   If the true size of the upper columns is 12 inches × 12 inches and $E = 4 \times 10^6$ psi, find the horizontal and vertical movements of the points *A* and *B* when the frame is loaded as shown.

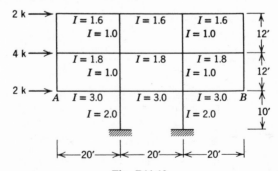

Fig. P11.10

CHAPTER 12

Relaxation Methods

In this chapter we propose to review two methods which are based on the application of the relaxation technique to the problem of solving the equilibrium equations (see equations 11.5). The brief outline presented here is intended only to demonstrate the relation of these methods to the general stiffness method. In practice many short cuts are employed, each of which improves the practical efficiency of the analysis, although at the same time tending to obscure its mathematical basis.

The method of moment distribution, in particular, has deservedly received a great deal of attention. The explanation given below makes no mention of the many techniques which are so useful in practice. It is expected, therefore, that before the method is put into operation, other works, more particularly devoted to this phase, will be consulted.

12.1 MOMENT DISTRIBUTION

Moment distribution is a method of analysis applicable primarily to plane frames in which only bending distortions in the plane of the frame are taken into account. It provides an extremely powerful tool for rectangular frames with prismatic members, and for this reason the two-bay frame of Example 11.1 will be used as an illustration. It will be assumed that the reader has some acquaintance with moment distribution, and the steps in the solution will not be given in detail.

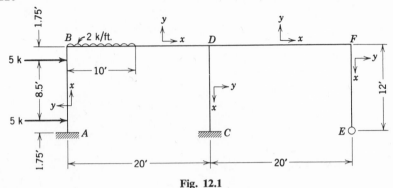

Fig. 12.1

Example 12.1 The frame (Fig. 12.1) of Example 11.1 is to be re-solved, using moment distribution. The process is to be compared with the procedure of Example 11.1.

Solution. As far as possible, the order of the steps adopted in Example 11.1 will be repeated so as to facilitate comparison.

(i) RESTRAINTS. The same restraints will be imposed as before, namely, rotation restraints at joints B, D, E and F respectively, and a restraint P_1 against horizontal movement (sway) of beam BDF.

(ii) END STIFFNESSES OF MEMBERS. The end stiffnesses for each member are calculated as before. For ease of reference they are summarized in the diagrams of Fig. 12.2. The direct stiffnesses due to joint rotation are shown in Fig. 12.2a. Since the members are prismatic, the carry-over couples induced at the "far end" of each member are half those induced at the near end. The horizontal force induced by unit rotation of each joint is 0.0417 and is shown as a column shear. In Fig. 12.2b are shown the couples induced by lateral translation (movement of restraint P_1). The horizontal force in each column induced by unit horizontal displacement of beam BDF is again shown as a column shear.

(iii) INITIAL END ACTIONS. The particular solution is the same as that for Example 11.1, namely, the solution when all joints are fully restrained. For this problem, the solution is readily obtainable from handbooks, as

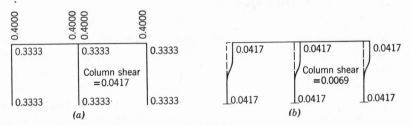

Fig. 12.2

was discussed in Chapter 11. The initial values of the end actions, expressed with signs consistent with the axes chosen for the joints, are shown in Fig. 11.5.

(iv) FINAL END ACTIONS. Expression for the final end actions are usually not stated explicitly in the moment distribution process. However, for the purpose of explanation it will be convenient to state them. These expressions were given previously in equations 11.4 and will be restated here for reference.

End Couples

$$
\begin{aligned}
p_B^A &= -7.500 + 0.3333u_B + &0u_D& &+& &0u_E& &+& &0u_F& &+ 0.0417u_1& \Bigg\} P_B \\
p_B^D &= +45.833 + 0.4000u_B + 0.2000u_D + &0u_E& &+& &0u_F& &+& &0u_1& \\[4pt]
p_D^B &= -20.833 + 0.2000u_B + 0.4000u_D + &0u_E& &+& &0u_F& &+& &0u_1& \\
p_D^C &= 0 &+ 0u_B& + 0.3333u_D + &0u_E& &+& &0u_F& &+ 0.0417u_1& \Bigg\} P_D \\
p_D^F &= 0 &+ 0u_B& + 0.4000u_D + &0u_E& &+ 0.2000u_F +& &0u_1& \\[4pt]
p_E^F &= 0 &+ 0u_B& + &0u_D& + 0.3333u_E + 0.1667u_F + 0.0417u_1\} P_E \\[4pt]
p_F^D &= 0 &+ 0u_B& + 0.2000u_D + &0u_E& &+ 0.4000u_F +& &0u_1& \Bigg\} P_F \\
p_F^E &= 0 &+ 0u_B& + &0u_D& + 0.1667u_E + 0.3333u_F + 0.0417u_1
\end{aligned}
\quad (12.1)
$$

End Horizontal Forces

$$
\begin{aligned}
p_1^A &= -5.000 + 0.0417u_B + &0u_D& &+& &0u_E& &+& &0u_F& &+ 0.0069u_1& \Bigg\} P_1 \\
p_1^C &= 0 &+ 0u_B& + 0.0417u_D + &0u_E& &+& &0u_F& &+ 0.0069u_1& \\
p_1^E &= 0 &+ 0u_B& + &0u_D& + 0.0417u_E + 0.0417u_F + 0.0069u_1
\end{aligned}
$$

(v) EQUILIBRIUM EQUATIONS. Again, these are not usually expressly stated but they are required here for reference. By grouping the expressions in equation 12.1 we obtain the equilibrium equations.

$$
\begin{aligned}
+38.333 &\quad + 0.7333u_B + 0.2000u_D + &0u_E& &+& &0u_F& &+ 0.0417u_1& = 0 \\
-20.833 &\quad + 0.2000u_B + 1.1333u_D + &0u_E& &+ 0.2000u_F& &+ 0.0417u_1& = 0 \\
0 &\quad + 0u_B + &0u_D& + 0.3333u_E + 0.1667u_F &+ 0.0417u_1& = 0 \quad (12.2)\\
0 &\quad + 0u_B + 0.2000u_D + 0.1667u_E + 0.7333u_F &+ 0.0417u_1& = 0 \\
-5.000 &\quad + 0.0417u_B + 0.0417u_D + 0.0417u_E + 0.0417u_F &+ 0.0208u_1& = 0
\end{aligned}
$$

The distribution process is concerned with the solution of these equations by relaxing the restraints one at a time.

Initially, since the joints are fully fixed, $u_B = u_D \ldots u_1 = 0$, and clearly the equations 12.2 are not satisfied.

The relaxing of restraint P_B, which allows the joint B to rotate to its position of temporary equilibrium, corresponds to making a variation in the unknown u_B such that the first equation of 12.2 is temporarily satisfied. The same variation of u_B will have an effect upon each of the other equations. The magnitudes of these effects are governed by the coefficients of u_B. In the same way, the second equation of 12.2 can be satisfied by a suitable variation of u_D, which corresponds physically to the release of joint D after B has been relocked. This last operation will also affect the other equations, and in particular it will upset the first equation of 12.2. The effect upon the various equations is governed by the coefficients of u_D, namely, the second column of the K matrix. Since the diagonal term (K_{22}) of this column is considerably larger than the others, the balancing of restraint P_D will unbalance the other restraints to only a relatively small extent. The rapid convergence of the process is seen to depend largely upon the fact that the diagonal terms of the K matrix are predominant as compared with others in the same column.

While this feature is true of the first four diagonal terms, it is certainly not true of the fifth. In other words, the equations of rotational equilibrium are eminently suitable for solution by relaxations, but the equation of translation is not. Although a solution could eventually be reached by a process such as that described above, convergence would be greatly retarded by the presence of the fifth equation. For this reason the distribution process is normally applied only to the equations of rotational equilibrium. For the time being the last equation of 12.2 is ignored, as also are the u_1 terms in the other equations. The first four equations are then solved by the relaxation process.

Furthermore, in order to eliminate the back-substitution process of the basic stiffness method (p. 191), it is usual in moment distribution to compute directly the variation of the end actions due to a given joint rotation. This amounts to operation on the equilibrium equations expressed in the form of equations 12.1 rather than 12.2. Suppose that at a particular stage of the process it is found that a variation of $+5$ in u_D is required to satisfy the second equation of 12.2; then the variations actually recorded are found from the u_D column of equations 12.1. These will be

$$
\left.
\begin{aligned}
\text{variation of } p_B^A &= \quad\ 0 \times 5 = 0 \\
\text{variation of } p_B^D &= +0.2000 \times 5 = +1.0
\end{aligned}
\right\} P_B
$$

$$
\left.
\begin{aligned}
\text{variation of } p_D^B &= +0.4000 \times 5 = +2.0 \\
\text{variation of } p_D^C &= +0.3333 \times 5 = 1.667 \\
\text{variation of } p_D^F &= +0.4000 \times 5 = +2.0
\end{aligned}
\right\} P_D
$$

$$
\left.
\begin{aligned}
\text{variation of } p_E^F &= \quad\ 0 \times 5 = 0
\end{aligned}
\right\} P_E
$$

$$
\left.
\begin{aligned}
\text{variation of } p_F^D &= +0.2000 \times 5 = +1.0 \\
\text{variation of } p_F^E &= \quad\ 0 \times 5 = 0
\end{aligned}
\right\} P_F
$$

The P_1 group is ignored at present. It will be observed that the total variation in the restraint action at the relaxed joint (D) is much greater than that at any other joint.

The foregoing process is continued until it is judged that the solution has been obtained with sufficient accuracy. The approximate solutions will approach the exact solutions as the process is continued indefinitely. It is important to note that the solution obtained by this method differs from the so-called exact solution only insofar as insufficient cycles are performed. In the present case, solution of the first four equations of 12.2 and direct calculation of end moments from equations 12.1 yields the following values:

$$
\begin{aligned}
p_B^A &= -27.5 \\
p_B^D &= +27.5
\end{aligned}\Bigg\}
\qquad
\begin{aligned}
p_D^B &= -20.8 \\
p_D^C &= +10.4 \\
p_D^F &= +10.4
\end{aligned}\Bigg\}
\qquad
p_E^F = 0\}
\qquad
\begin{aligned}
p_F^D &= +2.4 \\
p_F^E &= -2.4
\end{aligned}\Bigg\}
$$

These values, which satisfy only the rotation equations, will be denoted by p_r.

The translation equation is now introduced by a direct process. An arbitrary value is assigned to the displacement u_1. This value corresponds to a lateral displacement of the beam BDF while all joints are locked against rotation. The arbitrary value of u_1 assigns definite values to the last terms in equations 12.2. These become the constant terms in place of the figures $+38.333$ and -20.833, which are now omitted. The first four equations are again solved by the moment distribution procedure. When u_1 is given the value $+100/0.0417$ this second solution gives

$$
\begin{aligned}
p_B^A &= +59.5 \\
p_B^D &= -59.5
\end{aligned}\Bigg\}
\qquad
\begin{aligned}
p_D^B &= -46.5 \\
p_D^C &= +81.5 \\
p_D^F &= -35.0
\end{aligned}\Bigg\}
\qquad
p_E^F = 0\}
\qquad
\begin{aligned}
p_F^D &= -35.0 \\
p_F^E &= +35.0
\end{aligned}\Bigg\}
$$

These values, which satisfy the rotation equations for an arbitrary value of the *translation* u_1, will be denoted by p_t.

It is noted that if the value assigned to u_1 is c times as large as that assumed above, the solution will have values represented by $c \times p_t$. If, in addition, the fixed-end moment terms ($+38.333$ and -20.833) are included, the first four equations will have a solution ($p_r + c p_t$). Substitution of this expression in the equation of translational equilibrium yields the true value of c. In practice, the end moments are computed at all member ends, not only at those at which an artificial restraint is present. It is thus possible to calculate the column shear in terms of the end moments. The horizontal equilibrium of the beam BDF can then be expressed by the equation

$$-5 - 1.40 + 28.89c = 0 \tag{12.3}$$

where -5 is the constant term of the last equation of 12.2 and $(-1.40 + 28.89c)$ is the total shear at the top of the columns due to the end moments denoted by $(p_r + cp_t)$. From equation 12.3, $c = 0.22$, and the final end moments on the members are given by $(p_r + 0.22p_t)$. In detail

$$p_B^A = -27.50 + 0.22(+59.5) = -14.4$$

$$p_B^D = +27.50 + 0.22(-59.5) = +14.4$$

$$p_D^B = -20.8\ \ + 0.22(-46.5) = -31.0$$

$$p_D^C = +10.4\ \ + 0.22(+81.5) = +28.3$$

$$p_D^F = +10.4\ \ + 0.22(-35.0) = \ \ +2.7$$

$$p_E^F = \quad 0\ \ \ + 0.22(0) \qquad = \quad 0$$

$$p_F^D = \ \ +2.4\ \ + 0.22(-35.0) = \ \ -5.3$$

$$p_F^E = \ \ -2.4\ \ + 0.22(+35.0) = \ \ +5.3$$

These values agree with previous solutions to a degree of accuracy sufficient for most purposes.

In a problem with more than one translational restraint, the equations of rotational equilibrium are solved in the foregoing manner, first for the applied loads, giving the solution p_r, and then successively for arbitrary displacements of the translation restraints, giving solutions $p_{t1}, p_{t2} \ldots$. The true solution is then $(p_r + c_1 p_{t1} + c_2 p_{t2} \ldots)$. Substituting in the various equations of translation equilibrium gives a set of equations for the determination of $c_1, c_2 \ldots$.

In this form the method is clearly economical only when the number of sway operations is small, for otherwise the solution of the equations for $c_1, c_2 \ldots$ will itself become too extensive. Details of the numerous practical modifications of moment distribution will, however, not be pursued. It will be seen that moment distribution is ideally suitable for frames in which no joint suffers any translation. Approximations can be made which permit the process to be considerably extended. However, if it is desired to obtain, by iterative methods, the true solution of a frame many of whose joints can undergo translation, it is necessary to make more extensive use of relaxation techniques.

12.2 GROUP RELAXATIONS

The use of "group relaxations" has proved successful, in many problems of physical science, in the speeding up of the process of convergence.

It has been applied to the solution of plane frame problems, where the "sway" equations become embarrassing for moment distribution.

Given a set of simultaneous equations such as equations 12.2, variation of the value of one of the unknowns can be regarded as a unit relaxation operation, while variation of several unknowns simultaneously is called a "group operation." The effect on the equations of such a group operation can be calculated by adding the effects which occur when the unknowns are varied separately.

To illustrate the principle involved, Example 12.1 will be re-solved using group relaxations.

Example 12.2 The frame of Example 12.1 is to be re-solved (see Fig. 12.1).

Solution. The choice of restraints, the calculation of end stiffnesses and initial end actions, and the setting up of the equilibrium equations are all carried out as in Example 12.1. It is convenient, before proceeding, to set out the effects of the unit operations in diagrammatic form.

Each column of Table 12.1 summarizes the end actions which occur as a result of a particular unit operation. The values shown in any column of Table 12.1 are the same as the coefficients in the corresponding column of the matrix k (equations 12.1). In the table, the couples induced at joints A and C have also been included, although since there are no restraints at A and C, these coefficients do not appear in the matrix k. In this problem, and in many others, the arithmetic could be simplified by using scale factors so that the diagrams of Table 12.1 contain integral values. For instance, an operation $30 \times \rho_1$ would result in integral values of the induced couples and forces. The basic stiffness factors have been retained in order to simplify comparison with the other solutions.

Group operations can be built up by any linear grouping of the foregoing basic units. An operation $\rho_1 - 2\delta$ would affect predominantly the end couples at B, but would also create column shears which total zero. This is called a "no shear" operation, which is useful for relaxing the first rotation equation without any effect being carried over into the translation equation. A similar operation can be based on each rotation restraint.

Table 12.2 shows four group operations which can be used for relaxing rotation restraints without inducing any variation in restraint P_1. Other groups are possible. The group F is arranged to reduce the carry-over from F to E when F is relaxed. A zero carry-over could have been arranged had it been worth while. In Table 12.2 each number in brackets is the sum of the couples at the nearby joint. It gives the total variation of the restraint action due to that particular group operation. The foregoing groupings could have been obtained directly from equations 12.2. From an examination of the coefficients of the last equation it is clear that

Table 12.1
Unit Operations

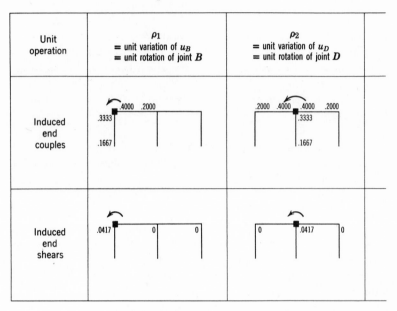

Unit operation	ρ_1 = unit variation of u_B = unit rotation of joint B	ρ_2 = unit variation of u_D = unit rotation of joint D
Induced end couples	.4000 .2000 / .3333 / .1667	.2000 .4000 .4000 .2000 / .3333 / .1667
Induced end shears	.0417 0 0	0 .0417 0

Table 12.2
Group Operations

Group operation	$B = \rho_1 - 2\delta$	$D = \rho_2 - 2\delta$
Induced end couples	(.650) .4000 .2000 +.2500 −.0833 −.0833 / +.0833 −.0833 −.0833	(1.050) .2000 .4000 .4000 .2000 −.0833 +.2500 −.0833 / −.0833 +.0833 −.0833
Induced end shears	+.0278 −.0139 −.0139	−.0139 +.0278 −.0139

216

Table 12.1 (continued)

ρ_3 = unit variation of u_E = unit rotation of joint E	ρ_4 = unit variation of u_F = unit rotation of joint F	δ = unit variation of u_1 = unit translation of joints B, D, F
.1667 .3333	.2000 .4000 .3333 .1667	.0417 .0417 .0417 .0417 .0417 .0417
0 0 .0417	0 0 .0417	.0069 .0069 .0069 .0069 .0069 .0069

Table 12.2 (continued)

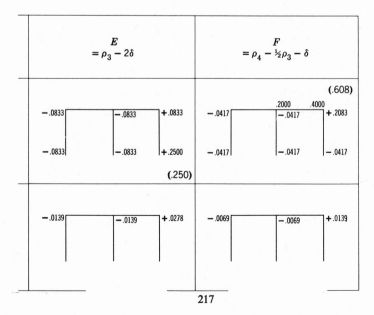

E $= \rho_3 - 2\delta$	F $= \rho_4 - \tfrac{1}{2}\rho_3 - \delta$
$-.0833$ $-.0833$ $+.0833$ $-.0833$ $-.0833$ $+.2500$ (.250)	(.608) .2000 .4000 $-.0417$ $-.0417$ $+.2083$ $-.0417$ $-.0417$ $-.0417$
$-.0139$ $-.0139$ $+.0278$	$-.0069$ $-.0069$ $+.0139$

217

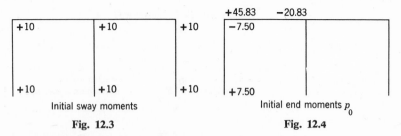

Initial sway moments	Initial end moments p_0
Fig. 12.3	**Fig. 12.4**

the equation will remain satisfied if $\Delta u_1 = -2\Delta u_B$, and leads to the group operator $B = \rho_1 - 2\delta$.

The sway equation is first balanced by using a suitable multiple of operation δ, namely, $(-5/0.021)\delta$, and this produces end couples as shown in Fig. 12.3. These moments can be written down directly by noting that they are all equal and that their sum, divided by the column height (12 feet), must give the required column shear of $+5$ kips. The addition of these moments to the initial end values, p_0, produces the figures of the first row of the relaxation table (Table 12.3). Thereafter the rotation equations are balanced by means of operations B, D, E and F. Since these do not disturb the sway equation, the latter remains satisfied.

The time, which in Example 12.1 was spent on the sway problem, is here avoided by the expenditure of more time in constructing basic operations and a more cumbersome relaxing procedure. The method shows to greater advantage as the ratio of translation restraints to rotation restraints increases. The arithmetic is simplified if the relative stiffness values are expressed as far as possible as integers. These points are illustrated by the solution of a vierendeel truss, the slope deflection equations for which would comprise seven equations of rotation and six of translation.

Example 12.3 Figure 12.5 shows a vierendeel truss. Each member is straight and symmetrical. The numbers against the members indicate their relative bending stiffnesses.

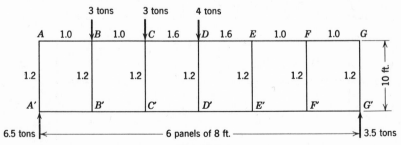

Fig. 12.5

Table 12.3
Relaxation Table

Operation	A	P_B		C	P_D			P_E	P_F	
		A	D		B	C	F		D	E
Initial end moment after balancing sway	+17.5	+2.5	+45.8	+10	−20.8	+10	0	+10	0	+10
(−48.3/.650)B	−6.2	−18.6	−29.7	+6.2	−14.9	+6.2		+6.2		+6.2
(−16.2/.250)E	+5.4	+5.4		+5.4		+5.4		−16.2		−5.4
(+14.1/1.050)D	−1.1	−1.1	+2.7	+1.1	+5.4	+3.3	+5.4	−1.1	+2.7	−1.1
(−12.4/.608)F	+0.9	+0.9		+0.9		+0.9	−4.1	+0.9	−8.2	−4.2
(−7.9/.650)B	−1.0	−3.0	−4.9	+1.0	−2.4	+1.0		+1.0		+1.0
(+4.6/1.050)D	−0.4	−0.4	+0.9	+0.4	+1.8	+1.1	+1.7	−0.4	+0.9	−0.4
(−1.5/.608)F	+0.1	+0.1		+0.1		+0.1	−0.5	+0.1	−1.0	−0.5
Final moments	+15.2	−14.2	+14.8	+25.1	−30.9	+28.0	+2.5	+0.5	−5.6	+5.6
		p_B^A	p_B^D		p_D^B	p_D^C	p_D^F	p_E^F	p_F^D	p_F^E

Solution. The truss is symmetrical about the horizontal center line. Since the loads are applied to the joints and axial deformations are neglected, it will make no difference if the loads are applied half to the top chord and half to the bottom chord. The loads will then be anti-symmetrical about the horizontal center line, and it follows that the final displacement will also be anti-symmetrical. This consideration suggests that when any top chord joint is rotated, the corresponding bottom chord joint should be rotated by an equal amount in the same direction. In effect, this distortion pattern constitutes a preliminary grouping of the unit operations.

Using integers proportional to the stiffnesses, we may write the moments induced by such a combined operation at C and C' (for example) as shown in Fig. 12.6.

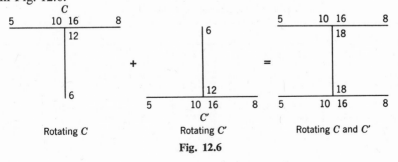

Fig. 12.6

Table 12.4
Basic Operations

Operation	ρ_1 = rotation of A and A'	ρ_2 = rotation of B and B'
Induced end couples		

Table 12.5
Group Operations

Operation	A $= \rho_1 + 7.5\delta_{AB}$	B $= \rho_2 + 7.5\delta_{AB} + 7.5\delta_{BC}$
Induced end couples		

Table 12.6 Relaxation Table

Operation	A		B			C		
	A'	B	A	B'	C	B	C'	D
Sway moments		+13.0	+13.0		+7.0	+7.0		+1.0
Distribution	−11.4	−1.6	−2.2	−15.6	−2.2	−0.8	−5.9	−1.3
Carry-over		+2.2	+1.6		+0.8	+2.2		−0.9
Distribution	−1.9	−0.3	−0.3	−1.9	−0.3	−0.1	−1.0	−0.2
Final moments	−13.3	+13.3	+12.1	−17.5	+5.3	+8.3	−6.9	−1.4

Table 12.4 (continued)

ρ_3 = rotation of C and C'	ρ_4 = rotation of D and D'	δ = shearing of any panel.
C 5　　10 16　　8 　　　18 　　　18 5　　10 16　　8	D 8　　16 16　　8 　　　18 　　　18 8　　16 16　　8	−1　−1 −1　−1

Table 12.5 (continued)

C = $\rho_3 + 7.5\delta_{BC} + 12\delta_{CD}$	D = $\rho_4 + 12\delta_{CD} + 12\delta_{DE}$
(24.5) −2.5　　2.5 C 4　　−4 　　18	(26) −4　　4 D 4　　−4 　　18

Table 12.6 (continued)

D			E			F			G	
C	D'	E	D	E'	F	E	F'	G	F	G'
+1.0		−7.0	−7.0		−7.0	−7.0		−7.0	−7.0	
+0.9	+4.2	+0.9	+2.3	+10.3	+1.4	+1.5	+11.0	+1.5	+0.9	+6.1
+1.3		−2.3	−0.9		−1.5	−1.4		−0.9	−1.5	
+0.2	+0.7	+0.2	+0.4	+1.8	+0.2	+0.2	+1.8	+0.2	+0.2	+1.3
+3.4	+4.9	−8.2	−5.2	+12.1	−6.9	−6.7	+12.8	−6.2	−7.4	+7.4

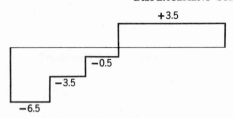

Fig. 12.7

In this way the operations in Table 12.4 are derived. Operations at joints E, F and G are symmetrical with those for A, B and C. If a rotation operation is combined with a panel shear such that the sum of the chord moments in the four corners of the panel is zero, the total shear force induced in the panel by such an operation will be zero. In this way the group operations of Table 12.5 are obtained from the basic operations of Table 12.4. Only the top joints are shown, since the numbers along the bottom chord will be the same.

The sway equations are first satisfied by making suitable shear distortions in each panel (without joint rotation). Figure 12.7 indicates the shear forces in the various panels of the truss.

As indicated by the operation δ of Table 12.4, the shearing of any panel will produce equal moments in the four corners. If a moment m is induced in each corner the total shear in the top and bottom chords is $-4m/8$ since the panel length is 8 feet. From this relationship it can be seen that the moments shown in Fig. 12.8 are those which give the required panel shears of Fig. 12.7. Since, in this instance, all the loads are applied directly to joints, the solution p_0 is uniformly zero and the sway moments of Fig. 12.8 provide the initial values to be relaxed by the operations A, B, C and D. In Table 12.6 a relaxation of every joint is shown on one line, and the corresponding carry-over effects are entered on the next. This does not imply that the joints are in fact unlocked simultaneously. It is assumed that each joint is relaxed separately, but the results are written on two lines for the purpose of saving space.

The two cycles of distribution shown give sufficient accuracy for many practical purposes, but further operations can be performed if greater accuracy is needed.

For a truss which lacks a horizontal axis of symmetry, the same approach can be used, but separate operations will be required for the top and bottom chords. If the loads are not applied directly to the joints

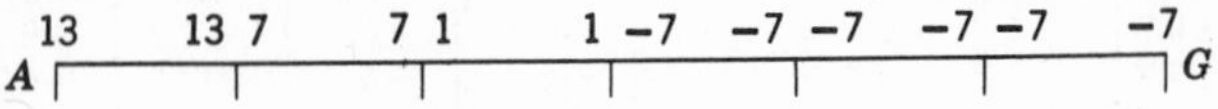

```
      13      13  7     7  1      1 -7    -7 -7    -7 -7     -7
  A ┌───────┬───────┬───────┬───────┬───────┬───────┐ G
```

Initial sway moments

Fig. 12.8

they cannot directly be divided between the top and bottom chords, as was done in Example 12.3, to obtain anti-symmetry.   However, the final analysis can be regarded as the superposition of two solutions.   The first serves to "transfer" the loads to the panel points, and the second is a solution similar to the above.

The use of group relaxations extends considerably the scope of the iteration technique.   In plane frames such as those of Examples 12.2 and 12.3, when only bending is considered, the nature of the group operations can be found readily.   For more complex frames these operations must be determined from the characteristics of the K matrix.   In extensive problems it is possible to use a relaxation technique based on matrix operations.

PROBLEMS

12.1. By the method of moment distribution solve Problem 11.6 for loading type (c).

12.2. By the method of moment distribution solve Problem 11.10.

12.3. Re-solve Problem 12.1 using group relaxations.   Take sidesway into account by using "no shear" operations.

12.4. Re-solve Problem 12.2 using suitable group relaxations in order to eliminate the necessity for solving simultaneous equations after the distribution process.

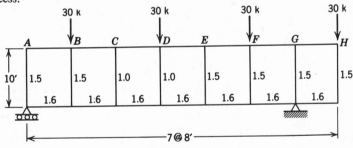

Fig. P12.5

12.5. Solve the vierendeel truss shown in Fig. P12.5 for the loads shown.   The numbers shown in the figure are proportional to the moments of inertia of the various members.   List the bending moments at the top and bottom of each column.

12.6. Figure P12.6 shows a vierendeel truss, the relative stiffnesses (I/l) of the members being indicated by the figures on the diagram.   The loading is applied through crossbeams, which join the truss at panel points.

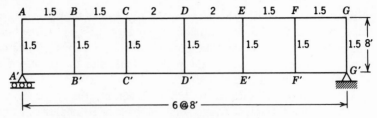

Fig. P12.6

Use the method of group relaxation to obtain an influence line for the moment at the top of the second vertical $M_{BB'}$.

CHAPTER 13

Stiffness Analysis
of a Single Member

When the ends of every member are completely fixed, any displacement of a joint implies a similar displacement of all the member ends attached to the joint. The action required to move the joint in a chosen direction is the sum of the actions required to move the member ends in that direction. The stiffness of the joint with respect to displacement in a given direction is, consequently, the sum of the relevant stiffness coefficients of the member ends adjacent to it, and for this reason the stiffness properties of an individual member will be studied as a preliminary to a study of frames of a general nature. Similar remarks apply to the initial out-of-balance values, since the initial value of a particular restraint action, P_0, is the sum of the corresponding end actions exerted by the joint upon the adjoining members.

13.1 END STIFFNESS

Consider a member AB, of any shape, cantilevered from A. The end B can then suffer six components of displacement. For the time being, these will be expressed in terms of the axes of the member at B. If one of these displacements, is imposed while the other five are inhibited, six component actions will, in general, be induced at B. Or, in other words, six end actions are associated with the required displacement. The same applies to the other displacements, and if all displacements are made simultaneously the values of the end actions will be given by

$$p_1 = k_{11}u_1 + k_{12}u_2 \cdots + k_{16}u_6$$

$$p_2 = k_{21}u_1 + k_{22}u_2 \cdots + k_{26}u_6$$

$$\vdots \qquad\qquad\qquad\qquad\qquad (13.1)$$

$$p_6 = k_{61}u_1 + k_{62}u_2 \cdots + k_{66}u_6$$

where k_{rs} is the action p_r induced at B by a unit displacement u_s, the other displacements being prevented.

Hence there are thirty-six stiffness coefficients relating the displacements at B to the actions induced at that end. If we let p_{BB} denote the matrix of end actions at B due to movements at B, we can write

$$p_{BB} = k_{BB}u_B \qquad\qquad (13.2)$$

and k_{BB} is the stiffness matrix at the end B.

The displacements at B will also cause end actions to be called into play at A, and these will be expressed by a further set of six equations, similar to equations 10.1 but with different coefficients. These can be written in matrix form

$$p_{AB} = k_{AB}u_B \qquad\qquad (13.3)$$

where p_{AB} implies actions at A due to displacements at B, and k_{AB} is a "carry-over" stiffness matrix.

If the same member is now cantilevered from B instead of A, it will be possible to make six displacements of the end A, which can be represented by a column matrix u_A. Using the member axes at A, we can express the actions induced at A by the equation

$$p_{AA} = k_{AA}u_A \qquad\qquad (13.4)$$

and those at B by

$$p_{BA} = k_{BA}u_A \qquad\qquad (13.5)$$

Suppose, now, that both ends are displaced at the same time. The total end actions induced at A and B will be

$$p_A = p_{AA} + p_{AB} = k_{AA}u_A + k_{AB}u_B$$

$$p_B = p_{BA} + p_{BB} = k_{BA}u_A + k_{BB}u_B$$

which can be written

$$\begin{bmatrix} p_A \\ \hline p_B \end{bmatrix} = \begin{bmatrix} k_{AA} & \vdots & k_{AB} \\ \hline k_{BA} & \vdots & k_{BB} \end{bmatrix} \begin{bmatrix} u_A \\ \hline u_B \end{bmatrix} \qquad\qquad (13.6)$$

This defines a stiffness matrix for this particular member which includes the direct stiffness coefficients for both ends and also the cross-coefficients which relate the displacements at one end to the actions induced at the other. It will be denoted by k^{AB} to signify the member to which it refers.

$$k^{AB} = \begin{bmatrix} k_{AA} & k_{AB} \\ \hline k_{BA} & k_{BB} \end{bmatrix} \tag{13.7}$$

In a general case the matrix k^{AB} will be of order (12 × 12), and the submatrices (6 × 6). In particular cases only a portion of the matrices may be relevant. For straight members which form part of a plane frame, end rotations in the xy plane and lateral end displacements are of paramount importance. These induce end couples and transverse end forces, and the relationships are given by submatrices of crder (2 × 2) in this case.

In general, the stiffness coefficients cannot be evaluated directly, but have to be obtained from the flexibility coefficients by inversion. This procedure is discussed in Section 13.4. However, in the special case in which the member is straight and in which only bending deformations are considered, the elementary differential equation of beam deflection can be used as a basis for finding k. The equation can be integrated either algebraically, or else graphically by the use of area-moment methods. In the following problem the former procedure will be followed.

Example 13.1 Figure 13.1 shows a homogeneous tapered beam of rectangular cross-section whose breadth and depth at A are half those at B. It is required to find the stiffness coefficients due to vertical and rotational displacements of A and B, when only bending deformations are taken into account.

Solution. If the origin of x is taken at O, and I_B is the moment of inertia at B, at any other section

$$I = I_B\left(\frac{x}{2L}\right)^4 = \left(\frac{I_B}{16L^4}\right)x^4$$

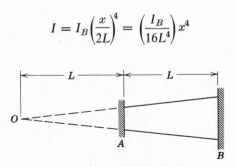

Fig. 13.1

With no applied loading, the beam differential equation is

$$\frac{d^2}{dx^2}\left(EI\frac{d^2y}{dx^2}\right) = 0 \tag{13.8}$$

whence, by integration,

$$-N^y = \frac{d}{dx}\left(EI\frac{d^2y}{dx^2}\right) = a_1 \tag{13.9}$$

$$M^z = \left(EI\frac{d^2y}{dx^2}\right) = a_1x + a_2 \tag{13.10}$$

$$\frac{M^z}{EI} = \left(\frac{d^2y}{dx^2}\right) = \frac{16L^4}{EI_B}(a_1x^{-3} + a_2x^{-4}) \tag{13.11}$$

$$\frac{dy}{dx} = \frac{16L^4}{EI_B}\left(\frac{-a_1}{2}x^{-2} - \frac{a_2}{3}x^{-3} + a_3\right) \tag{13.12}$$

$$y = \frac{16L^4}{EI_B}\left(\frac{+a_1}{2}x^{-1} + \frac{a_2}{6}x^{-2} + a_3x + a_4\right) \tag{13.13}$$

The stiffness coefficients can be found by specifying the appropriate end displacements, and then finding the integration constants $a_1 \ldots a_4$ from equations 13.12 and 13.13. When these constants are substituted, equations 13.9 and 13.10 give the shear force and bending moment at every section and consequently allow the end forces to be determined. These operations can be performed in groups if matrix methods are used.

The vertical displacement and rotation at A are denoted by u_{A2} and u_{A6} respectively. The corresponding displacements at B are called u_{B2} and u_{B6}. These four displacements are first expressed in terms of the integration constants a_1, a_2, a_3 and a_4, by the use of equations 13.12 and 13.13.

From (13.13), $u_{A2} = y_A = \frac{16L^4}{EI_B}\left(\frac{1}{2L}a_1 + \frac{1}{6L^2}a_2 + La_3 + a_4\right)$

from (13.12), $u_{A6} = \left.\frac{dy}{dx}\right)_A = \frac{16L^4}{EI_B}\left(\frac{-1}{2L^2}a_1 - \frac{1}{3L^3}a_2 + a_3\right)$

from (13.13), $u_{B2} = y_B = \frac{16L^4}{EI_B}\left(\frac{1}{4L}a_1 + \frac{1}{24L^2}a_2 + 2La_3 + a_4\right)$

from (13.12), $u_{B6} = \left.\frac{dy}{dx}\right)_B = \frac{16L^4}{EI_B}\left(\frac{-1}{8L^2}a_1 - \frac{1}{24L^3}a_2 + a_3\right)$

Since these are linear equations relating the end displacements to the integration constants, they can be expressed in matrix form

$$
\begin{bmatrix} u_{A2} \\ u_{A6} \\ u_{B2} \\ u_{B6} \end{bmatrix} = \frac{16L^4}{EI_B} \begin{bmatrix} \dfrac{1}{2L} & \dfrac{1}{6L^2} & L & 1 \\[2mm] \dfrac{-1}{2L^2} & \dfrac{-1}{3L^3} & 1 & 0 \\[2mm] \dfrac{1}{4L} & \dfrac{1}{24L^2} & 2L & 1 \\[2mm] \dfrac{-1}{8L^2} & \dfrac{-1}{24L^3} & 1 & 0 \end{bmatrix} \begin{bmatrix} a_1 \\ a_2 \\ a_3 \\ a_4 \end{bmatrix} \qquad (13.14)
$$

$$\text{or} \quad u = L_1 a$$

where L_1 is a matrix depending on the beam dimensions.

The end actions at A and B are denoted by p_{A2}, p_{A6}, p_{B2} and p_{B6}. By using equations 13.9 and 13.10, we can also express these as linear functions of the integration constants, in the same way as we did for the end displacements.

$$
\begin{bmatrix} p_{A2} \\ p_{A6} \\ p_{B2} \\ p_{B6} \end{bmatrix} = \begin{bmatrix} -N_A^y \\ -M_A^z \\ N_B^y \\ M_B^z \end{bmatrix} = \begin{bmatrix} 1 & 0 & 0 & 0 \\ -L & -1 & 0 & 0 \\ -1 & 0 & 0 & 0 \\ 2L & 1 & 0 & 0 \end{bmatrix} \begin{bmatrix} a_1 \\ a_2 \\ a_3 \\ a_4 \end{bmatrix} \qquad (13.15)
$$

$$\text{or} \quad p = L_2 a$$

The required relationship between p and u can now be obtained by eliminating a from equations 13.14 and 13.15.

From equation 13.14 $a = L_1^{-1} u$, and when substituted in equation 13.15 this gives

$$p = L_2 L_1^{-1} u = ku$$

so that $k = L_2 L_1^{-1}$.   Thus

$$
k = L_2 L_1^{-1} = \frac{EI_B}{16L^4} \left[\begin{array}{cc|cc} +56L & -16L^2 & -56L & +40L^2 \\ +16L^2 & +8L^3 & -16L^2 & +8L^3 \\ \hline -56L & -16L^2 & +56L & -40L^2 \\ +40L^2 & +8L^3 & -40L^2 & +32L^3 \end{array} \right] \qquad (13.16)
$$

This is in the form indicated in equation (13.7), the submatrices being of order (2×2) in this case since only two displacements are considered.

13.2 RELATIONSHIPS BETWEEN END STIFFNESSES

A system of displacements u_B will induce actions p_{BB} at B and another set p_{AB} at A, such that

$$p_{BB} = k_{BB}u_B$$

and $$p_{AB} = k_{AB}u_B$$

We note that actions p_{BB} are expressed in the axes at B, while actions p_{AB} are expressed in the axes at A. Furthermore, these are the only external actions upon the member so that the two sets form a system in equilibrium. Therefore, after transforming p_{BB} to the axes at A (giving $A_{AB}p_{BB}$), we can write

$$p_{AB} + A_{AB}p_{BB} = 0$$

whence $$p_{AB} = -A_{AB}p_{BB} \tag{13.17}$$

Therefore $$k_{AB}u_B = -A_{AB}k_{BB}u_B$$

and $$k_{AB} = -A_{AB}k_{BB} \tag{13.18}$$

In a similar manner it can be shown that

$$k_{BA} = -A_{BA}k_{AA} \tag{13.19}$$

Since $A_{BA} = A_{AB}^{-1}$ see equation (5.24), the transformation matrices can be eliminated from equations 13.18 and 13.19. This elimination leads to the relationship

$$k_{AA}k_{BA}^{-1} = k_{AB}k_{BB}^{-1} \tag{13.20}$$

The stiffness k_{AA} and k_{BB} are also related to one another. The relationship can be derived from the corresponding relationships between the flexibilities f_{AA} and f_{BB} based on equation 9.9 in Chapter 9. However, it is easier to make use of the fact that the complete matrix k^{AB} is symmetrical, as it must be by the reciprocal law. From this it follows that

$$-A_{AB}k_{BB} = (-A_{BA}k_{AA})^T$$
$$= -k_{AA}^T A_{BA}^T$$

and hence $$k_{BB} = A_{AB}^{-1}k_{AA}^T A_{BA}^T \tag{13.21}$$

But $A_{AB}^{-1} = A_{BA}$, and $k_{AA}^T = k_{AA}$ since the latter is a symmetrical matrix. Therefore equation 13.21 becomes

$$k_{BB} = A_{BA}k_{AA}A_{BA}^T \tag{13.22}$$

Not only is the matrix k^{AB} symmetrical, but, by virtue of the sign convention for actions and displacements, all the terms on the diagonal will be positive.

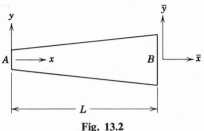

Fig. 13.2

In Example 13.1 all four stiffness matrices were derived directly. It can be shown that they obey the foregoing relationships. Suppose that only k_{AA} is known.

$$k_{AA} = \begin{bmatrix} 56L & 16L^2 \\ 16L^2 & 8L^3 \end{bmatrix}$$

A change of axes from A to B in this case requires only translation, with a shift of origin to the point $(L, 0, 0)$, see Fig. 13.2. With all rows and columns other than the second and sixth omitted, the axis translation matrix becomes

$$T = \begin{bmatrix} 1 & 0 \\ -X & 1 \end{bmatrix} = \begin{bmatrix} 1 & 0 \\ -L & 1 \end{bmatrix} = A_{BA}$$

Then

$$k_{BA} = -A_{BA}k_{AA} = \begin{bmatrix} -1 & 0 \\ L & -1 \end{bmatrix} \begin{bmatrix} 56L & 16L^2 \\ 16L^2 & 8L^3 \end{bmatrix} = \begin{bmatrix} -56L & -16L^2 \\ 40L^2 & 8L^3 \end{bmatrix}$$

$$k_{BB} = (-A_{BA})k_{AA}(-A_{BA}^T)$$

$$= k_{BA}(-A_{BA}^T) = \begin{bmatrix} -56L & -16L^2 \\ 40L^2 & 8L^3 \end{bmatrix} \begin{bmatrix} -1 & L \\ 0 & -1 \end{bmatrix} = \begin{bmatrix} 56L & -40L^2 \\ -40L^2 & 32L^3 \end{bmatrix}$$

$$k_{AB} = k_{AA}(-A_{BA}^T) = \begin{bmatrix} +56L & +16L^2 \\ +16L^2 & +8L^3 \end{bmatrix} \begin{bmatrix} -1 & L \\ 0 & -1 \end{bmatrix} = \begin{bmatrix} -56L & +40L^2 \\ -16L^2 & +8L^3 \end{bmatrix}$$

The last matrix, k_{AB}, could have been obtained by the transposition of k_{BA}. It will be seen that these values agree with those obtained directly in equation 13.16.

13.3 CHANGE OF AXES

Before the analysis of a frame can be undertaken, the stiffness coefficients for all the members meeting at a given joint must be stated in common

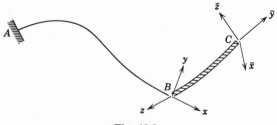

Fig. 13.3

axes in order that equilibrium relationships may be expressed. This will almost invariably necessitate an axis change for the stiffness of some members. A general axis change involving both translation and rotation will be considered.

It will be assumed that the end stiffness matrix, k_{BB}, at B (Fig. 13.3) in axes x, y, z, is known, and it is required to re-express this matrix in axes $\bar{x}$, $\bar{y}$, $\bar{z}$ at C. For convenience a rigid arm can be imagined to join B and C. Suppose that C suffers displacements u_C, and that the actions required to produce these are p_C. These are related by

$$p_C = k_{CC} u_C$$

and it is required to find the value of k_{CC}.

We proceed in the same way as we did in Section 7.1 for the transformation of the flexibility of a cantilever. The point C is given displacements u_C. The corresponding displacements of B are

$$u_B = A_{CB}^T u_C$$

and these give rise to actions p_B at B such that

$$p_B = k_{BB} u_B$$
$$ = k_{BB} A_{CB}^T u_C \tag{13.23}$$

Transforming these actions back to C we have finally,

$$p_C = A_{CB} p_B$$
$$ = A_{CB} k_{BB} A_{CB}^T u_C$$

from which we conclude that the stiffness k_{CC} is given by

$$k_{CC} = A_{CB} k_{BB} A_{CB}^T \tag{13.24}$$

This is a congruent transformation of exactly the same type as that which gives the ends stiffness at A in terms of that at B (equation 13.22). Taking into account equation 13.24 as well as the relationship derived

Fig. 13.4

in the last section, we can summarize the effect of axis change upon the stiffness characteristics of a member. We suppose that, for a member AB (Fig. 13.4), any one of the stiffness matrices is known, say k_{BB}. The first subscript can be changed from B to C, where B and C are at the same end of the member, by premultiplying by A_{CB}. If the first subscript is to be changed to D, where B and D are at opposite ends of the member, it is necessary to premultiply by $-A_{DB}$. In a similar way the second subscript is changed from B to C by postmultiplying by A_{CB}^{T}, B and C being at the same end. To change the second subscript from B to D, where these are at opposite ends, it is necessary to postmultiply by $-A_{DB}^{T}$.

It will be seen that all the relationships developed above can be written down immediately by using this rule. By means of a simple axis transformation, either the direct stiffness in any axes or the carry-over stiffness between one set of axes and another can be found from a known stiffness matrix provided the actions are deemed to be transmitted through the original member AB.

It is to be remembered that if the member CD (Fig. 13.4) is deformed by end actions, the set of actions applied at C statically equilibrate those at D. In other words, one set is, statically the negative of the other even though they may be expressed in different axes. Similarly end displacements are relative. Displacement of C means displacement relative to D. The same deformation would result from an equal and opposite displacement of D relative to C. Moreover, since the only elements which contribute to the deformation are those between A and B, the "rigid arms" AD and BC are irrelevant except that they serve to express the actions and displacements in different axes and consequently to change their appearance. It is interesting to observe that if C is any point joined to the end of a member AB by a rigid arm (Fig. 13.5), the stiffness of C in any chosen axes is the same whether C is joined to the end A or the end B. This result follows from the foregoing transformation rule, since to obtain

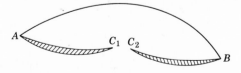

Fig. 13.5

the stiffness matrix k_{CC} we can start with any other stiffness matrix, k_{AB} for instance, and change it to k_{CC} by suitable axis transformations without reference to the position of the rigid arm. This can be appreciated physically by inserting both the arms AC_1 and BC_2. Deformation of the member AB is effected by applying equal and opposite actions at C_1 and C_2. Since the resulting displacements of C_1 and C_2 are also equal and opposite, the stiffness of C_1 will be the same as that of C_2.

13.4 STIFFNESS OF A MEMBER OF GENERAL SHAPE

In the general case, where deformations other than those due to bending must also be considered, the stiffness cannot be obtained from the differential equation of bending. Instead, the stiffness is found from the end flexibility. The flexibility matrix for the end B of a cantilever AB has been discussed in Chapter 6. Equation 6.5 provides, in an explicit form, the expression for the flexibility matrix f_{BB}. In terms of f_{BB} the displacements and actions at B are related by

$$u_B = f_{BB}p_B \tag{13.25}$$

In terms of the stiffness matrix k_{BB} the same actions and displacements are related by

$$p_B = k_{BB}u_B \tag{13.26}$$

and since f_{BB} and k_{BB} are square matrices it follows that

$$k_{BB} = f_{BB}^{-1} \tag{13.27}$$

This provides a means of evaluating the direct stiffness at either end. Once we have obtained one of the submatrices of k^{AB} (see equation 13.7), it is possible to find the others by transformations, since the various stiffness matrices are related to one another.

Example 13.2 Suppose that the elliptical beam (Fig. 13.6) of Example 6.3 is to be used as part of a frame which is to be analyzed by the stiffness method. The solution previously obtained (p. 104) constitutes the particular solution for the present analysis.

It is now required to find the direct stiffnesses at each end, k_{AA} and k_{BB},

Fig. 13.6

as well as the cross-stiffnesses k_{AB} and k_{BA}. The axes at A and B in which these stiffnesses must be expressed will depend upon the orientation of the member in the frame. For this example, it will be assumed that the required axes at A are parallel to those at B.

Solution. Since the flexibility matrix at B has already been determined, we obtain first the stiffness matrix k_{BB} by inversion of the flexibility matrix.

$$f_{BB} = \begin{bmatrix} 19317.2313 & -14205.5362 & 21528.6122 & -864.0293 & -2031.7258 & -402.6785 \\ -14205.5362 & 72725.1638 & -16456.3384 & 2165.1912 & 1547.2649 & 3310.7853 \\ 21528.6122 & -16456.3384 & 29659.0996 & -1088.8530 & -3408.8225 & -683.2356 \\ -864.0293 & 2165.1912 & -1088.8530 & 574.7193 & 110.4763 & -115.6055 \\ -2031.7258 & 1547.2649 & -3408.8225 & 110.4763 & 606.0416 & 89.4837 \\ -402.6785 & 3310.7853 & -683.2356 & -115.6055 & 89.4837 & 423.0267 \end{bmatrix}$$

and

$$k_{BB} = f_{BB}^{-1} = 10^{-3} \times \begin{bmatrix} 0.3807 & 0.0264 & -0.3579 & -0.1240 & -0.7372 & -0.3005 \\ 0.0264 & 0.0372 & -0.0125 & -0.1947 & 0.0093 & -0.3417 \\ -0.3579 & -0.0125 & 0.4421 & 0.1555 & 1.2537 & 0.2483 \\ -0.1240 & -0.1947 & 0.1555 & 3.0779 & 0.0268 & 2.4925 \\ -0.7372 & 0.0093 & 1.2537 & 0.0268 & 6.2100 & -0.0562 \\ -0.3005 & -0.3417 & 0.2483 & 2.4925 & -0.0562 & 5.8459 \end{bmatrix}$$

The matrix k_{BB} contains the whole of the stiffness characteristics of the member. The stiffness matrix k_{AA} is obtained purely by axis transformation without further reference to the geometry of the member itself. The change of axes from B to A is one of translation only in this case, and the transformation matrix is therefore

$$A_{AB} = T =$$

$$\begin{bmatrix} 1 & 0 & 0 & 0 & 0 & 0 \\ 0 & 1 & 0 & 0 & 0 & 0 \\ 0 & 0 & 1 & 0 & 0 & 0 \\ \hline 0 & Z & -Y & 1 & 0 & 0 \\ -Z & 0 & X & 0 & 1 & 0 \\ Y & -X & 0 & 0 & 0 & 1 \end{bmatrix} = \begin{bmatrix} 1 & 0 & 0 & 0 & 0 & 0 \\ 0 & 1 & 0 & 0 & 0 & 0 \\ 0 & 0 & 1 & 0 & 0 & 0 \\ \hline 0 & 25.00 & 0 & 1 & 0 & 0 \\ -25.00 & 0 & -15.00 & 0 & 1 & 0 \\ 0 & 15.00 & 0 & 0 & 0 & 1 \end{bmatrix}$$

For the purpose of calculation it is convenient to obtain one of the cross-stiffnesses first since the evaluation of k_{AA} involves two matrix multiplications, either one of which produces k_{AB} or k_{BA}. Accordingly we have

$$k_{AB} = -A_{AB}k_{BB}$$

$$= 10^{-3} \times \begin{bmatrix} -0.3807 & -0.0264 & 0.3579 & 0.1240 & 0.7372 & 0.3005 \\ -0.0264 & -0.0372 & 0.0125 & 0.1947 & -0.0093 & 0.3417 \\ 0.3579 & 0.0125 & -0.4421 & -0.1555 & -1.2537 & -0.2483 \\ -0.5370 & -0.7364 & 0.1564 & 1.7901 & -0.2602 & 6.0491 \\ 4.8869 & 0.4646 & -3.5694 & -0.7953 & -5.8341 & -3.7326 \\ -0.0961 & -0.2170 & -0.0612 & 0.4283 & -0.0838 & -0.7209 \end{bmatrix}$$

$k_{AA} = k_{AB}(-A_{AB}^T)$

$$= 10^{-3} \times \begin{bmatrix} 0.3807 & 0.0264 & -0.3579 & 0.5370 & -4.8869 & 0.0961 \\ 0.0264 & 0.0372 & -0.0125 & 0.7364 & -0.4646 & 0.2170 \\ -0.3579 & -0.0125 & 0.4421 & -0.1564 & 3.5694 & 0.0612 \\ 0.5370 & 0.7364 & -0.1564 & 16.6203 & -10.8196 & 4.9971 \\ -4.8869 & -0.4646 & 3.5694 & -10.8196 & 74.4649 & -3.2364 \\ 0.0961 & 0.2170 & 0.0612 & 4.9971 & -3.2364 & 3.9762 \end{bmatrix}$$

$k_{BA} = k_{BB}(A_{AB}^T)$

$$= 10^{-3} \times \begin{bmatrix} -0.3807 & -0.0264 & 0.3579 & -0.5370 & 4.8869 & -0.0961 \\ -0.0264 & -0.0372 & 0.0125 & -0.7364 & 0.4646 & -0.2170 \\ 0.3579 & 0.0125 & -0.4421 & 0.1564 & -3.5694 & -0.0612 \\ 0.1240 & 0.1947 & -0.1555 & 1.7901 & -0.7953 & 0.4283 \\ 0.7372 & -0.0093 & -1.2537 & -0.2602 & -5.8341 & -0.0838 \\ 0.3005 & 0.3417 & -0.2483 & 6.0491 & -3.7326 & -0.7209 \end{bmatrix}$$

An expression which is very frequently required is that for the end stiffness of a prismatic member. If shear deformations are ignored, this matrix can easily be written down from elementary principles. If shear deformations are to be taken into account, the stiffness is more easily derived by inversion of the flexibility matrix. If the member is called AB, the flexibility of the end B was derived on page 91. By inversion of this we obtain

$$k_{BB} = \begin{bmatrix} \dfrac{EA^x}{L} & 0 & 0 & 0 & 0 & 0 \\ 0 & \dfrac{12EI^z}{L^3}\phi_1 & 0 & 0 & 0 & \dfrac{-6EI^z}{L^2}\phi_1 \\ 0 & 0 & \dfrac{12EI^y}{L^3}\phi_2 & 0 & \dfrac{6EI^y}{L^2}\phi_2 & 0 \\ 0 & 0 & 0 & \dfrac{GI^x}{L} & 0 & 0 \\ 0 & 0 & \dfrac{6EI^y}{L^2}\phi_2 & 0 & \dfrac{4EI^y}{L}\psi_2 & 0 \\ 0 & \dfrac{-6EI^z}{L^2}\phi_1 & 0 & 0 & 0 & \dfrac{4EI^z}{L}\psi_1 \end{bmatrix} \tag{13.28}$$

where

$$\alpha_1 = \frac{6EI^z}{L^2 GA^y} \qquad \alpha_2 = \frac{6EI^y}{L^2 GA^z}$$

$$\phi_1 = \frac{1}{2\alpha_1 + 1} \qquad \phi_2 = \frac{1}{2\alpha_2 + 1}$$

$$\psi_1 = \frac{\alpha_1/2 + 1}{2\alpha_1 + 1} \qquad \psi_2 = \frac{\alpha_2/2 + 1}{2\alpha_2 + 1}$$

13.5 INTERNAL ACTIONS INDUCED BY END DISPLACEMENTS

When the end stiffnesses of a member are known it is possible to express the internal actions at any section along the member in terms of the displacement of one end, the other end being assumed fixed. Thus if, in the member AB, the end B is fixed and A suffers displacements u_A, the corresponding end actions at A are p_{AA}, and according to equation 13.4

$$p_{AA} = k_{AA}u_A$$

But the internal actions at any point Q due to end actions p_{AA} at A are

$$M_Q = m_{QA}p_{AA}$$

where m_{QA} is a matrix whose form is discussed in Chapter 6. Hence, in terms of the end displacements u_A, we have

$$M_Q = m_{QA}k_{AA}u_A \tag{13.29}$$

In a similar manner it can be shown that when A is fixed, the internal actions at Q due to displacement of B are

$$M_Q = m_{QB}k_{BB}u_B \tag{13.30}$$

For any displacements the internal actions at Q will be found by considering the displacements at the two ends consecutively and applying both equations 13.29 and 13.30.

13.6 PARTICULAR SOLUTION

With the member initially in a fixed-ended condition, the particular solution is itself the solution of a statically indeterminate structure. Essentially, this solution is always obtained by the methods of Part I. The details will depend upon the problem. The fixed-ended solutions for various load conditions when members are of simple geometrical shape are given in handbooks, and for frames composed of such members the stiffness method is thereby facilitated.

For a straight beam loaded normally to its axis, integration of the differential equation of bending will yield the required result, provided that bending is the only deformation to be considered. Such an integration process contains the same steps as the general flexibility method.

Example 13.2 The tapered beam of Example 13.1 is fixed at each end and sustains a uniformly distributed load of w pounds per foot normal to its axis.   If only bending is to be considered, find the bending moment at any point along the beam.

Solution.   As in the previous example, the point O (Fig.13.7) is taken as the origin, so that (see page 227) at any point

$$I = \left(\frac{I_B}{16L^4}\right)x^4$$

The differential equation of bending is

$$\frac{d^2}{dx^2}\left(EI\frac{d^2y}{dx^2}\right) = w$$

whence, by integration,

$$-N^y = \frac{d}{dx}\left(EI\frac{d^2y}{dx^2}\right) = wx + a_1$$

and

$$M^z = EI\frac{d^2y}{dx^2} = \frac{wx^2}{2} + a_1x + a_2 \tag{13.31}$$

In equation 13.31 the term $wx^2/2$ represents the particular solution and $(a_1x + a_2)$ represents the complementary solution, corresponding to redundants a_1 and a_2 acting at the origin (Fig. 13.8).   The redundants are determined by postulating zero slope and deflection at A relative to the support B.   In order to achieve this, the slope and deflection corresponding to the functions of equation 13.31 must be found.

$$\frac{d^2y}{dx^2} = \frac{1}{EI}\left(\frac{wx^2}{2} + a_1x + a_2\right)$$

$$= \frac{16L^4}{EI_B}\left(\frac{w}{2}x^{-2} + a_1x^{-3} + a_2x^{-4}\right)$$

$$\frac{dy}{dx} = \frac{16L^4}{EI_B}\left(-\frac{w}{2}x^{-1} - \frac{a_1}{2}x^{-2} - \frac{a_2}{3}x^{-3} + a_3\right) \tag{13.32}$$

$$y = \frac{16L^4}{EI_B}\left(-\frac{w}{2}\ln x + \frac{a_1}{2}x^{-1} + \frac{a_2}{6}x^{-2} + a_3x + a_4\right) \tag{13.33}$$

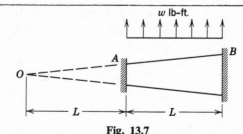

Fig. 13.7

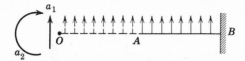

Fig. 13.8

The support conditions at B are specified by putting dy/dx and y equal to zero with $x = 2L$ in equations 13.32 and 13.33. Compatibility at A is expressed by putting dy/dx and y equal to zero with $x = L$. Solving the resulting equations for the four integration constants gives

$$a_1 = -1.4068wL$$

$$a_2 = 0.0952wL^2$$

$$a_3 = 0.1138w/L$$

$$a_4 = \tfrac{1}{2}\ln L + 0.431$$

The bending moment at any point is, therefore, from equation 13.31

$$M^z = \frac{w}{2}\,x^2 + 1.4068wLx + 0.0952wL^2$$

As an alternative to algebraic integration, area-moment methods can sometimes be employed. However, when the problem is simple enough for these methods the solution will generally be available in a handbook.

Where the problem assumes a more general character than that of Example 13.2, a more explicit use of the flexibility method can be adopted. A problem of this type is solved completely in Example 6.3 (elliptical beam).

13.7 INCOMPLETE END FIXITY

It sometimes happens that a member is not fully continuous at each end with the remainder of the structure. That is to say, the end connection is such that it is not possible to transmit all force components. For instance, a hinged joint will not transmit moment about the axis of the hinge.

Where the end connection is limited in this way, the end stiffness matrix of the member is correspondingly reduced in size. The end stiffness can be computed by the foregoing methods, the forces which are applied to the member end being limited to those which can actually be transmitted by the connection.

In the pin-connected member of Fig. 13.9a only the axial force is relevant at each end. It is easily seen that the stiffness matrix k_{BB} is of order (1×1) and is equal to EA^x/L.

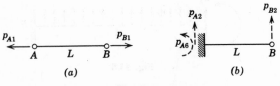

Fig. 13.9

The member of Fig. 13.9*b* is fixed at *A* and pinned at *B*. If the member is part of a plane frame, and if we neglect axial deformation, then the only relevant end forces are those shown. The stiffness matrix is obtained by successively imposing unit displacements u_{A2}, u_{A6} and u_{B2}, and calculating the three induced forces in each case.

The first operation ($u_{A2} = 1$) is indicated in Fig. 13.10*a*, and the resulting forces are the elements of the first column of the stiffness matrix. The other columns are obtained as shown in Figs. 13.10*b* and 13.10*c*. The end forces and displacements are then related by the following equations.

$$
\begin{bmatrix} p_{A2} \\ \\ p_{A6} \\ \\ p_{B2} \end{bmatrix} =
\begin{bmatrix}
\dfrac{3EI}{L^3} & \dfrac{3EI}{L^2} & -\dfrac{3EI}{L^3} \\[2mm]
\dfrac{3EI}{L^2} & \dfrac{3EI}{L} & -\dfrac{3EI}{L^2} \\[2mm]
-\dfrac{3EI}{L^3} & -\dfrac{3EI}{L^2} & \dfrac{3EI}{L^3}
\end{bmatrix}
\begin{bmatrix} u_{A2} \\ \\ u_{A6} \\ \\ u_{B2} \end{bmatrix}
\tag{13.34}
$$

For a beam of this kind fixed at *A* and pinned at *B*, and with $L = 6$ feet and $EI = 30 \times 10^3$ kip-ft^2, the member stiffness matrix is evaluated as follows

$$
\begin{bmatrix} k_{AA} & k_{AB} \\ \hline k_{BA} & k_{BB} \end{bmatrix} = 10^3
\begin{bmatrix}
0.42 & 2.5 & -0.42 \\
2.5 & 15 & -2.5 \\ \hline
-0.42 & -2.5 & 0.42
\end{bmatrix}
\tag{13.35}
$$

Even where the derivation of the stiffness matrix necessitates the determination of the flexibility as a preliminary step, the above procedure

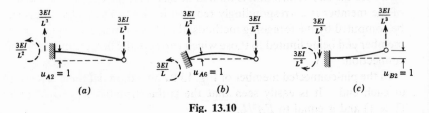

Fig. 13.10

can be used. The flexibility is computed only for the relevant terms. For the above problem the flexibility at B is

$$f_{BB} = L^3/3EI$$

hence $$k_{BB} = 3EI/L^3$$

The elements of the transformation matrix A_{AB} are the actions at A induced by a unit value of p_{B2} at B. Thus

$$A_{AB} = \begin{bmatrix} 1 \\ L \end{bmatrix}$$

From the relationship $k_{AA} = A_{AB}k_{BB}A_{AB}^T$ we then obtain the stiffness at end A.

$$k_{AA} = \begin{bmatrix} 1 \\ L \end{bmatrix} [3EI/L^3][1 \quad L] = \begin{bmatrix} \dfrac{3EI}{L^3} & \dfrac{3EI}{L^2} \\ \dfrac{3EI}{L^2} & \dfrac{3EI}{L} \end{bmatrix}$$

The cross-stiffnesses are obtained in a similar manner.

It may happen that the member stiffness is known for the case where the ends are fully continuous. The stiffness for incomplete end fixity can then be derived from this by a simple modification. The above problem will be used as an illustration. For a prismatic beam in a plane frame, the fully fixed-ended stiffness was given in equation 11.2. From this we obtain, for the values $L = 6$ and $EI = 30 \times 10^3$, the following relationship

$$\begin{bmatrix} p_{A2} \\ p_{A6} \\ \hline p_{B2} \\ p_{B6} \end{bmatrix} = 10^3 \begin{bmatrix} 1.67 & 5 & -1.67 & 5 \\ 5 & 20 & -5 & 10 \\ \hline -1.67 & -5 & 1.67 & -5 \\ 5 & 10 & -5 & 20 \end{bmatrix} \begin{bmatrix} u_{A2} \\ u_{A6} \\ \hline u_{B2} \\ u_{B6} \end{bmatrix} \qquad (13.36)$$

If we now decide to make the member pin-ended at B we must put $p_{B6} = 0$. The last equation of 13.36 gives u_{B6} in terms of the other three displacements

$$0 = 5u_{A2} + 10u_{A6} - 5u_{B2} + 20u_{B6}$$

This equation can be used to eliminate u_{B6} from the first three equations. In effect we divide through the last row of equation 13.36 by the diagonal element ($= 20$) and use the resulting equation to eliminate the last column of the matrix. This gives

$$\begin{bmatrix} p_{A2} \\ \hline p_{A6} \\ \hline p_{B2} \end{bmatrix} = 10^3 \begin{bmatrix} 0.42 & 2.5 & \vdots & -0.42 \\ 2.5 & 15 & \vdots & -2.5 \\ \hline -0.42 & -2.5 & \vdots & 0.42 \end{bmatrix} \begin{bmatrix} u_{A2} \\ \hline u_{A6} \\ \hline u_{B2} \end{bmatrix}$$

which agrees with the previous result.

Where more than one end action is reduced to zero the process is repeated for each articulation. The procedure is simply that of Gauss-Jordan elimination (see Appendix, page 296).

Alternatively we can describe the process in matrix notation. If the end forces at A and B are arranged so that the ones to be set to zero are stated last, we have

$$\begin{bmatrix} p_1 \\ --- \\ 0 \end{bmatrix} = \begin{bmatrix} k_{11} & \vdots & k_{12} \\ ----- & \vdots & ----- \\ k_{21} & \vdots & k_{22} \end{bmatrix} \begin{bmatrix} u_1 \\ --- \\ u_2 \end{bmatrix}$$

where the p values are subdivided not into those at A and those at B, but into those which can be applied to the member and those which cannot. Then by multiplying out the right-hand side we obtain

$$p_1 = k_{11}u_1 + k_{12}u_2$$
$$0 = k_{21}u_1 + k_{22}u_2 \tag{13.37}$$

From the second of 13.37

$$u_2 = -k_{22}^{-1}k_{21}u_1$$

and when this is substituted into the first of 13.37 we obtain

$$p_1 = k_{11}u_1 - k_{12}k_{22}^{-1}k_{21}u_1$$

or

$$p_1 = (k_{11} - k_{12}k_{22}^{-1}k_{21})u_1 \tag{13.38}$$

The term in brackets is thus the reduced stiffness matrix, which is required.

PROBLEMS

13.1. Find the end stiffness and carry-over stiffness of a member which is pinned at each end. The length is 16 feet, the area of cross-sections is 2.7 square inches and $E = 16 \times 10^3$ ksi.

13.2. The bar in Fig. P13.2 has the same dimensions as that in Problem 13.1. It is part of a pin-jointed frame. Restraints p_1 and p_2 are exerted on the joint B

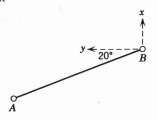

Fig. P13.2

in the directions x and y as shown. Find the restraint forces induced by displacements u_1 and u_2 respectively of the joint B in the x and y directions, while A remains stationary. Hence express the relationship between $\{p_1 \ p_2\}$ and $\{u_1 \ u_2\}$ in the form of a stiffness matrix.

13.3. A member of a plane frame is rigidly attached to other members at each end. The length of the member is 18 feet; $E = 5 \times 10^3$ ksi and $I = 0.04$ ft.^{4}. Find the end stiffness matrices and the cross-stiffness matrices for this member. Neglect deformation due to shear and axial force. Express the answer in units of kips and feet.

13.4. The member AB of Fig. P13.4 has the dimensions given in Problem 13.3, where the end stiffnesses were computed. Re-express the end stiffness of the member in the axes shown in Figs. P13.4a, b and c respectively. First assume that the axial deformations of the member are zero; then assume finite deformations with $A = 0.5$ square feet.

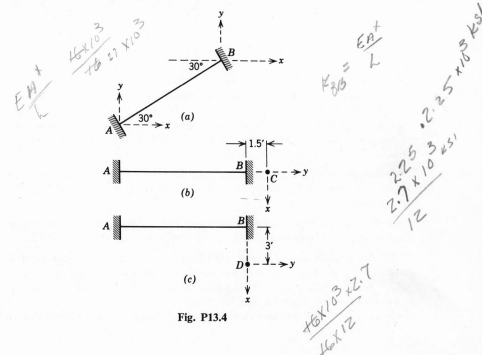

Fig. P13.4

13.5. A member AB of the same size as that in Problem 13.3 is used in a plane frame. It is rigidly connected to the other members of the frame at A, but at B it is connected to the other members through a pin joint. Compute the end stiffnesses and cross-stiffnesses.

13.6. PQ is a straight tapered beam of rectangular section and is 25 feet long. The depth varies from 20 inches at P to 10 inches at Q. The width is constant at 10 inches. The member is part of a three-dimensional frame and is fully continuous at both ends. Find the stiffness matrix at the end Q in terms of the shear modulus G. Take $E = 2.3G$ and neglect deformation due to shear force. Indicate the transformation required to obtain the stiffness at end P and the cross-stiffnesses. Evaluate one of the transformation matrices.

13.7. The circular girder $ACDEB$ of Fig. P13.7 lies in the horizontal plane. The cross-section is rectangular, the width being 1 foot and the depth 2 feet. The radius of the circle is 30 feet.

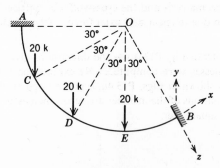

Fig. P13.7

The beam supports vertical loads at C, D and E as shown. Compute the end stiffnesses at A and B in member axes, and also the cross-stiffnesses. Assume that the member is part of a three-dimensional structure, so that each stiffness matrix is of order (6×6). Find also the fixed-end reactions on the beam due to the given loading. Take $E = 2.3$, $G = 1$, and neglect deformation due to shear.

13.8. Re-solve Problem 13.7 with the beam fully fixed at A but attached to the adjacent structure at B through a universal joint which permits all rotations but no translation.

13.9. For the helical girder of Problem 6.4 find the stiffness matrix for the end B. Express this stiffness in axes such that y is vertical and z is radially inwards.

13.10. The helical girder of Problems 6.4 and 13.9 carries a uniformly distributed load of 1 kip per foot length of the member. The load acts vertically on a helix 9 inches outside the centroidal axis of the beam. In plan the line of loading is a circle of radius 8 feet 9 inches.

Find the fixed-end reactions due to this load. Express these end actions in axes such that at B the y axis is vertical and the z axis radially inwards, while the axes at A are parallel to those at B.

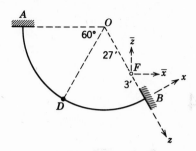

Fig. P13.11

13.11. The circular beam of Fig. P13.11 has the same dimensions as that of Fig. P13.7. Express the stiffness of the end B in the axes at F as shown. The beam lies in the plane xz which is the same as the plane $\bar{x}\bar{z}$. If the joint F undergoes displacements given by the vector

$$\{0.025 \quad 0.050 \quad -0.008 \quad -0.005 \quad 0.001 \quad 0.003\}$$

find the stress-resultants induced at the section D by these end displacements. Take $E = 2.3 \times 10^6$ ksf.

CHAPTER 14

Stiffness of a Frame in Terms of Unassembled Members

14.1 FRAME STIFFNESS

Just as the flexibility of a frame can be expressed in terms of the flexibility of its various components, so the stiffness of a frame can similarly be expressed in terms of the stiffness of its components. As we should expect, it is possible to express the frame stiffness in a form exactly analagous to the one previously derived for frame flexibility. The derivation could in fact be carried out in an exactly similar manner. To do so, however, would be to overlook several simplifications which are inherent in the stiffness method.

In the flexibility method, the application of a redundant force might well cause deformation to every member in the frame. In the stiffness method, displacement of a node point will cause deformation only of those members connected to the node. Moreover, the restraints are almost invariably grouped as orthogonal components at the node points. For this reason it is convenient to deal with all restraints at one node as a group rather than dealing with them individually. We shall first examine a typical member PQ and consider the contribution which this member makes to the stiffness of the whole frame.

Deformation of PQ occurs only as a result of displacement either of P or of Q; therefore we need discuss only these two joints of the frame. The node points at which the restraints are grouped need not necessarily

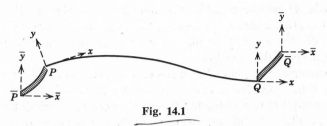

Fig. 14.1

coincide with the ends of the member. The nodes will be denoted by $\bar{P}$ and $\bar{Q}$, and for generality it will be assumed that these points are not identical with the member ends P and Q (Fig. 14.1).

We suppose that the member stiffness k_Q is known at the end Q. From this we can easily derive the stiffness of the member expressed in the axes at $\bar{P}$ and $\bar{Q}$. We require the stiffness at $\bar{P}$, the stiffness at $\bar{Q}$ and the cross-stiffness between these points. We know from Chapter 13 that these stiffnesses are obtained by transformations of the following form:

$$k_{\bar{Q}\bar{Q}} = A_{\bar{Q}Q}k_Q A_{\bar{Q}Q}^T$$
$$k_{\bar{P}\bar{P}} = A_{\bar{P}Q}k_Q A_{\bar{P}Q}^T$$
$$k_{\bar{P}\bar{Q}} = -A_{\bar{P}Q}k_Q A_{\bar{Q}Q}^T$$
$$k_{\bar{Q}\bar{P}} = -A_{\bar{Q}Q}k_Q A_{\bar{P}Q}^T$$

(14.1)

The size of the member stiffness matrix will depend on the number of force components which it is capable of exerting on the joint or node. For example, a pin-ended member can exert only one component, namely a force in the direction PQ. Consequently the stiffness matrix for such a member is of order (1×1).

On the other hand, the number of restraints at a node will depend on the type and orientation of *all* members meeting at the node. Thus, at a node in a planar pin-jointed frame the restraints will usually be required to resist forces in both the x and y directions, and two restraints will be needed. If two or more of the members are rigidly connected, so that moments may be developed at their ends, a moment restraint will also be required. Hence the number of restraints at a node may be greater than the number of force components exerted by a particular member joined to that node. In other words, the size of the node stiffness matrix may be greater than that of any one of the members joined thereto. In such a case the transformation matrix A referred to in equations 14.1 will not be square.

The significance of the transformation matrix A^T may be appreciated by analogy with the corresponding matrix B which was developed in the flexibility analysis (Chapter 8). At a node C the number of columns in the matrix A^T will be equal to the number of restraints at C. If one restraint is given a unit displacement, the elements in the corresponding column of A^T, for a particular member, represent the relevant end displacements of that member.

For example, the pin-ended member CD (Fig. 14.2) has a (1×1) stiffness EA/L, only forces and displacements along CD being relevant. The joint requires two restraints, P_1 and P_2, since the member forces are not all parallel. A unit displacement of P_1 will produce an axial displacement at the end of CD equal to $\cos \theta$. Similarly a unit displacement of P_2 will cause a member end displacement of $\sin \theta$. For the member CD the matrix A^T will thus take the form [$\cos \theta$ $\sin \theta$]. When the member stiffness is re-expressed in joint axes it will have the form

$$AkA^T = \begin{bmatrix} \cos \theta \\ \sin \theta \end{bmatrix} [EA/L][\cos \theta \quad \sin \theta]$$

$$= \frac{EA}{L} \begin{bmatrix} \cos^2 \theta & \cos \theta \sin \theta \\ \sin \theta \cos \theta & \sin^2 \theta \end{bmatrix}$$

It will be seen that irrespective of the size of the member stiffness matrix, its size after transformation to node axes will be that of the node stiffness.

The transformations referred to in equations 14.1 are of this type. After the transformation, the four matrices k_{QQ}, k_{PP}, k_{PQ} and k_{QP} may be regarded as submatrices of k^{PQ}. Thus

$$k^{PQ} = \begin{bmatrix} k_{PP} & k_{PQ} \\ k^{QP} & k_{QQ} \end{bmatrix}$$

In the complete frame stiffness matrix, the member PQ will contribute the four submatrices which are submatrices of k^{PQ}. The location of these submatrices will depend on where the node points $\bar{P}$, $\bar{Q}$ occur in the sequence of numbering throughout the frame (Fig. 14.3).

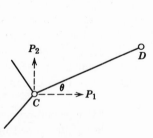

Fig. 14.2

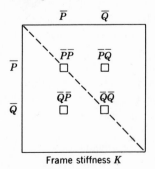

Frame stiffness K

Fig. 14.3

In a similar manner each other member of the frame contributes four submatrices of the total frame stiffness matrix.   Insofar as there are other members connected to the node $\bar{P}$, the on-diagonal submatrix $k_{\bar{P}\bar{P}}$ will receive further contribution from such members.   Hence finally the term $K_{\bar{P}\bar{P}}$ will be $\sum k_{\bar{P}\bar{P}}$, namely the summation of the stiffness of the adjacent members each expressed in the joint axes.   On the other hand, off-diagonal matrices such as $K_{\bar{P}\bar{Q}}$ will receive only one contribution, namely that from the member joining $\bar{P}$ to $\bar{Q}$ (except in the unlikely event of two separate members spanning between the same two nodes).

The size of the frame K is equal to the number of restraints imposed on the whole frame.

14.2   PARTICULAR SOLUTION

The restraint displacements are determined from equilibrium equations (one for each restraint) and these take the form

$$\underset{(n\times l)}{P_0} + \underset{(n\times n)}{K}\ \underset{(n\times l)}{u} = \underset{(n\times l)}{0}$$

where n is the number of restraints in the frame, and l is the number of loading conditions.

If there is only one load condition, P_0 is a column vector containing the initial values of the restraints when the loads are applied to the fully restrained frame.   If there are a number of load conditions, P_0 contains a corresponding number of columns.

It is convenient to divide P_0 into submatrices, one for each joint.   The submatrix $P_{\bar{Q}0}$ contains initial restraint values at joint $\bar{Q}$.   It has as many rows as there are restraints at $\bar{Q}$.   The number of columns corresponds to the number of different load conditions considered.   In this regard it should be remembered that a particular solution can arise as a result of temperature change and lack of fit.   The restraint forces called into play by such effects will constitute additional columns of the matrix P_0.

If loads are applied to the member PQ, we first find the fixed-end reactions.   The forces exerted by the joint *on the member* are denoted by P_{P0} and P_{Q0} respectively.   It is convenient to deal with all load cases for PQ before considering other members.   These forces are then transformed to joint axes, $A_{\bar{P}P}P_{P0}$ and $A_{\bar{Q}Q}P_{Q0}$ respectively.   These are then the contributions from this particular member to the matrices $P_{\bar{P}0}$ and $P_{\bar{Q}0}$.   The matrix $P_{\bar{Q}0}$ will, of course, receive further contributions from other members fixed to joint $\bar{Q}$ provided such members are loaded.

After the loading on all members has been dealt with in this way, we must consider loads applied directly to the joints.   If loads are applied

directly to joint $\bar{Q}$, for instance, the restraints needed to *resist* these loads will constitute the value to be added into matrix $P_{\bar{Q}0}$.

14.3 COMPLETE SOLUTION

The joint displacements are now found by solving the equilibrium equations $P_0 + Ku = 0$. The solution $u \; (= -K^{-1}P_0)$ contains one column for each load condition considered.

We are now in a position to find the total end actions for every member. Consider the end Q of member PQ as typical. The forces acting on the member end in the particular solution were calculated and denoted by P_{Q0} (these are in member axes). To this we must add the forces induced by the displacements of joints $\bar{P}$ and $\bar{Q}$.

The known displacements of joint $\bar{Q}$ are transferred to $Q \; (= A_{\bar{Q}Q}^T u_{\bar{Q}})$ and the corresponding member forces then computed. The forces are $k_{QQ}A_{\bar{Q}Q}^T u_{\bar{Q}}$. Similarly, the displacements of $\bar{P}$ give rise to forces $k_{QQ}(-A_{\bar{P}Q}^T)u_{\bar{P}}$ acting at Q.

The total end forces at Q are therefore given by

$$p_Q = p_{Q0} + [k_{QQ}A_{\bar{Q}Q}^T u_{\bar{Q}} + k_{QQ}(-A_{\bar{P}Q}^T)u_{\bar{P}}]$$

$$= p_{Q0} + k_{QQ}[A_{\bar{Q}Q}^T \quad -A_{\bar{P}Q}^T]\begin{bmatrix} u_{\bar{Q}} \\ u_{\bar{P}} \end{bmatrix} \tag{14.2}$$

Similarly the total end forces at the end P will be given by

$$p_P = p_{P0} + k_{PP}[-A_{\bar{Q}P}^T \quad A_{\bar{P}P}^T]\begin{bmatrix} u_{\bar{Q}} \\ u_{\bar{P}} \end{bmatrix} \tag{14.3}$$

The size of matrices $A_{\bar{Q}Q}^T$ and $A_{\bar{P}Q}^T$ was discussed in Section 14.1.

Alternatively, we can first calculate the total end actions at $\bar{P}$ and $\bar{Q}$ in *joint axes*. The contributions of the particular solution have already been computed, $\{p_{\bar{P}0} \quad p_{\bar{Q}0}\}$. The contributions of the complementary solution are given by the matrix product

$$\begin{bmatrix} k_{\bar{P}\bar{P}} & k_{\bar{P}\bar{Q}} \\ k_{\bar{Q}\bar{P}} & k_{\bar{Q}\bar{Q}} \end{bmatrix}\begin{bmatrix} u_{\bar{P}} \\ u_{\bar{Q}} \end{bmatrix}$$

The submatrices $k_{\bar{P}\bar{P}}$ and so on are expressed in joint axes and their sizes are determined by the number of restraints at the joint.

The final end actions (in joint axes) are thus

$$\begin{bmatrix} p_{\bar{P}} \\ p_{\bar{Q}} \end{bmatrix} = \begin{bmatrix} p_{\bar{P}0} \\ p_{\bar{Q}0} \end{bmatrix} + \begin{bmatrix} k_{\bar{P}\bar{P}} & k_{\bar{P}\bar{Q}} \\ k_{\bar{Q}\bar{P}} & k_{\bar{Q}\bar{Q}} \end{bmatrix}\begin{bmatrix} u_{\bar{P}} \\ u_{\bar{Q}} \end{bmatrix} \tag{14.4}$$

All the quantities on the R.H.S. of equation 14.4 have already been evaluated.   If required, p_P and p_Q can be transformed to member axes, but this is frequently not necessary.

The foregoing theory will be illustrated by means of a small frame of a fairly general character.   The members are chosen so that the necessary preliminary calculations have been performed in previous chapters.

Example 14.1   Figure 14.4 shows a frame which is built up mainly from elliptical elements identical in geometrical form with that analyzed in

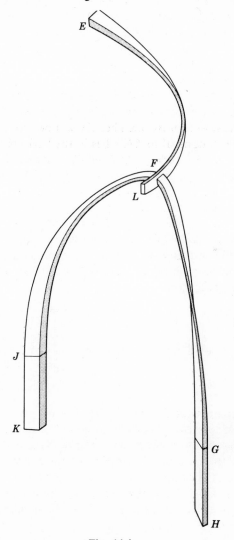

Fig. 14.4

Example 6.3. Stiffness properties of this member were determined in Example 13.2. The present frame has two such members, *JF* and *GF*, standing in vertical planes at an angle of 120° to one another. At *G* and *J* these members are joined to vertical prismatic columns 10 feet long which have a rectangular section 20 inches by 10 inches. The member *EF* again has the same elliptical form as *JF* and *GF*, but *EF* lies in a horizontal plane and the tangent at *F* bisects the angle between *JF* and *GF*. A 2-foot cantilever *FL* carries a 5-kip vertical load at its end *L*. The member *EF* carries two loads each of 5 kips situated in the same position as the loads in Example 6.3. The other members of the frame are not loaded. The support joints *H*, *K* and *E* are completely fixed.

Only the relative values of *E* and *G* are of significance, and it will therefore be assumed that $G = 1$ and $E = 2.5$.

Solution. (i) RESTRAINTS. Six restraints are required at each end of the joints *F*, *G* and *J*. The displacements of these restraints will be grouped into (6×1) matrices denoted by u_F, u_G and u_J respectively.

At *F* the natural axes of the member *EF* will be used as the axes of the joint, so that x is tangential to *EF*, z lies in the horizontal plane, and y is vertically upwards (Fig. 14.5a). At *J* and *G*, joint axes chosen as shown in Figs. 14.5b and c. The stiffness matrices k_{JJ}^F and k_{GG}^F are then identical with the stiffness matrix k_{AA}^B determined in Example 13.2.

The joint axes are indicated by $\bar{x}$, $\bar{y}$, $\bar{z}$ in Figs. 14.5a, b and c.

The appearance of the frame stiffness matrix (i.e., the equilibrium equations from which the joint displacements will be determined) will be governed by the sequence in which we arrange the moving joints. Suppose we take them in the order *F*, *G* and *J*. The final equations will then have the appearance

$$\begin{bmatrix} P_{F0} \\ \hline P_{G0} \\ \hline P_{J0} \end{bmatrix} + \begin{bmatrix} K_{FF} & K_{FG} & K_{FJ} \\ \hline K_{GF} & K_{GG} & K_{GJ} \\ \hline K_{JF} & K_{JG} & K_{JJ} \end{bmatrix} \begin{bmatrix} u_F \\ \hline u_G \\ \hline u_J \end{bmatrix} = \begin{bmatrix} 0 \\ \hline 0 \\ \hline 0 \end{bmatrix} \qquad (14.5)$$

where the submatrices of *K* are of order (6×6).

We now have to evaluate the submatrices of *K* and of P_0.

(ii) END STIFFNESSES OF MEMBERS. The frame is built up of members which have either the form of *AB* (Fig. 14.6a) or the form of *CD* (Fig. 14.6b). The axes shown for the elliptical member *AB* are those which were used in Example 13.2. The axes at *B* are the member axes, and the axes at *A* are parallel to those at *B*. The stiffness matrices k_{BB} and k_{AA} are known (see pages 235, 236).

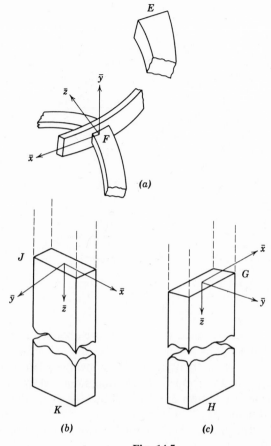

Fig. 14.5

An expression for the end stiffness, k_{DD}^C, of a prismatic member such as CD was derived in Section 13.4. By inserting the numerical values of this problem we obtain

$$k_{DD}^C = \begin{bmatrix} 0.3472 & \cdot & \cdot & \cdot & \cdot & \cdot \\ \cdot & 0.0024 & \cdot & \cdot & \cdot & -0.0121 \\ \cdot & \cdot & 0.0096 & \cdot & 0.0482 & \cdot \\ \cdot & \cdot & \cdot & 0.0221 & \cdot & \cdot \\ \cdot & \cdot & 0.0482 & \cdot & 0.3125 & \cdot \\ \cdot & -0.0121 & \cdot & \cdot & \cdot & 0.0804 \end{bmatrix}$$

This matrix is in terms of the axes of the member as shown in Fig. 14.6b.

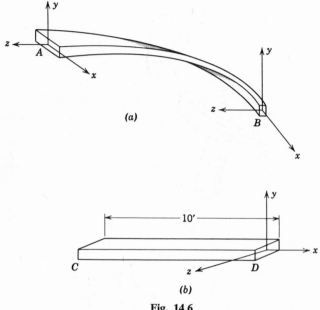

(a)

(b)

Fig. 14.6

The stiffness matrices required in the frame are obtained from the basic properties of AB and CD by means of the necessary axis transformations. This may be thought of as orienting the basic members into the position they are to occupy in the frame. In the diagrams below, the axes in which the stiffnesses are known are denoted by x, y, z and the joint axes, where these are different, by $\bar{x}$, $\bar{y}$, $\bar{z}$.

Member GH. The transformation matrix from axes x, y, z to axes $\bar{x}$, $\bar{y}$, $\bar{z}$ (Fig. 14.7) is $A_{\bar{G}G}^{H}$, where

$$
A_{\bar{G}G}^{H} = \begin{bmatrix}
0 & 0 & +1 & 0 & 0 & 0 \\
0 & +1 & 0 & 0 & 0 & 0 \\
-1 & 0 & 0 & 0 & 0 & 0 \\
\hline
0 & 0 & 0 & 0 & 0 & +1 \\
0 & 0 & 0 & 0 & +1 & 0 \\
0 & 0 & 0 & -1 & 0 & 0
\end{bmatrix}
$$

Then
$$
k_{\bar{G}G}^{H} = (A_{\bar{G}G}^{H}) k_{DD}^{C} (A_{\bar{G}G}^{H})^{T}
$$

This value of $k_{\bar{G}G}^{H}$ is now entered into the square K_{GG} of equations 14.5. It is the contribution of member GH to this joint stiffness.

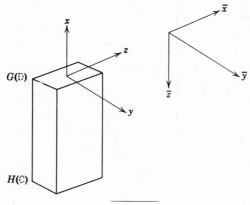

Fig. 14.7

Since H is an immovable joint, no further stiffness properties are required for GH.

Member JK. From a consideration of the axes shown in Figs. 14.5b and c we see that

$$k_{JJ}^K = k_{GG}^H$$

This value of k_{JJ}^K is entered into the submatrix K_{JJ} of equations 14.5.

Member JF. At J, which is to be compared with end A of member AB (Fig. 14.6a), the joint axes have been so chosen that they correspond to the axes at A in AB. For this reason no axis change is required at J.

At F, which corresponds to end B of member AB, a change of axes is required (Fig. 14.8). Axes x, y, $\bar{x}$ and $\bar{z}$ lie in the horizontal plane, while $\bar{y}$ and z are vertical. The matrix $A'_{\bar{F}F}$ is

$$A'_{\bar{F}F} = \begin{bmatrix} -0.5000 & +0.8660 & 0 & 0 & 0 & 0 \\ 0 & 0 & -1 & 0 & 0 & 0 \\ -0.8660 & -0.5000 & 0 & 0 & 0 & 0 \\ 0 & 0 & 0 & -0.5000 & +0.8660 & 0 \\ 0 & 0 & 0 & 0 & 0 & -1 \\ 0 & 0 & 0 & -0.8660 & -0.5000 & 0 \end{bmatrix}$$

We then have

$$k_{JJ}^F = k_{AA}^B$$
$$k_{FF}^J = (A'_{\bar{F}F})k_{BB}^A(A'_{\bar{F}F})^T$$
$$k_{FJ} = (A'_{\bar{F}F})k_{BA}$$
$$k_{JF} = k_{AB}(A'_{\bar{F}F})^T$$

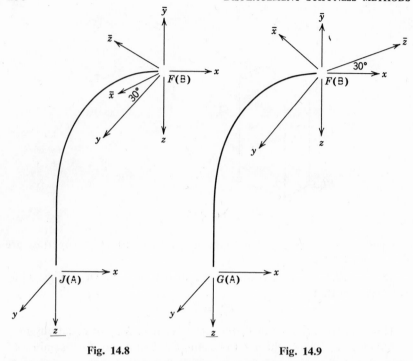

Fig. 14.8   Fig. 14.9

When these four matrices have been computed they are entered into submatrices K_{JJ}, K_{FF}, K_{FJ} and K_{JF} respectively of equations 14.5.

Member GF. Again, *GF* is to be compared with member *AB*. At *G* no axis change is required. At *F* a change is required. The axes x, y, $\bar{x}$ and $\bar{z}$ (Fig. 14.9) lie in the horizontal plane, while $\bar{y}$ and z are vertical. The matrix $A_{\bar{F}F}^{G}$ is

$$A_{\bar{F}F}^{G} = \begin{bmatrix} -0.5000 & -0.8660 & 0 & 0 & 0 & 0 \\ 0 & 0 & -1 & 0 & 0 & 0 \\ +0.8660 & -0.5000 & 0 & 0 & 0 & 0 \\ \hline 0 & 0 & 0 & -0.5000 & -0.8660 & 0 \\ 0 & 0 & 0 & 0 & 0 & -1 \\ 0 & 0 & 0 & +0.8660 & -0.5000 & 0 \end{bmatrix}$$

We then have

$$k_{GG}^{F} = k_{AA}^{B}$$
$$k_{FF}^{G} = (A_{\bar{F}F}^{G})k_{BB}^{A}(A_{\bar{F}F}^{G})^{T}$$
$$k_{FG} = (A_{\bar{F}F}^{G})k_{BA}$$
$$k_{GF} = k_{AB}(A_{\bar{F}F}^{G})^{T}$$

When these matrices have been computed they are entered into sub-matrices K_{GG}, K_{FF}, K_{FG} and K_{GF} respectively of equations 14.5.

Member EF. This member is to be compared with member *AB*. The axes at *F* have been chosen to correspond with those at *B* so that no change is required. We have

$$k_{FF}^E = k_{BB}^A$$

This value of k_{FF}^E is entered into submatrix K_{FF} of equations 14.5.

Since *E* is an immovable joint, no further stiffness properties are required for *EF*.

It will be observed that the submatrices of the frame *K* which are on the diagonal have received contributions from each member meeting at the relevant joint. Off-diagonal submatrices receive a contribution from one member only. The submatrices K_{GJ} and K_{JG} remain zero since there is no member *GJ*.

(iii) INITIAL END ACTIONS. The initial end actions are obtained from the particular solution. The only loaded member is *EF*. The particular solution for this member, with both ends fixed, was evaluated in Example 6.3. Table 6.4 shows the values of the internal actions at various points along the member. The top row of Table 6.4 gives the values of the internal actions at *B*, which are identical with the end actions applied to the member *FE* by the joint *F* in the problem. Three of the six actions are indicated in Fig. 14.10. The six actions are denoted by p_{F0}^E, and from Table 6.4 we have

$$p_{F0}^E = \begin{bmatrix} -0.3568 \\ 3.3701 \\ 0.9074 \\ -4.3855 \\ 2.2934 \\ -21.4651 \end{bmatrix}$$

This value of p_{F0}^E is entered into submatrix P_{F0} of equations 14.5.

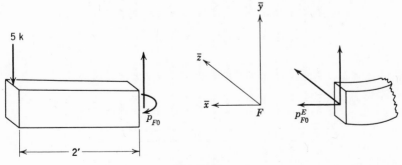

Fig. 14.10

$$
\begin{Bmatrix}
-0.3568 \\ 8.3701 \\ 0.9074 \\ -4.3855 \\ 2.2934 \\ -11.4651 \\ 0 \\ 0 \\ 0 \\ 0 \\ 0 \\ 0 \\ 0 \\ 0 \\ 0 \\ 0 \\ 0 \\ 0
\end{Bmatrix}
+
\begin{bmatrix} F & \vdots & G & \vdots & J \end{bmatrix}
\begin{Bmatrix}
u_{F1} \\ u_{F2} \\ u_{F3} \\ u_{F4} \\ u_{F5} \\ u_{F6} \\ \cdots \\ u_{G1} \\ u_{G2} \\ u_{G3} \\ u_{G4} \\ u_{G5} \\ u_{G6} \\ \cdots \\ u_{J1} \\ u_{J2} \\ u_{J3} \\ u_{J4} \\ u_{J5} \\ u_{J6}
\end{Bmatrix}
= 0 \qquad (14.6)
$$

Coefficient matrix $[\,F \mid G \mid J\,]$ (18 rows × 18 columns):

	F1	F2	F3	F4	F5	F6	G1	G2	G3	G4	G5	G6	J1	J2	J3	J4	J5	J6
1	.000627	−.000331	−.000384	−.000172	−.001038	−.000377	.000213	.000045	−.000190	.000906	−.002846	.000236	.000167	−.000019	.000168	−.000369	−.002041	−.000140
2	−.000331	.000921	−.000025	−.000039	.000506	.000912	−.000358	−.000012	.000442	.000156	.003569	.000061	−.000358	−.000012	.000442	−.000156	.003569	.000061
3	−.000384	−.000025	.001032	.001164	.000912	.000067	−.000316	−.000004	.000304	−.000097	−.004000	.000025	.000343	.000042	−.000316	.000833	−.004464	.000192
4	−.000172	−.000039	.001164	.013932	.002519	.002466	−.000700	−.000089	.001163	−.000670	.005450	−.000142	.000576	−.000105	−.001008	−.001120	−.004655	−.000287
5	−.001038	.000506	.000912	.002519	.017902	.000112	−.000301	−.000342	.000248	−.006049	.003733	.000721	−.000301	−.000342	.000248	−.006049	.003733	.000721
6	−.000377	.000912	.000067	.002466	.000112	.013568	−.000261	.000173	.000492	.001680	.002228	.000413	−.000476	−.000164	.000762	−.001420	.003606	−.000329
7	.000213	−.000358	−.000316	−.000700	−.000301	−.000261	.010026	.000026	−.000358	.000537	.043338	.000096	0	0	0	0	0	0
8	.000045	−.000012	−.000004	−.000089	−.000342	.000173	.000026	.002448	−.000012	−.011320	−.000465	.000217	0	0	0	0	0	0
9	−.000190	.000442	.000304	.001163	.000248	.000492	−.000358	−.000012	.347664	−.000156	.003569	.000061	0	0	0	0	0	0
10	.000906	.000156	−.000097	−.000670	−.006049	.001680	.000537	−.011320	−.000156	.096996	−.010820	.004997	0	0	0	0	0	0
11	−.002846	.003569	−.004000	.005450	.003733	.002228	.043338	−.000465	.003569	−.010820	.386965	−.003236	0	0	0	0	0	0
12	.000236	.000061	.000025	−.000142	.000721	.000413	.000096	.000217	.000061	.004997	−.003236	.026031	0	0	0	0	0	0
13	.000167	.000358	.000343	.000576	.000301	−.000476	0	0	0	0	0	0	.010026	.000026	−.000358	.000537	.043338	.000096
14	−.000019	−.000012	.000042	−.000105	−.000342	.000164	0	0	0	0	0	0	.000026	.002448	−.000012	−.011320	−.000465	.000217
15	.000168	.000442	−.000316	−.001008	.000248	.000762	0	0	0	0	0	0	−.000358	−.000012	.347664	−.000156	.003569	.000061
16	−.000369	−.000156	.000833	−.001120	−.006049	−.001420	0	0	0	0	0	0	.000537	−.011320	−.000156	.096996	−.010820	.004997
17	−.002041	.003569	−.004464	−.004655	.003733	.003606	0	0	0	0	0	0	.043338	−.000465	.003569	−.010820	.386965	−.003236
18	−.000140	.000061	.000192	−.000287	.000721	−.000329	0	0	0	0	0	0	.000096	.000217	.000061	.004997	−.003236	.026031

The vertical 5-kip force acting at the end of the 2-foot cantilever FL can be transformed to a force and a couple applied directly to joint F. The actions which the joint has to exert in opposition to these are denoted by p_{F0} (Fig. 14.10). The matrix p_{F0} is, therefore,

$$p_{F0} = \begin{bmatrix} 0 \\ +5 \\ 0 \\ 0 \\ 0 \\ +10 \end{bmatrix}$$

This value of p_{F0} is entered into submatrix P_{F0} of equations 14.5.

Initial actions on the ends of other members are zero; hence submatrices P_{G0} and P_{J0} remain zero in this problem.

(iv) EQUILIBRIUM EQUATIONS. The stiffness and end actions of all members have been transformed to joint axes. The equilibrium equations outlined in equations 14.5 are therefore now available in numerical form, equations 14.6 (see chart).

The equations are now solved by a technique suitable for the number of equations (Gauss-Jordan elimination was used in this problem). This gives the joint displacements as follows:

$$U_F = \begin{bmatrix} -8624.32 \\ -17197.85 \\ -7179.88 \\ 224.74 \\ 189.00 \\ 1575.42 \end{bmatrix} \quad U_G = \begin{bmatrix} -2552.86 \\ 1094.12 \\ 13.19 \\ 218.00 \\ 449.49 \\ 110.88 \end{bmatrix} \quad U_J = \begin{bmatrix} -502.18 \\ 751.61 \\ 7.00 \\ 135.52 \\ 77.74 \\ 43.33 \end{bmatrix}$$

(v) FINAL END ACTIONS. The final end actions on each member end are expressed in terms of the initial end actions, the joint displacements and the member stiffness. Since the joint displacements are known in joint axes the initial actions and stiffnesses must also be in joint axes. These have already been calculated.

$$\begin{aligned}
p_F^E &= p_{F0}^E + k_{FF}^E u_F \\
p_F^G &= p_{F0}^G + k_{FF}^G u_F + k_{FG} u_G \\
p_G^F &= p_{G0}^F + k_{GF} u_F + k_{GG}^F u_G \\
p_F^J &= p_{F0}^J + k_{FF}^J u_F + k_{FJ} u_J \\
p_J^F &= p_{J0}^F + k_{JF} u_F + k_{JJ}^F u_J \\
p_G^H &= p_{G0}^H + k_{GG}^H u_G \\
p_J^K &= p_{J0}^K + k_{JJ}^K u_J
\end{aligned} \qquad (14.7)$$

(vi) INTERNAL ACTIONS. Once the final end actions have been computed for a particular member, the internal actions at any point can be calculated by statics, since the member loading is known.

For reasons of space a complete solution will be given only for member *EF*. From the first equation of 14.7 we have

$$
p_F^E = p_{F0}^E + k_{FF}^E u_F = \begin{bmatrix} -0.3568 \\ 3.3701 \\ 0.9074 \\ -4.3855 \\ 2.2934 \\ -21.4651 \end{bmatrix}
$$

$$
+ \begin{bmatrix} .000381 & .000026 & -.000358 & -.000124 & -.000737 & -.000301 \\ .000026 & .000037 & -.000012 & -.000195 & .000009 & -.000342 \\ -.000358 & -.000012 & .000442 & .000155 & .001254 & .000248 \\ -.000124 & -.000195 & .000155 & .003078 & .000027 & .002492 \\ -.000737 & .000009 & .001254 & .000027 & .006210 & -.000056 \\ -.000301 & -.000342 & .000248 & .002492 & -.000056 & .005846 \end{bmatrix} \begin{bmatrix} -8624.32 \\ -17197.85 \\ -7179.88 \\ 224.74 \\ 189.00 \\ 1575.42 \end{bmatrix}
$$

$$
= \begin{bmatrix} -2.17 \\ 2.01 \\ 1.70 \\ 3.54 \\ 0.58 \\ -5.02 \end{bmatrix}
$$

Due to these end actions and to the external loading on the beam, the internal actions can be calculated at any desired sections along the member. The internal actions have been computed at the points 1, 2 ... 7 which divide the beam into six equal segments. These actions are given in Table 14.1.

Table 14.1

Point	N^x	N^y	N^z	M^x	M^y	M^z
7	−2.17	2.01	1.70	3.54	0.58	−5.02
6	−2.73	2.03	−0.19	2.93	−2.66	8.74
5	−2.68	1.43	−1.55	−1.72	6.04	18.20
4	−2.46	−2.98	1.24	−6.35	10.85	9.17
3	−2.22	−2.91	1.77	−7.37	1.85	−9.17
2	−1.96	−3.93	7.22	−5.24	−28.45	−26.62
1	−1.70	−2.17	7.99	1.99	−77.18	−29.27

14.4 CHANGE OF RESTRAINTS

In the flexibility method, the question of choosing among various possible sets of releases is usually given careful consideration. The corresponding question regarding various systems of restraints in the

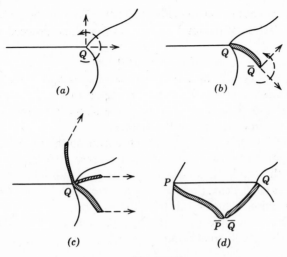

Fig. 14.11

stiffness method is rarely given much thought.   The question is of some interest, however.

Consider the joint Q in a two-dimensional frame (Fig. 14.11a).   In order to inhibit all movement at Q it is usual to provide three restraints situated at Q and forming an orthogonal set (Fig. 14.11a).   The only question considered as a rule is the direction of the joint axes.

However, there is no necessity for the restraints to be located at Q. If we imagine any other point $\bar{Q}$ to be joined to Q by a rigid arm (Fig. 14.11b) then three restraints at $\bar{Q}$ will effectively prevent movement of Q.

An analogy exists between the flexibility and the stiffness methods. The joint in the stiffness method corresponds to a cell (space surrounded by members) in the flexibility method.   Just as the cell can be made statically determinate by a complete cut in any of the surrounding members, so the joint Q can be made rigid by a set of restraints $\bar{Q}$ where $\bar{Q}$ can be located anywhere in the plane.   Just as the cut implies three releases grouped at one point, the restraints at $\bar{Q}$ are also grouped at one point.

However, a cell can be made statically determinate by three releases which are not necessarily grouped at the one point.   Similarly we note that the restraints need not be so grouped.   Any three *independent* restraints will serve the purpose.   One possible system is indicated in Fig. 14.11c.   In effect, the restraint system must be capable of exerting an x force component, a y force component and a moment about any point for a planar frame.

Since the restraints for a given joint can be located anywhere, it is possible to locate the restraints for joint P at the same place as those for

Q, i.e., $\bar{P}$ and $\bar{Q}$ could coincide (Fig. 14.11d). To find the stiffnesses of member PQ in terms of the joint axes $\bar{P}$ and $\bar{Q}$ we first proceed as before to find $k_{\bar{Q}\bar{Q}}$.

$$k_{\bar{Q}\bar{Q}} = A_{\bar{Q}Q}k_{QQ}A_{\bar{Q}Q}^T$$

However, since $A_{\bar{P}Q} = I$, we now have that $k_{\bar{P}\bar{P}} = k_{\bar{Q}\bar{Q}}$. Furthermore, the cross-stiffnesses $k_{\bar{P}\bar{Q}}$ and $k_{\bar{Q}\bar{P}}$ are each equal to $-k_{\bar{Q}\bar{Q}}$. This occurs because axes $\bar{P}$ and $\bar{Q}$ coincide, and the minus sign occurs because $\bar{P}$ and $\bar{Q}$ are joined to opposite ends of the member.

Theoretically it would thus be possible to locate all the nodes of a frame at the same point in space and in the same axes. However, this will usually cause the equilibrium equations to be ill-conditioned, particularly if some stiffness coefficients (in member axes) are much larger than others.

The simplifications which result from the adoption of such a procedure are illustrated in Example 14.2. In this example the frame has been chosen so that severe ill-conditioning is avoided.

Example 14.2 The frame shown in Fig. 14.12 is built up from eight identical members, each forming part of a circular arc and similar to the member whose flexibility was determined in Example 6.2. The cross-section of a member is a rectangle 1 foot × 0.5 foot, the longer side being in the plane of the member.   Take $G = 360 \times 10^3$ ksf and $E = 2.5G$.

In the analysis the nodes corresponding to joints B, E and H will all be located at the same point in space.

Solution.   The point V at which the nodes are to be located is arbitrary.   The point V will be taken as coincident with E, and the nodal axes will be as shown in Fig. 14.13.   Although the nodes corresponding to B, E and H are located at the same point in space, they will of course

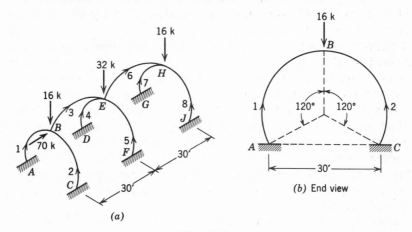

(a)

(b) End view

Fig. 14.12

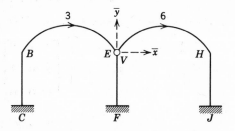

Fig. 14.13

undergo relative movement when *B*, *E* and *H* move. They must be regarded as three separate nodes, and to distinguish them they will be labeled *VB*, *VE* and *VH*.

Member Stiffness. From Fig. 14.12*b* we see that $R = 17.32$ feet. Using the results of Example 6.2 we obtain the flexibility matrix for the basic component member.

$$f = G \begin{bmatrix} 59565 & 0 & -56126 & 0 & 3537 & 0 \\ 0 & 469128 & 0 & -14193 & 0 & 16126 \\ -56126 & 0 & 63098 & 0 & -4320 & 0 \\ 0 & -14193 & 0 & 1344 & 0 & -22 \\ 3537 & 0 & -4320 & 0 & 348 & 0 \\ 0 & 16126 & 0 & -22 & 0 & 1319 \end{bmatrix}$$

Then by inversion the member stiffness is obtained.

$$k = \frac{1}{G} \begin{bmatrix} 45.85 & 0 & 59.15 & 0 & 268.31 & 0 \\ 0 & 2.82 & 0 & 29.22 & 0 & -33.98 \\ 59.15 & 0 & 114.33 & 0 & 818.05 & 0 \\ 0 & 29.22 & 0 & 570.73 & 0 & -347.71 \\ 268.31 & 0 & 818.05 & 0 & 8462.57 & 0 \\ 0 & -33.98 & 0 & -347.71 & 0 & 682.63 \end{bmatrix}$$

Transformation to Nodal Axes. We need to transfer forces from the end of each member in turn to the nodal axes at *V*. It is convenient in this instance to perform the rotation first. When the axes of members 1 and 2 meeting at *B* have been oriented to the common *direction*, the *translation* to *V* is identical for both.

For member 1, the rotation from axes B to axes V (Fig. 14.14) is given by

$$R_1 = \begin{bmatrix} \lambda_1 & 0 \\ 0 & \lambda_1 \end{bmatrix} \quad \text{and} \quad \lambda_1 = \begin{bmatrix} 0 & 1 & 0 \\ 0 & 0 & 1 \\ 1 & 0 & 0 \end{bmatrix}$$

For member 2,

$$R_2 = \begin{bmatrix} \lambda_2 & 0 \\ 0 & \lambda_2 \end{bmatrix} \quad \text{and} \quad \lambda_2 = \begin{bmatrix} 0 & -1 & 0 \\ 0 & 0 & 1 \\ -1 & 0 & 0 \end{bmatrix}$$

Translation from B to V is effected by T_B, where

$$T_B = \begin{bmatrix} I & 0 \\ X_B & I \end{bmatrix} \quad \text{and} \quad X_B = \begin{bmatrix} 0 & 0 & 0 \\ 0 & 0 & 30 \\ 0 & -30 & 0 \end{bmatrix}$$

The stiffness of member 3 is most conveniently taken at the end E, which saves translation. Rotation from axes E to axes V (Fig. 14.15) is given by

$$R_3 = \begin{bmatrix} \lambda_3 & 0 \\ 0 & \lambda_3 \end{bmatrix} \quad \text{where} \quad \lambda_3 = \begin{bmatrix} 0.500 & 0 & 0.866 \\ -0.866 & 0 & 0.500 \\ 0 & -1 & 0 \end{bmatrix}$$

Members 4 and 7 are oriented similarly to member 1, so axis rotation for these members is effected by R_1. We can now express the transformation for each member.

$$A_1 = \begin{bmatrix} \lambda_1 & 0 \\ X_B\lambda_1 & \lambda_1 \end{bmatrix} \quad A_2 = \begin{bmatrix} \lambda_2 & 0 \\ X_B\lambda_2 & \lambda_2 \end{bmatrix}$$

$$A_3 = \begin{bmatrix} \lambda_3 & 0 \\ 0 & \lambda_3 \end{bmatrix} \quad A_4 = \begin{bmatrix} \lambda_1 & 0 \\ 0 & \lambda_1 \end{bmatrix}$$

$$A_5 = \begin{bmatrix} \lambda_2 & 0 \\ 0 & \lambda_2 \end{bmatrix} \quad A_6 = \begin{bmatrix} \lambda_3 & 0 \\ X_H\lambda_3 & \lambda_3 \end{bmatrix}$$

$$A_7 = \begin{bmatrix} \lambda_1 & 0 \\ X_H\lambda_1 & \lambda_1 \end{bmatrix} \quad A_8 = \begin{bmatrix} \lambda_2 & 0 \\ X_H\lambda_2 & \lambda_2 \end{bmatrix}$$

where $X_H = -X_B$.

For computing purposes, it is convenient to stack these A matrices in a three-dimensional array (Fig. 14.16) which can be denoted by A. For

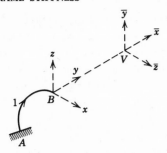

Fig. 14.14

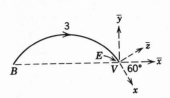

Fig. 14.15

member 1, the stiffness in the V axes is given by

$$\bar{k}_1 = A_1 k A_1^T$$

Similar expressions apply for the other members. The multiplication indicated diagrammatically in Fig. 14.16 thus gives the member stiffnesses (expressed at V) stacked in a matrix $\bar{k}$. We may suppose that

$$kA^T = C \qquad (14.8)$$

and $$AC = \bar{k} \qquad (14.9)$$

The equilibrium equations can be written in the form

$$
\begin{array}{|c|}
\hline
P_{VB\cdot 0} \\
\hline
P_{VH\cdot 0} \\
\hline
P_{VE\cdot 0} \\
\hline
\end{array}
\; + \;
\begin{array}{|c|c|c|}
\hline
VB & 0 & -\bar{k}_3 \\
\hline
0 & VH & -\bar{k}_6 \\
\hline
-\bar{k}_3 & -\bar{k}_6 & VE \\
\hline
\end{array}
\begin{array}{|c|}
\hline
u_{VB} \\
\hline
u_{VH} \\
\hline
u_{VE} \\
\hline
\end{array}
\; = 0 \quad (14.10)
$$

$P_{VB\cdot 0}$ are the initial restraints at B expressed in V axes.

$$VB = \bar{k}_1 + \bar{k}_2 + \bar{k}_3$$
$$VH = \bar{k}_6 + \bar{k}_7 + \bar{k}_8$$
$$VE = \bar{k}_3 + \bar{k}_4 + \bar{k}_5 + \bar{k}_6$$

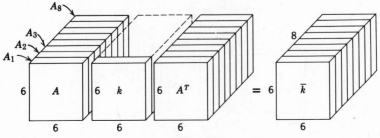

Fig. 14.16

Each member has only one stiffness since both its ends are joined to points situated at the same location. This matrix serves as the stiffness of each end and also as the cross-stiffness. Formation of the joint stiffness matrices is thus only a matter of summation for the relevant members. The sequence in which the joints are selected is arbitrary.

Solution of equations 14.10 yields the joint displacements expressed in axes V.

$$u_{VB} = \begin{bmatrix} 4.7457 \\ -0.1107 \\ 0 \\ 0 \\ 0 \\ -0.0022 \end{bmatrix} \qquad u_{VH} = \begin{bmatrix} 4.0517 \\ 1.6189 \\ 0 \\ 0 \\ 0 \\ -0.0586 \end{bmatrix} \qquad u_{VE} = \begin{bmatrix} 4.2987 \\ -0.0960 \\ 0 \\ 0 \\ 0 \\ -0.0349 \end{bmatrix}$$

The member end forces will depend on the displacement at both ends of the member, or in other words on the *relative* end displacements. Usually we should deal with the displacement of each end separately. But in the present analysis, the displacements of both ends of a member are expressed in the same axis. Consequently the relative end displacements may be found by simple subtraction. For example, for member 3 the displacement of end E relative to end B is simply $u_{VE} - u_{VB}$.

$$u_3 = u_{VE} - u_{VB}$$

We subtract u_{VB} from u_{VE} (and not vice versa) since the x axis was taken (arbitrarily) from B to E. The relative displacement u_3 may be transformed to member axes, $A_3^T \cdot u_3$, and the member end forces then found (in member axes) by multiplying by k.

$$p_3 = kA_3^T \cdot u_3 = C_3 u_3$$

The product kA^T has already been evaluated for each member and stored in the matrix C (equation 14.8). Thus if we suitably stack the member relative displacements as in Fig. 14.17, a single multiplication will give

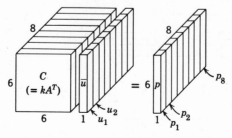

Fig. 14.17

Table 14.2

Member	N^x	N^y	N^z	M^x	M^y	M^z
1	−2.61	13.32	−5.04	137.40	−36.09	−160.51
2	−2.61	−13.32	−5.04	−137.40	−36.09	160.51
3	−24.52	0	−30.65	0	−97.40	0
4	−5.68	11.10	−10.98	105.68	−78.56	−133.95
5	−5.68	−11.10	−10.98	−105.68	−78.56	133.95
6	−22.12	0	−6.40	0	169.86	0
7	−8.27	9.71	−15.98	84.93	−114.32	−117.31
8	−8.27	−9.71	−15.98	−84.93	−114.32	117.31

the forces at the end of every member. For this problem the member end forces are tabulated in Table 14.2, which has the same form as matrix p of Fig. 14.17.

The arithmetic sum of the N^z forces (vertical shears) on members 1, 2, 4, 5, 7 and 8 is 64.00, which agrees well with the sum of the vertical loads on the frame. The arithmetic sum of the N^y forces (horizontal shears) on the same members is 68.26, which agrees only approximately with the horizontal 70-kip force. The difference is due to roundoff and indicates the ill-conditioning introduced by the method.

The method of coincident nodes can be used easily with the frame of Example 14.2 because the members are such that all elements of the stiffness matrix are finite. When some of the elements are extremely large, the transformation to a node remote from the member end introduces computational difficulty. As a consequence, the method is not recommended for general use.

PROBLEMS

14.1. Write down the stiffness matrix for the plane frame of Fig. P14.1. Assume
(a) extensible members;
(b) inextensible members.

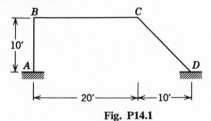

Fig. P14.1

Take
$$EA = \text{constant} = 30$$
$$EI = \text{constant} = 100$$

14.2. Write down the stiffness matrix for the gabled portal frame shown in Fig. P14.2   Assume that bending deformations only are to be considered, and that $EI = 1$ throughout the frame.

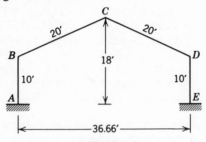

Fig. P14.2

14.3. A rigid-jointed frame composed of five members is shown in plan and elevation in Fig. P14.3.   Each of the four inclined members has a cross-section of 1 foot square and is orientated so that two of its sides lie in vertical planes. The horizontal member is 1 foot wide and 1.5 feet deep.   The supports at A, B, C, and D are fully fixed.

    (a) Determine the frame stiffness matrix taking axial deformations into account.

    (b) Determine the frame stiffness matrix neglecting axial deformations.
        Joint translation is prevented by a horizontal restraint in the direction EF.

  In both cases neglect shear deformations.   Express the answer in feet and kip units, and take frame axes so that x is in the direction EF and y is vertically upward. $E = 2000$ ksi and $G = 800$ ksi.

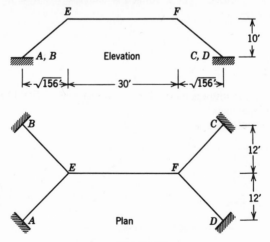

Fig. P14.3

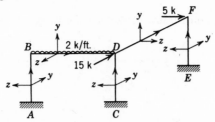

Fig. P14.4

14.4. In the frame of Fig. P14.4, the beams *BD* and *DF* are at right angles to one another in the horizontal plane. The beams are 15 feet long and the columns are 10 feet long. The relative rigidity values of the members are as follows:

Columns	Beams
$GI^x = 0.5$	$GI^x = 1$
$EI^y = 4$	$EI^y = 2$
$EI^z = 4$	$EI^z = 8$

Deformations due to axial force and shear force are to be neglected.

Use the stiffness method to determine the reactions at the base of each column, and the internal actions at the mid-point of *BD* for the given loading.

14.5. The planar reinforced concrete frame of Fig. P14.5 has constant rectangular cross section 2 feet × 1 foot 6 inches. A stiffness analysis of the frame is to be carried out based on the stiffness of the unassembled members with due allowance for finite-sized joints at *B* and *D* only. Assume that the effective length of a member is equal to its clear length plus $d/4$ (= 6 inches) for each finite-sized joint into which it frames. Take $E = 2.3G$.

Determine the support reactions when the frame is loaded by the following load systems:

(*a*) uniformly distributed load of 4 kips per foot along *BDF*;
(*b*) vertical load of 40 kips at *F*;
(*c*) uniformly distributed load of 2 kips per foot along *AB*;
(*d*) any combination of load systems (*a*), (*b*) and (*c*).

In each case the loading extends as far as the intersection of center lines.

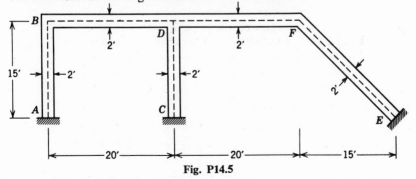

Fig. P14.5

14.6. Solve the pin-jointed frame of Problem 4.4 (page 63) using the stiffness method.

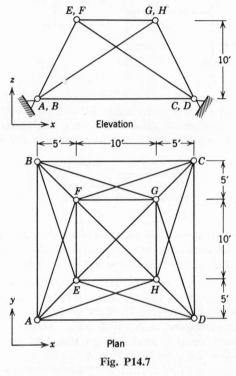

Fig. P14.7

14.7. The pin-jointed frame of Fig. P14.7 is supported by universal joints at *A*, *B*, *C* and *D*. It can be loaded at joints *E*, *F*, *G* and *H* by loads of 4 kips in the *x* and *y* direction, and 10 kips in the (−ve) *z* direction. Assuming that all members have the same cross-sectional area of 4 square inches find the member forces by stiffness methods for the following load combinations:

Load Case	4 kips in *x* Direction	4 kips in *y* Direction	10 kips in (−ve) *z* Direction
(*a*)	*E*	*E*	*E*
(*b*)	*E*	*H*	*G*
(*c*)	*E, F*		
(*d*)	*E, F*	*G, H*	*E, F, G, H*
(*e*)	*E, F, G, H*	*E, F, G, H*	*E, F, G, H*
(*f*)			*E, F*

14.8. A straight uniform member AB has a length of 10 feet, $EA = 1$ and $EI = 16$. It is fixed at A and is pin-connected to a joint B in a two-dimensional frame. Other members frame into joint B in a fully continuous manner as shown in Fig. P14.8. Restraints at joint B are numbered 1, 2 and 6 as shown.

Find the end stiffness of member AB at B, and its contribution to the joint stiffness matrix at B when θ is 0°, 30° and 45°.

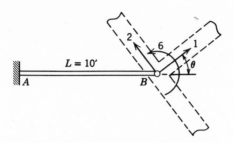

Fig. P14.8

14.9. The homogeneous tapered beam AB of rectangular cross-section (Fig. P14.9) is 20 feet long. At B the breadth is 15 inches and the depth is 9 inches. The breadth and depth at A are one-third those at B. The member is fixed at B and is pinned at A to a fully continuous finite-size joint C in a plane frame. Determine the (2×2) member stiffness matrix for member AB, and its contribution to the joint stiffness matrix at C when θ is 0°, 30° and 45°. ($E = 2.5 \times 10^7$ psi.)

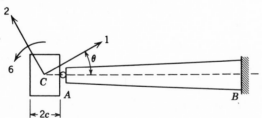

Fig. P14.9

14.10. Re-solve the braced portal example of page 143 by the stiffness method.

14.11. Re-solve Problem 4.11.

14.12. Re-solve Problem 4.13.

14.13. Figure P14.13 shows the plan layout of a fully rigid dome-type structure. Compare the appearance and the band width of the non-zero entries in the frame stiffness matrix when the joints are numbered
    (*a*) at random;
    (*b*) in rings;
    (*c*) as shown in Fig. P14.13.

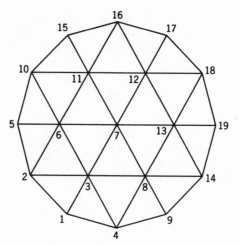

Fig. P14.13

14.14. Re-solve Problem 8.7.
14.15. Re-solve Problem 8.5.
14.16. Re-solve Problem 8.6.
14.17. Re-solve Problem 8.8.
14.18. Re-solve Problem 8.9.

APPENDIX

Some Notes
on Matrix Algebra

A.1 INTRODUCTION

The notation of matrix algebra represents a system of grouping algebraic or numerical quantities in such a way that a single symbol suffices to denote the whole group.   In this way a considerable economy of symbols is effected, and matrices may be thought of as a type of algebraic shorthand. The elementary parts of matrix algebra are closely associated with linear simultaneous equations.   It is because the latter feature so prominently in this book that the matrix notation has been used so extensively.   Moreover, many electronic computers can be programmed directly for matrix operations.   The matrix formulation of the problem thus saves considerable programming time.

The notes of this appendix are limited to those portions of matrix algebra which have been used in the body of the text.   They are provided with a view to convenient reference and not as an exhaustive treatment of the subject.   For those wishing to pursue the study of matrix algebra in more detail, a number of excellent textbooks are available which are devoted entirely to this subject.

A.2 MATRIX NOTATION AND DEFINITIONS

A matrix is defined as a rectangular array of elements arranged in rows and columns.   The array is enclosed within square brackets to indicate that it is being regarded as a matrix.   The elements may be numbers, algebraic functions, differential operators and so on.   The array is denoted collectively by a single symbol which is sometimes bracketed.   If no ambiguity arises the brackets are often omitted. Individual elements of the matrix are usually represented by a letter with two subscripts of which the first denotes the row and the second denotes the column which the element occupies. Thus, we write

$$\begin{bmatrix} a_{11} & a_{12} & a_{13} & a_{14} & a_{15} \\ a_{21} & a_{22} & a_{23} & a_{24} & a_{25} \\ a_{31} & a_{32} & a_{33} & a_{34} & a_{35} \end{bmatrix}_{(3 \times 5)} \equiv [A] \equiv A$$

In this array A stands for a group comprising 3 rows and 5 columns. A typical element is often referred to as a_{ij}, which signifies the element in the ith row and the jth column.

A matrix should not be confused with a determinant. A determinant is a *square* array enclosed within vertical lines, and it signifies a certain relationship among the elements. If the elements are numerical the determinant can be evaluated. The matrix, on the other hand, merely represents the array and does not imply a relationship among the elements.

The *order* of a matrix refers to its size. A matrix containing m rows and n columns is said to be of order $(m \times n)$. The number of rows is always specified first. Figures A.1 and A.2 show different types of matrices and in each case the order is shown in round brackets below the matrix concerned.

A *row* matrix is one containing a single row. Its order is $(1 \times n)$.

A *column* matrix is one containing a single column. Its order is $(m \times 1)$.

A row matrix (or column matrix) is often referred to as a *row vector*

$$[1 \quad 16 \quad -172]$$
$$(1 \times 3)$$

Row matrix
(a)

$$\begin{bmatrix} 2 \\ 6 \\ 1 \\ 3 \\ 5 \end{bmatrix}_{(5 \times 1)}$$

Column matrix
(b)

$$\begin{bmatrix} 6.5L & 2.0L^2 & 0.1L^3 \\ 20.6L & -18.7L^2 & 2.4L^3 \end{bmatrix}$$
$$(2 \times 3)$$

Rectangular matrix
(c)

$$\begin{bmatrix} O & O \\ O & O \\ O & O \end{bmatrix}$$
$$(3 \times 2)$$

Null matrix
(d)

$$\text{If } A = \begin{bmatrix} 6 & 14 \\ 7 & 8 \\ -2 & 0 \end{bmatrix}$$
$$(3 \times 2)$$

$$\text{then } A^T = \begin{bmatrix} 6 & 7 & -2 \\ 14 & 8 & 0 \end{bmatrix}$$
$$(2 \times 3)$$

Transposed matrices
(e)

Fig. A.1

$$\begin{bmatrix} \dfrac{L^3}{3EI} & \dfrac{-L^2}{2EI} \\[2mm] \dfrac{-L^2}{2EI} & \dfrac{L}{EI} \end{bmatrix}$$
(2×2)

Square matrix
(symmetrical)
(a)

$$\begin{bmatrix} a & 0 & 0 & 0 \\ 0 & b & 0 & 0 \\ 0 & 0 & c & 0 \\ 0 & 0 & 0 & d \end{bmatrix}$$
(4×4)

Diagonal matrix
(b)

$$\begin{bmatrix} 1 & 0 & 0 \\ 0 & 1 & 0 \\ 0 & 0 & 1 \end{bmatrix} = I$$
(3×3)

Unit matrix of
order (3×3)
(c)

$$\begin{bmatrix} 2 & 1 & 7 \\ 0 & 4 & -2 \\ 0 & 0 & 5 \end{bmatrix}$$
(3×3)

Upper triangular
matrix
(d)

$$\begin{bmatrix} 4 & 0 & 0 & 0 \\ 1 & -11 & 0 & 0 \\ 0 & 8 & 0 & 0 \\ 5 & 2 & -1 & 3 \end{bmatrix}$$
(4×4)

Lower triangular
matrix
(e)

$$[p_1 \quad p_2 \quad p_3] \quad \begin{bmatrix} p_1 \\ p_2 \\ p_3 \end{bmatrix}$$
$A_{(1 \times 3)}$ $B_{(3 \times 1)}$
$A^T = B$ and
$B^T = A$

Transposed matrices
(f)

Fig. A.2

(or *column vector*) because of the significance of this form when matrix algebra is used in the study of vector quantities.

A *null* matrix is one each of whose elements is zero. It is denoted by O and serves the same function in matrix algebra as zero does in ordinary algebra.

If matrices A and B are such that each row of B is identical with the corresponding column of A, then B is said to be the *transpose* of A and is denoted by A^T. If A is of order $(m \times n)$, then A^T will be of order $(n \times m)$. Transposition of a row vector will result in a column vector and vice versa.

A *square* matrix is one having the same number of rows as columns. The following definitions apply specifically to square matrices.

The *principal diagonal* of a square matrix is the diagonal which commences with the element in the top left-hand corner, and comprises the elements $a_{11}, a_{22} \ldots a_{ii} \ldots a_{nn}$. It is usually referred to merely as the *diagonal*.

A *diagonal matrix* is one which has zero elements everywhere except on the diagonal.

A *unit* matrix is one which has unit elements on the diagonal and zeros elsewhere. The unit matrix is denoted by I and serves the same function in matrix algebra as unity does in ordinary algebra. A unit matrix must be square, but there is one unit matrix of each order. The unit matrix of order (3×3), for example, is sometimes denoted by I_3.

If all the elements on one side of the diagonal of a square matrix are zero, the matrix is said to be *triangular*. The terms *upper triangular* matrix and *lower triangular* matrix are explained in Fig. A.2.

A *symmetrical* matrix is a square matrix which is symmetrical about its diagonal. That is to say, $a_{ij} = a_{ji}$. We note that a symmetrical matrix is unchanged by the process of transposition.

A.3 EQUALITY, ADDITION, SUBTRACTION AND SCALAR MULTIPLICATION

Two matrices are said to be equal if each element of one is equal to the corresponding element of the other. The equality of two matrices therefore implies as many relationships as there are elements in each matrix. The matrix equation

$$\begin{bmatrix} a & b & c \\ d & e & f \end{bmatrix} = \begin{bmatrix} 2 & 1 & 9 \\ 10 & 0 & -3 \end{bmatrix} \tag{A.1}$$

implies six equations of ordinary algebra, namely

$$\begin{aligned} a &= 2 \\ b &= 1 \\ c &= 9 \\ d &= 10 \\ e &= 0 \\ f &= -3 \end{aligned} \tag{A.2}$$

If corresponding elements of two matrices are added, the resulting elements form a third matrix, which is the sum of the first two. We may imagine the two matrices of the same order being superimposed one upon the other and the corresponding elements added. We say that $C = A + B$ if $c_{ij} = a_{ij} + b_{ij}$.

$$\underbrace{\begin{bmatrix} 6 & 2 & 17 & 5 \\ -10 & 4 & 6 & 9 \end{bmatrix}}_{A_{(2\times4)}} + \underbrace{\begin{bmatrix} 1 & 4 & 3 & 7 \\ 2 & 8 & -6 & 11 \end{bmatrix}}_{B_{(2\times4)}} = \underbrace{\begin{bmatrix} 7 & 6 & 20 & 12 \\ -8 & 12 & 0 & 20 \end{bmatrix}}_{C_{(2\times4)}} \tag{A.3}$$

In a similar manner, if the elements of one matrix are subtracted from the corresponding elements of another, the resulting elements form a

third matrix, which is the difference of the first two. We say that
$D = A - B$ if $d_{ij} = a_{ij} - b_{ij}$.

$$\underset{A_{(2\times4)}}{\begin{bmatrix} 6 & 2 & 17 & 5 \\ -10 & 4 & 6 & 9 \end{bmatrix}} - \underset{B_{(2\times4)}}{\begin{bmatrix} 1 & 4 & 3 & 7 \\ 2 & 8 & -6 & 11 \end{bmatrix}} = \underset{D_{(2\times4)}}{\begin{bmatrix} 5 & -2 & 14 & -2 \\ -12 & -4 & 12 & -2 \end{bmatrix}} \quad (A.4)$$

From the definitions of equality, addition and subtraction it is clear
that these processes cannot be used except among matrices of the same
order. We say that matrices of the same order are *conformable* for
addition, subtraction and equation, while matrices of different order are
not conformable. It also follows from the definitions that addition and
subtraction obey the commutative and associative laws. That is,

$$\left. \begin{aligned} A + B &= B + A \\ A + (B + C) &= (A + B) + C \end{aligned} \right\} \quad (A.5)$$

A matrix is said to be multiplied by a scalar if every element of the
matrix is multiplied by the scalar. Thus if k is a single element, or
scalar quantity,

$$k \begin{bmatrix} a & b & c \\ d & e & f \\ x & y & z \end{bmatrix} = \begin{bmatrix} ka & kb & kc \\ kd & ke & kf \\ kx & ky & kz \end{bmatrix} \quad (A.6)$$

A.4 PARTITIONED MATRICES

Often the elements of a matrix fall naturally into different physical
groups. It may be convenient to refer to these groups individually, in
which case the groups are called *submatrices*. The submatrices are often
isolated by dotted lines. The original matrix is referred to as a *partitioned
matrix*.

$$A = \begin{bmatrix} 1 & 2 & 4 & -1 & \vdots & 1 & 0 \\ 0 & 1 & 0 & 2 & \vdots & 0 & 1 \\ \cdots & \cdots & \cdots & \cdots & & \cdots & \cdots \\ 3 & 5 & -2 & 7 & \vdots & 0 & 0 \end{bmatrix} = \begin{bmatrix} A_{11} & A_{12} \\ A_{21} & A_{22} \end{bmatrix}$$

If the matrix A, above, is partitioned as shown we notice that the
submatrix A_{12} is a unit matrix while the submatrix A_{22} is a null matrix.
In a particular context this fact might have some significance.

In this book, extensive use has been made of partitioning. On p. 52 a
flexibility matrix has been partitioned so as to distinguish the locations

to which the various coefficients refer. In Chapter 5 the axis transformation matrices have been partitioned to emphasize their composition. In Chapter 14 the stiffness matrix of a frame has been written in terms of elements which are themselves submatrices, being the stiffness matrices of individual members. Apart from other considerations, this method of writing has the merit of brevity.

It will be shown that matrices whose elements are themselves submatrices conform to the usual laws of matrix algebra subject only to the usual limitations of these laws.

From the definition of matrix addition and subtraction it follows that the sums and differences of partitioned matrices can be written in terms of their submatrices provided that these are individually conformable. That is to say, if A and B are submatrices we can write

$$\begin{bmatrix} A_{11} & A_{12} & A_{13} \\ A_{21} & A_{22} & A_{23} \end{bmatrix} + \begin{bmatrix} B_{11} & B_{12} & B_{13} \\ B_{21} & B_{22} & B_{23} \end{bmatrix} = \begin{bmatrix} (A_{11} + B_{11})(A_{12} + B_{12})(A_{13} + B_{13}) \\ (A_{21} + B_{21})(A_{22} + B_{22})(A_{23} + B_{23}) \end{bmatrix}$$

provided that A_{11} is of the same order as B_{11}, A_{12} is of the same order as B_{12} and so on.

A.5 MATRIX MULTIPLICATION

Suppose that it is required to find the product, C, of the two matrices A and B shown below.

$$\begin{bmatrix} a_{11} & a_{12} & a_{13} & a_{14} \\ a_{21} & a_{22} & a_{23} & a_{24} \\ a_{31} & a_{32} & a_{33} & a_{34} \end{bmatrix} \begin{bmatrix} b_{11} & b_{12} & b_{13} & b_{14} \\ b_{21} & b_{22} & b_{23} & b_{24} \\ b_{31} & b_{32} & b_{33} & b_{34} \\ b_{41} & b_{42} & b_{43} & b_{44} \end{bmatrix}$$
$$(3 \times 4)(4 \times 4)$$

The element c_{ij} of the matrix C is formed by taking the inner product of the ith row of A and the jth column of B. The *inner product* is defined as the sum of the products of corresponding elements. For example, if we select the third row of A and the second column of B, the inner product of these is $(a_{31}b_{12} + a_{32}b_{22} + a_{33}b_{32} + a_{34}b_{42})$. This expression is equal to the element c_{32} in the product matrix C.

This process implies that the number of elements in a row of A is equal to the number of elements in a column of B. If this is true, the matrices are said to be *conformable* for multiplication. Otherwise the multiplication process is not defined. When the matrices are conformable, the number of rows in the product is equal to the number of rows in A, and the number of columns in the product is equal to the number of columns in B.

Thus two matrices of order $(a \times b)$ and $(c \times d)$ respectively can be multiplied only if $b = c$, in which case the product will be of order $(a \times d)$.

The schematic layout shown below helps in visualizing the size of the product matrix, and also indicates how any element in the product is related to the row and column from which it is formed.*

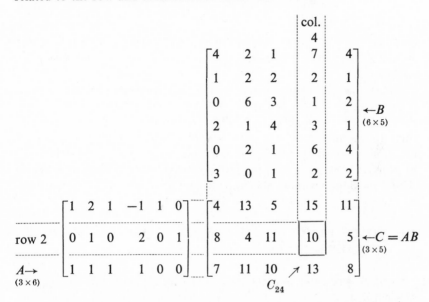

Any element of C is the inner product of the row of A and the column of B at the intersection of which it lies. An extension of this layout for continued multiplication is shown in Section A.6.

It follows from the law of multiplication that although two matrices may be conformable in the sequence $A \times B$, this may not be the case if they are interchanged. Even if they can still be multiplied, the product will not in general be the same. The commutative law therefore does not hold for matrix multiplication. In general $AB \neq BA$. Because the sequence of the terms in multiplication is significant, we say that A is premultiplied by X if the product XA is intended. To signify the product AX, we say that A is postmultiplied by X.

The associative and distributive laws apply to multiplication, provided that the sequence of the terms is strictly maintained.

$$A(BC) = (AB)C = ABC$$
$$A(B + C) = AB + AC$$

Suppose that two partitioned matrices A and B are conformable for

* A similar layout was first suggested by Kurt Eisemann of IBM, New York.

multiplication. It is possible to express the product in terms of the submatrices of A and B, provided that these are individually conformable for multiplication. That is to say, we can write

$$\begin{bmatrix} A_{11} & A_{12} & A_{13} \\ A_{21} & A_{22} & A_{23} \end{bmatrix} \begin{bmatrix} B_{11} & B_{12} \\ B_{21} & B_{22} \\ B_{31} & B_{32} \end{bmatrix} = \begin{bmatrix} (A_{11}B_{11} + A_{12}B_{21} + A_{13}B_{31})(A_{11}B_{12} + A_{12}B_{22} + A_{13}B_{32}) \\ (A_{21}B_{11} + A_{22}B_{21} + A_{23}B_{31})(A_{21}B_{12} + A_{22}B_{22} + A_{23}B_{32}) \end{bmatrix}$$

provided that A_{11} and B_{11} are conformable, A_{12} and B_{21} are conformable and so on. Each of the individual matrix products and additions must be possible.

For this condition to be fulfilled it is only necessary for the vertical partitioning of A to be similar to the horizontal partitioning of B. Since A and B are conformable, the number of elements in a row of A must be equal to the number of elements in a column of B. If the matrices are partitioned as indicated in Fig. A.3, multiplication of the submatrices will be possible. Matrix A may be further subdivided by horizontal lines and B by vertical lines without affecting the conformability of the submatrices.

A.6 COMPUTATIONAL CHECKS ON MATRIX MULTIPLICATION

Let Z_1 be a row matrix every element of which is unity, and consider the product $Z_1 A$.

$$\underbrace{\begin{bmatrix} 1 & 1 & 1 \end{bmatrix}}_{Z_1} \underbrace{\begin{bmatrix} 4 & 3 & 1 \\ 2 & 5 & 0 \\ 1 & 0 & 4 \end{bmatrix}}_{A} = \underbrace{\begin{bmatrix} 7 & 8 & 5 \end{bmatrix}}_{Z_1 A} \tag{A.7}$$

The elements of this product consist of the column sums of A. In a similar way, if Z_2 is a column matrix of unit elements, the product AZ_2 will be a column matrix whose elements are the row sums of A.

Suppose now that two matrices A and B are to be multiplied to produce the matrix C.

$$AB = C \tag{A.8}$$

Premultiplying both sides of equation A.8 by Z_1, we obtain

$$Z_1 AB = Z_1 C$$

or $$(Z_1 A)B = (Z_1 C) \tag{A.9}$$

Equation A.9 indicates that if the row matrix $(Z_1 A)$ consisting of the column sums of A is postmultiplied by B, the product is the row matrix of the column sums of C. This fact can be used as a computational check on the multiplication AB.

Alternatively the row sums can be used as a check. Postmultiplying equation A.8 by Z_2 we obtain

$$ABZ_2 = CZ_2$$

or $$A(BZ_2) = (CZ_2) \qquad (A.10)$$

Equation A.10 indicates that when A is postmultiplied by the column

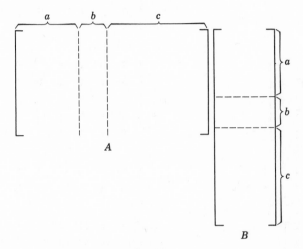

Fig. A.3

matrix (BZ_2) consisting of the row sums of B, the product will be the column matrix of the row sums of C.

One or the other of the foregoing checks is always used in matrix multiplication.

From equation A.8 we can also obtain

$$Z_1ABZ_2 = Z_1CZ_2 \qquad (A.11)$$

which indicates that

$$[\text{col. sums of } A] \times \begin{bmatrix} \text{row} \\ \text{sums} \\ \text{of } B \end{bmatrix} = \begin{bmatrix} \text{sum of all} \\ \text{elements of } C \end{bmatrix}_{(1 \times 1)}$$

A continued matrix product is given below in Fig. A.4, using the schematic layout discussed in Section A.5. At the same time a row sum check will be incorporated. It is required to determine the product $E = ABCD$.

The product CD is computed first. The matrices C and D are set down in the positions shown, and the row sums of D are calculated. These row sums appear as an extra column on D. When the product CD is computed this final column is included and gives rise to an extra column on (CD). The rows of (CD) are now summed, and if these row sums agree with the values obtained by the multiplication process, the elements

Row sums

$$
D \rightarrow
\begin{bmatrix}
1 & 0 & 1 & 2 & 1 & 0 & 0 \\
0 & 1 & 1 & 1 & 0 & 1 & 0 \\
0 & 0 & 1 & 0 & 0 & 0 & 1
\end{bmatrix}
\quad
\begin{matrix}
5 \\ 4 \\ 2
\end{matrix}
$$
(3×7)

$$
C \rightarrow
\begin{bmatrix}
2 & 0 & 0 \\
0 & 1 & 0 \\
1 & 1 & 1 \\
0 & 1 & 1 \\
1 & 1 & 1
\end{bmatrix}
\qquad
CD \rightarrow
\begin{bmatrix}
2 & 0 & 2 & 4 & 2 & 0 & 0 \\
0 & 1 & 1 & 1 & 0 & 1 & 0 \\
1 & 1 & 3 & 3 & 1 & 1 & 1 \\
0 & 1 & 2 & 1 & 0 & 1 & 1 \\
1 & 1 & 3 & 3 & 1 & 1 & 1
\end{bmatrix}
\quad
\begin{matrix}
10 \\ 4 \\ 11 \\ 6 \\ 11
\end{matrix}
$$
(5×3) (5×7)

$$
B \rightarrow
\begin{bmatrix}
1 & 1 & 1 & 1 & 1 \\
0 & 1 & 0 & 1 & 0
\end{bmatrix}
\qquad
B(CD) \rightarrow
\begin{bmatrix}
4 & 4 & 11 & 12 & 4 & 4 & 3 \\
0 & 2 & 3 & 2 & 0 & 2 & 1
\end{bmatrix}
\quad
\begin{matrix}
42 \\ 10
\end{matrix}
$$
(2×5) (2×7)

$$
A \rightarrow
\begin{bmatrix}
1 & 2 \\
3 & 4 \\
1 & 1 \\
2 & 1 \\
2 & 2 \\
4 & 5
\end{bmatrix}
\qquad
\begin{matrix} A(BCD) \rightarrow \\ = E \end{matrix}
\begin{bmatrix}
4 & 8 & 17 & 16 & 4 & 8 & 5 \\
12 & 20 & 45 & 44 & 12 & 20 & 13 \\
4 & 6 & 14 & 14 & 4 & 6 & 4 \\
8 & 10 & 25 & 26 & 8 & 10 & 7 \\
8 & 12 & 28 & 28 & 8 & 12 & 8 \\
16 & 26 & 59 & 58 & 16 & 26 & 17
\end{bmatrix}
\quad
\begin{matrix}
62 \\ 166 \\ 52 \\ 94 \\ 104 \\ 218
\end{matrix}
$$
(6×2) (6×7)

Fig. A.4

of CD can be taken as being correct. The matrix B is now set down below C, and the product of B with (CD) gives the matrix BCD. The row sum check is used in the same way as before. Finally A is set down below B, and the product of A with (BCD) is evaluated.

The order of the final product E depends upon the order of the individual matrices as follows:

$$
\underset{(6 \times 7)}{E} = \underset{(6 \times 2)}{A} \times \underset{(2 \times 5)}{B} \times \underset{(5 \times 3)}{C} \times \underset{(3 \times 7)}{D} \tag{A.12}
$$

A.7 EXPRESSION OF SIMULTANEOUS EQUATIONS IN MATRIX FORM

The matrix equation

$$u_0 + fp = 0 \qquad\qquad (A.13)$$

can be expanded by means of the rules discussed above. We suppose that

$$u_0 = \begin{bmatrix} u_{10} \\ u_{20} \\ u_{30} \\ u_{40} \end{bmatrix} \quad f = \begin{bmatrix} f_{11} & f_{12} & f_{13} & f_{14} \\ f_{21} & f_{22} & f_{23} & f_{24} \\ f_{31} & f_{32} & f_{33} & f_{34} \\ f_{41} & f_{42} & f_{43} & f_{44} \end{bmatrix} \quad p = \begin{bmatrix} p_1 \\ p_2 \\ p_3 \\ p_4 \end{bmatrix} \quad 0 = \begin{bmatrix} 0 \\ 0 \\ 0 \\ 0 \end{bmatrix}$$

Considering first the product fp we have

$$f_{(4\times 4)} \times p_{(4\times 1)} = \begin{bmatrix} (f_{11}p_1 + f_{12}p_2 + f_{13}p_3 + f_{14}p_4) \\ (f_{21}p_1 + f_{22}p_2 + f_{23}p_3 + f_{24}p_4) \\ (f_{31}p_1 + f_{32}p_2 + f_{33}p_3 + f_{34}p_4) \\ (f_{41}p_1 + f_{42}p_2 + f_{43}p_3 + f_{44}p_4) \end{bmatrix}_{(4\times 1)}$$

Note that each row of fp contains only a single element, which is the sum of four terms. The product fp is therefore a column matrix. It has the same order as u_0, and the addition $u_0 + fp$ can therefore be performed. Using the addition rule, we have

$$u_0 + fp = \begin{bmatrix} (u_{10} + f_{11}p_1 + f_{12}p_2 + f_{13}p_3 + f_{14}p_4) \\ (u_{20} + f_{21}p_1 + f_{22}p_2 + f_{23}p_3 + f_{24}p_4) \\ (u_{30} + f_{31}p_1 + f_{32}p_2 + f_{33}p_3 + f_{34}p_4) \\ (u_{40} + f_{41}p_1 + f_{42}p_2 + f_{43}p_3 + f_{44}p_4) \end{bmatrix}_{(4\times 1)}$$

The equating of the matrix $[u_0 + fp]$ to the null matrix $[O]$ signifies that corresponding elements are equal and therefore gives rise to four relationships in ordinary algebra. These relationships are

$$u_{10} + f_{11}p_1 + f_{12}p_2 + f_{13}p_3 + f_{14}p_4 = 0$$
$$u_{20} + f_{21}p_1 + f_{22}p_2 + f_{23}p_3 + f_{24}p_4 = 0$$
$$u_{30} + f_{31}p_1 + f_{32}p_2 + f_{33}p_3 + f_{34}p_4 = 0 \qquad (A.14)$$
$$u_{40} + f_{41}p_1 + f_{42}p_2 + f_{43}p_3 + f_{44}p_4 = 0$$

By the rules of matrix algebra the single matrix equation A.13 therefore implies the four simultaneous equations of (A.14).

A.8　TRANSFORMATION MATRICES

Any matrix multiplication, TA, might be regarded as a process for transforming a matrix A into a different matrix B. Very often the *transformation matrix* T is a square matrix, so that the product, TA, leaves the order of A unchanged, but rectangular transformation matrices are also used. Frequently, the matrix T has a fairly simple form and serves to rearrange the elements of A, or to multiply the elements by scaling factors, or to combine one row or column with another and so on. Since the given matrix A can be transformed either by premultiplication or by postmultiplication, a general transformation can be written

$$T_1 A T_2 = B \qquad (A.15)$$

where T_1 and T_2 are both square matrices and B has the same order as A.

Transformation matrices are used extensively in this book, where they have a physical significance. In Chapter 5, transformation matrices are used to provide scaling factors and in Chapter 6 they are used to effect change of axes. Below, the more elementary properties of transformation are illustrated by reference to matrices of order (3×3).

(i) MULTIPLICATION BY DIAGONAL MATRICES. We note first that the multiplication of a given matrix A by a unit matrix I leaves A unchanged. Thus

$$IA = AI = A \qquad (A.16)$$

Premultiplication of A by a diagonal matrix T serves to multiply each element of a particular row of A by the corresponding element of T. Thus

$$\begin{bmatrix} k_1 & 0 & 0 \\ 0 & k_2 & 0 \\ 0 & 0 & k_3 \end{bmatrix} \begin{bmatrix} a_1 & a_2 & a_3 \\ b_1 & b_2 & b_3 \\ c_1 & c_2 & c_3 \end{bmatrix} = \begin{bmatrix} k_1 a_1 & k_1 a_2 & k_1 a_3 \\ k_2 b_1 & k_2 b_2 & k_2 b_3 \\ k_3 c_1 & k_3 c_2 & k_3 c_3 \end{bmatrix} \qquad (A.17)$$
$$\quad\ \ T_{11} \qquad\qquad\quad\ A \qquad\qquad\qquad\quad B$$

Postmultiplication of A by a diagonal matrix T serves to multiply each element of a particular column of A by the corresponding element of T. Thus

$$\begin{bmatrix} a_1 & a_2 & a_3 \\ b_1 & b_2 & b_3 \\ c_1 & c_2 & c_3 \end{bmatrix} \begin{bmatrix} k_1 & 0 & 0 \\ 0 & k_2 & 0 \\ 0 & 0 & k_3 \end{bmatrix} = \begin{bmatrix} k_1 a_1 & k_2 a_2 & k_3 a_3 \\ k_1 b_1 & k_2 b_2 & k_3 b_3 \\ k_1 c_1 & k_2 c_2 & k_3 c_3 \end{bmatrix} \qquad (A.18)$$
$$\quad\ \ A \qquad\qquad\quad\ T_{21} \qquad\qquad\qquad\quad B$$

Multiplication by a diagonal matrix can be used to provide scaling factors without rearrangement of the elements of A.

(ii) MULTIPLICATION BY OFF-DIAGONAL MATRICES.   Rearrangement of the rows of A can be effected by premultiplying A by a suitable matrix. Scaling factors can be provided at the same time.   Thus

$$\begin{bmatrix} 0 & k_1 & 0 \\ k_2 & 0 & 0 \\ 0 & 0 & k_3 \end{bmatrix} \begin{bmatrix} a_1 & a_2 & a_3 \\ b_1 & b_2 & b_3 \\ c_1 & c_2 & c_3 \end{bmatrix} = \begin{bmatrix} k_1 b_1 & k_1 b_2 & k_1 b_3 \\ k_2 a_1 & k_2 a_2 & k_2 a_3 \\ k_3 c_1 & k_3 c_2 & k_3 c_3 \end{bmatrix} \qquad (A.19)$$

$$\quad\; T_{12} \qquad\qquad\quad A \qquad\qquad\qquad B$$

In comparison with matrix T_{11} of equation A.17, the elements k_1 and k_2 in T_{12} have changed columns.   The effect of this is to interchange rows 1 and 2 of A and also to provide scaling factors.

Similarly, an interchange of columns can be effected by postmultiplication.

$$\begin{bmatrix} a_1 & a_2 & a_3 \\ b_1 & b_2 & b_3 \\ c_1 & c_2 & c_3 \end{bmatrix} \begin{bmatrix} 0 & k_2 & 0 \\ 0 & 0 & k_3 \\ k_1 & 0 & 0 \end{bmatrix} = \begin{bmatrix} k_1 a_3 & k_2 a_1 & k_3 a_2 \\ k_1 b_3 & k_2 b_1 & k_3 b_2 \\ k_1 c_3 & k_2 c_1 & k_3 c_2 \end{bmatrix} \qquad (A.20)$$

$$\qquad A \qquad\qquad\quad T_{22} \qquad\qquad\qquad B$$

(iii) GENERAL CASE OF TRANSFORMATION.   Combination of the rows of A is effected when the premultiplying matrix contains more than one element in a given row.

$$\begin{bmatrix} 1 & k_1 & 0 \\ 0 & k_2 & 0 \\ 0 & 0 & k_3 \end{bmatrix} \begin{bmatrix} a_1 & a_2 & a_3 \\ b_1 & b_2 & b_3 \\ c_1 & c_2 & c_3 \end{bmatrix} = \begin{bmatrix} (a_1 + k_1 b_1) & (a_2 + k_1 b_2) & (a_3 + k_1 b_3) \\ k_2 b_1 & k_2 b_2 & k_2 b_3 \\ k_3 c_1 & k_3 c_2 & k_3 c_3 \end{bmatrix}$$

$$\;\; T_{13} \qquad\qquad A \qquad\qquad\qquad\qquad\qquad B$$

$$(A.21)$$

Here the first row of B is equal to the first row of A plus k_1 times the second row.   This combination is determined by the form of the top row of T_{13}.

Combination of the columns of A is similarly effected by the use of a postmultiplying matrix which contains more than one element in a given column.

Successive transformations can be made of a given matrix A, so that a general transformation can be expressed in the form

$$(T_{1n} \cdots T_{13}T_{12}T_{11}) A(T_{21}T_{22}T_{23} \cdots T_{2n}) = B \qquad (A.22)$$

Such a successive transformation is discussed in Section A.10, where it is used for the purpose of inversion.

A.9 THE INVERSE MATRIX AND MATRIX DIVISION

Given a square matrix A, it is possible to find another square matrix B of the same order such that $AB = I$ provided that A is non-singular. The matrix A is said to be singular if the determinant containing the same elements as A is equal to zero or infinite. The matrix B is called the *inverse* of A and is denoted by A^{-1}. The process of finding A^{-1} is called *inversion*. If $AA^{-1} = I$, then $A^{-1}A = I$. This is a special case where it is not only possible to reverse the sequence of the terms in the product, but the value of the product is unchanged.

The inverse matrix is used to perform a function in matrix algebra similar to division in ordinary algebra. Suppose we have a set of linear simultaneous equations represented by the matrix equation

$$AX = C \qquad (A.23)$$

where A is a square matrix while X and C are column vectors. Provided that A is non-singular, we can determine its inverse, A^{-1}. Premultiplying both sides of equation A.23 by A^{-1}, we have

$$A^{-1}AX = A^{-1}C$$

But since $A^{-1}A = I$, this can be written

$$X = A^{-1}C \qquad (A.24)$$

The operation of multiplying by A^{-1} is therefore analogous to the operation of dividing by A. Just as we must distinguish between premultiplying and postmultiplying, so we must also distinguish between predividing and postdividing. In a matrix equation such as

$$BA + MA = C$$

the matrix A can be eliminated from the left-hand side by postmultiplying by A^{-1}, giving

$$B(AA^{-1}) + M(AA^{-1}) = CA^{-1}$$
$$B + M = CA^{-1}$$

The process analogous to division can be effected if the inverse of a matrix can be determined. It should be noted that only a square matrix can be inverted.

A.10 INVERSION BY SUCCESSIVE TRANSFORMATION

Suppose that A is a non-singular square matrix. Then it is possible to find a transformation matrix T such that

$$TA = I \qquad (A.25)$$

T is, of course, the required inverse, A^{-1}. We transform A to I by stages

$$T_n \cdots T_3 T_2 T_1 A = I$$

so that T is finally obtained as a matrix product

$$T = (T_n T_{n-1} \cdots T_2 T_1) = A^{-1} \tag{A.26}$$

This matrix multiplication can be carried out at the same time by commencing with a unit matrix and multiplying successively by $T_1, T_2 \ldots T_n$. Then, while the given matrix A is systematically reduced to I, the unit matrix is converted to A^{-1}. In Fig. A.5 the two transformations are performed in parallel columns.

Consider the matrix

$$A = \begin{bmatrix} a_{11} & a_{12} & a_{13} \\ a_{21} & a_{22} & a_{23} \\ a_{31} & a_{32} & a_{33} \end{bmatrix} = \begin{bmatrix} 4 & 4 & 8 \\ 1 & 2 & 0 \\ 2 & 6 & 16 \end{bmatrix}$$

The determinant which contains the same elements, and which is usually denoted by $|A|$, has the value $+80$. Since $|A|$ is non-zero, the matrix A has an inverse. Referring back to equation A.21, we notice that a transformation matrix T_1 can be found which will, by premultiplication, convert the elements of the first column of A to the values $\{1, 0, 0\}$. The required matrix is

$$T_1 = \begin{bmatrix} 1/a_{11} & 0 & 0 \\ -a_{21}/a_{11} & 1 & 0 \\ -a_{31}/a_{11} & 0 & 1 \end{bmatrix} = \begin{bmatrix} +1/4 & 0 & 0 \\ -1/4 & 1 & 0 \\ -2/4 & 0 & 1 \end{bmatrix}$$

The first row of T_1 divides the first row of A by its initial element. The second row of T_1 so combines the first and second rows of A as to replace a_{21} by zero. The third row of T_1 performs the same function for a_{31}. In Fig. A.5 the matrix A is multiplied by T_1 in the left-hand column while I is multiplied by T_1 in the right-hand column.

A second matrix T_2 is now determined which will convert the elements of the second column of $(T_1 A)$ to the values $\{0, 1, 0\}$. Provided the first column of T_2 is

$$\begin{bmatrix} 1 & \cdot & \cdot \\ 0 & \cdot & \cdot \\ 0 & \cdot & \cdot \end{bmatrix}$$

the elements of the first column of (T_1A) are unaltered. The required matrix is

$$T_2 = \begin{bmatrix} 1 & -\dfrac{1}{1} & 0 \\[2ex] 0 & +\dfrac{1}{1} & 0 \\[2ex] 0 & -\dfrac{4}{1} & 1 \end{bmatrix}$$

In a similar way, the elements of the third column of (T_2T_1A) are now

$$
\begin{bmatrix} 4 & 4 & 8 \\ 1 & 2 & 0 \\ 2 & 6 & 16 \end{bmatrix} \leftarrow A
\qquad
\left\|
\begin{bmatrix} 1 & 0 & 0 \\ 0 & 1 & 0 \\ 0 & 0 & 1 \end{bmatrix} \leftarrow I
\right.
$$

$$
T_1 \rightarrow
\begin{bmatrix} 0.25 & 0 & 0 \\ -0.25 & 1 & 0 \\ -0.50 & 0 & 1 \end{bmatrix}
\begin{bmatrix} 1 & 1 & 2 \\ 0 & 1 & -2 \\ 0 & 4 & 12 \end{bmatrix} \leftarrow T_1A
\qquad
\left\|
\begin{bmatrix} 0.25 & 0 & 0 \\ -0.25 & 1 & 0 \\ -0.50 & 0 & 1 \end{bmatrix} \leftarrow T_1I
\right.
$$

$$
T_2 \rightarrow
\begin{bmatrix} 1 & -1 & 0 \\ 0 & 1 & 0 \\ 0 & -4 & 1 \end{bmatrix}
\begin{bmatrix} 1 & 0 & 4 \\ 0 & 1 & -2 \\ 0 & 0 & 20 \end{bmatrix} \leftarrow T_2T_1A
\qquad
\left\|
\begin{bmatrix} 0.50 & -1 & 0 \\ -0.25 & 1 & 0 \\ 0.50 & -4 & 1 \end{bmatrix} \leftarrow T_2T_1I
\right.
$$

$$
T_3 \rightarrow
\begin{bmatrix} 1 & 0 & -0.20 \\ 0 & 1 & 0.10 \\ 0 & 0 & 0.05 \end{bmatrix}
\begin{bmatrix} 1 & 0 & 0 \\ 0 & 1 & 0 \\ 0 & 0 & 1 \end{bmatrix} \begin{matrix} \leftarrow T_3T_2T_1A \\ \equiv I \end{matrix}
\qquad
\left\|
\begin{bmatrix} 0.400 & -0.200 & -0.200 \\ -0.200 & 0.600 & 0.100 \\ 0.025 & -0.200 & 0.050 \end{bmatrix} \begin{matrix} \leftarrow T_3T_2T_1I \\ \equiv A^{-1} \end{matrix}
\right.
$$

Fig. A.5

reduced to the values $\{0, \quad 0, \quad 1\}$ by a matrix T_3. Provided the first and second columns of T_3 are

$$\begin{bmatrix} 1 & 0 & \cdot \\ 0 & 1 & \cdot \\ 0 & 0 & \cdot \end{bmatrix}$$

the first two columns of (T_2T_1A) are unaltered. The required matrix is

$$T_3 = \begin{bmatrix} 1 & 0 & -\dfrac{4}{20} \\[2ex] 0 & 1 & -\dfrac{-2}{20} \\[2ex] 0 & 0 & +\dfrac{1}{20} \end{bmatrix}$$

In Fig. A.5 the progressive formation of the unit matrix from A is indicated by dotted lines.

When the inverse matrix A^{-1} has been determined it is most important that either the matrix product AA^{-1} or $A^{-1}A$ be calculated as a check on the arithmetic. Either product must be equal to I.

A corresponding process can be developed in which postmultiplying transformation matrices are employed. In this process the *rows* of A are successively transformed to the rows of the unit matrix by suitable combinations of the columns of A. The procedure is essentially the same as that outlined above.

A set of simultaneous equations

$$4x_1 + 4x_2 + 8x_3 = c_1$$

$$x_1 + 2x_2 + 0x_3 = c_2 \qquad \text{(A.26)}$$

$$2x_1 + 6x_2 + 16x_3 = c_3$$

can be expressed in the matrix form

$$\begin{bmatrix} 4 & 4 & 8 \\ 1 & 2 & 0 \\ 2 & 6 & 16 \end{bmatrix} \begin{bmatrix} x_1 \\ x_2 \\ x_3 \end{bmatrix} = \begin{bmatrix} c_1 \\ c_2 \\ c_3 \end{bmatrix} \qquad \text{(A.27)}$$

$$\qquad A \qquad\quad X \qquad\quad C$$

Premultiplying both sides of equation A.27 by the inverse A^{-1}, which has been determined above, we have

$$\begin{bmatrix} x_1 \\ x_2 \\ x_3 \end{bmatrix} = \begin{bmatrix} +0.400 & -0.200 & -0.200 \\ -0.200 & +0.600 & +0.100 \\ +0.025 & -0.200 & +0.050 \end{bmatrix} \begin{bmatrix} c_1 \\ c_2 \\ c_3 \end{bmatrix} \qquad \text{(A.28)}$$

which corresponds, in longhand form, to the equations

$$x_1 = +0.400c_1 \quad -0.200c_2 \quad -0.200c_3$$

$$x_2 = -0.200c_1 \quad +0.600c_2 \quad +0.100c_3 \qquad \text{(A.29)}$$

$$x_3 = +0.025c_1 \quad -0.200c_2 \quad +0.050c_3$$

It is now a simple matter to determine x_1, x_2 and x_3 for any prescribed values of c_1, c_2 and c_3.

It should be noted that if the matrix A is a diagonal matrix, then A^{-1} is also a diagonal matrix. The elements of A^{-1} are the reciprocals of the corresponding elements of A. This can be checked by multiplying A by A^{-1}.

$$\begin{bmatrix} a & 0 & 0 & 0 \\ 0 & b & 0 & 0 \\ 0 & 0 & c & 0 \\ 0 & 0 & 0 & d \end{bmatrix} \begin{bmatrix} 1/a & 0 & 0 & 0 \\ 0 & 1/b & 0 & 0 \\ 0 & 0 & 1/c & 0 \\ 0 & 0 & 0 & 1/d \end{bmatrix} = \begin{bmatrix} 1 & 0 & 0 & 0 \\ 0 & 1 & 0 & 0 \\ 0 & 0 & 1 & 0 \\ 0 & 0 & 0 & 1 \end{bmatrix}$$

A.11 INVERSION BY FACTORIZATION

Since the product AB of two conformable matrices yields another matrix C, then C can be said to have factors A and B. Even when A, B and C are all square matrices it is possible to find an infinite number of factors A and B for a given matrix C. The matrix equation

$$\underset{A}{\begin{bmatrix} a_{11} & a_{12} & a_{13} \\ a_{21} & a_{22} & a_{23} \\ a_{31} & a_{32} & a_{33} \end{bmatrix}} \underset{B}{\begin{bmatrix} b_{11} & b_{12} & b_{13} \\ b_{21} & b_{22} & b_{23} \\ b_{31} & b_{32} & b_{33} \end{bmatrix}} = \underset{C}{\begin{bmatrix} 4 & 4 & 8 \\ 1 & 2 & 0 \\ 2 & 6 & 16 \end{bmatrix}}$$

implies nine relationships of ordinary algebra since there are nine elements in C and nine in the product AB. Nine of the elements of A and B can be specified in such a way that the remainder can be determined from the relationships referred to. When factorization is used for the purpose of inversion, it is usual to specify that A is a lower triangular matrix with unit elements on the diagonal, and that B is an upper triangular matrix. That is to say, we write

$$\underset{L}{\begin{bmatrix} 1 & 0 & 0 \\ l_{21} & 1 & 0 \\ l_{31} & l_{32} & 1 \end{bmatrix}} \underset{U}{\begin{bmatrix} u_{11} & u_{12} & u_{13} \\ 0 & u_{22} & u_{23} \\ 0 & 0 & u_{33} \end{bmatrix}} = \underset{C}{\begin{bmatrix} 4 & 4 & 8 \\ 1 & 2 & 0 \\ 2 & 6 & 16 \end{bmatrix}} \qquad \text{(A.30)}$$

The nine unknown elements on the left-hand side of equation A.30 can be determined one at a time by generating the elements of C in order. Thus, the element c_{11} is the inner product of the first row of L with the first column of U. This gives

$$1 \cdot u_{11} = 4$$

In the same way, generation of c_{12} and c_{13} leads to the values of u_{12} and u_{13}.

By generating the elements of the second row of C, we obtain the values of u_{22} and u_{23}. In this manner we obtain, finally,

$$\begin{bmatrix} 1 & 0 & 0 \\ 0.25 & 1 & 0 \\ 0.50 & 4 & 1 \end{bmatrix} \begin{bmatrix} 4 & 4 & 8 \\ 0 & 1 & -2 \\ 0 & 0 & 20 \end{bmatrix} = \begin{bmatrix} 4 & 4 & 8 \\ 1 & 2 & 0 \\ 2 & 6 & 16 \end{bmatrix}$$
$$\qquad\quad L \qquad\qquad\quad U \qquad\qquad\quad C$$

Suppose now that C is to be inverted.

Since $$C = LU$$

then $$CU^{-1} = LUU^{-1} = L$$

and $$C^{-1}CU^{-1} = C^{-1}L$$

therefore $$U^{-1} = C^{-1}L \qquad\qquad\qquad (A.31)$$

Because of the special nature of the matrices U and L first U^{-1} and then C^{-1} can be determined element by element using a procedure similar to that used in the calculation of L and U. In the first place we have, by definition,

$$\begin{bmatrix} 4 & 4 & 8 \\ 0 & 1 & -2 \\ 0 & 0 & 20 \end{bmatrix} \begin{bmatrix} v_{11} & v_{12} & v_{13} \\ v_{21} & v_{22} & v_{23} \\ v_{31} & v_{32} & v_{33} \end{bmatrix} = \begin{bmatrix} 1 & 0 & 0 \\ 0 & 1 & 0 \\ 0 & 0 & 1 \end{bmatrix} \qquad (A.32)$$
$$\qquad\quad U \qquad\qquad\quad U^{-1} \qquad\qquad\quad I$$

Taking the inner product of the last row of U with the last column of U^{-1}, we have
$$20v_{33} = 1$$

The other elements of U^{-1} are found in the same way by generating successively the terms of I commencing with the last and working back along the rows. We find that

$$U^{-1} = \begin{bmatrix} 0.25 & -1 & -0.20 \\ 0 & 1 & 0.10 \\ 0 & 0 & 0.05 \end{bmatrix}$$

It should be noted that the inverse of an upper triangular matrix is always another upper triangular matrix.

Having determined U^{-1}, we can write, using equation A.31,

$$
\begin{bmatrix} 0.25 & -1 & -0.20 \\ 0 & 1 & 0.10 \\ 0 & 0 & 0.05 \end{bmatrix} = \begin{bmatrix} d_{11} & d_{12} & d_{13} \\ d_{21} & d_{22} & d_{23} \\ d_{31} & d_{32} & d_{33} \end{bmatrix} \begin{bmatrix} 1 & 0 & 0 \\ 0.25 & 1 & 0 \\ 0.50 & 4 & 1 \end{bmatrix}
$$
$$
\quad\quad U^{-1} \quad\quad\quad\quad C^{-1} \quad\quad\quad\quad\quad L
$$

Here again, if the terms of U^{-1} are generated by the relevant inner products of C^{-1} and L, the elements of C^{-1} can be determined one at a time. In this case we start with the bottom right-hand element of U^{-1} and work up the columns. Taking the last row of C^{-1} and the last column of L, we have

$$d_{33} \times 1 = 0.05$$

Continuing in this manner, we finally obtain

$$
C^{-1} = \begin{bmatrix} +0.400 & -0.200 & -0.200 \\ -0.200 & +0.600 & +0.100 \\ +0.025 & -0.200 & +0.050 \end{bmatrix}
$$

This result must now be checked by ensuring that its product with C is equal to a unit matrix.

A.12   INVERSION BY PARTITIONING

Consider a square matrix A and its inverse B, each partitioned into four submatrices in such a way that the submatrices on the diagonal are square. We can then write

$$
\left[\begin{array}{c|c} A_1 & A_2 \\ \hline A_3 & A_4 \end{array}\right] \left[\begin{array}{c|c} B_1 & B_2 \\ \hline B_3 & B_4 \end{array}\right] = \left[\begin{array}{c|c} I & O \\ \hline O & I \end{array}\right] \tag{A.33}
$$
$$
\quad\quad A \quad\quad\quad\quad B \quad\quad\quad\quad I
$$

The unit matrix on the right-hand side of equation A.33 is similarly partitioned, so that its two diagonal submatrices are unit matrices of the same order as A_1 and A_4, while its other submatrices are null matrices. Forming the product AB and equating its terms to those of I, we have

$$
\begin{aligned}
A_1 B_1 + A_2 B_3 &= I \\
A_1 B_2 + A_2 B_4 &= O \\
A_3 B_1 + A_4 B_3 &= O \\
A_3 B_2 + A_4 B_4 &= I
\end{aligned} \tag{A.34}
$$

These four equations can be solved in order to express the unknown values B_1, B_2, B_3 and B_4 in terms of the known quantities A_1, A_2, A_3 and A_4. These relationships may be shown to be

$$B_1 = A_1^{-1} + A_1^{-1} A_2 (A_4 - A_3 A_1^{-1} A_2)^{-1} A_3 A_1^{-1}$$

$$B_2 = -A_1^{-1} A_2 (A_4 - A_3 A_1^{-1} A_2)^{-1}$$

$$B_3 = -(A_4 - A_3 A_1^{-1} A_2)^{-1} A_3 A_1^{-1}$$

$$B_4 = (A_4 - A_3 A_1^{-1} A_2)^{-1}$$

(A.35)

Although these expressions appear to be extensive it must be remembered that the operations of multiplication, addition and subtraction can be carried out much more quickly than inversion. Furthermore, the presence of common terms enables B_1, B_2, B_3 and B_4 to be carried out progressively. If we put

$$\alpha = (A_4 - A_3 A_1^{-1} A_2)$$

$$\beta = A_3 A_1^{-1}$$

and

$$\gamma = A_1^{-1} A_2$$

then we have

$$B_4 = \alpha^{-1}$$

$$B_3 = -\alpha^{-1} \beta$$

$$B_2 = -\gamma \alpha^{-1}$$

$$B_1 = A_1^{-1} + \gamma \alpha^{-1} \beta$$

(A.36)

This process requires the inversion of A_1 and the inversion of α, which has the same order as A_4. For large matrices a step-by-step procedure for inversion can be based upon the foregoing method. If the partitioning of a matrix of order $(n \times n)$ is so arranged that A_4 is a single element, α is also a single element (or scalar quantity) and α^{-1} is merely the reciprocal of α. The only inversion then required is that of A_1, which is of order $(n - 1) \times (n - 1)$. This inversion again can be made to depend on the inversion of a submatrix of order $(n - 2) \times (n - 2)$ by the same process. This reduction is repeated until the whole inversion depends upon the inversion of the first element only of A, which is effected by taking its reciprocal.

In Chapter 5, the axis transformation matrix was expressed in terms of its submatrices (see p. 76) of order (3×3)

$$A = \left[\begin{array}{c|c} \lambda & O \\ \hline \lambda X & \lambda \end{array} \right]$$

By reference to equation A.33 we can put

$$A_1 = \lambda$$
$$A_2 = O$$
$$A_3 = \lambda X$$
$$A_4 = \lambda$$

Then, since $A_2 = O$,

$$\alpha = A_4 = \lambda$$

$$\beta = A_3 A_1^{-1} = \lambda X \lambda^{-1}$$

$$\gamma = O$$

Substituting these values in equations A.36, we obtain

$$B_4 = \lambda^{-1}$$
$$B_3 = -\lambda^{-1}(\lambda X \lambda^{-1}) = -X\lambda^{-1}$$
$$B_2 = O$$
$$B_1 = \lambda^{-1}$$

or

$$A^{-1} = \left[\begin{array}{c|c} \lambda^{-1} & O \\ \hline -X\lambda^{-1} & \lambda^{-1} \end{array}\right] \tag{A.37}$$

A.13 GAUSS-JORDAN ELIMINATION

The systematic process known as Gauss-Jordan elimination can be used to obtain the inverse of a matrix A, or it can be used to obtain the solution of a set of linear simultaneous equations without the inverse being specifically expressed. The latter application will be discussed first.

Suppose that it is required to solve a set of equations expressed in the form

$$AX = B \tag{A.38}$$

The first of these equations is divided through by the coefficient a_{11}, and the resulting equation is used to eliminate the x_1 term from each succeeding equation. The set then has the appearance

$$\begin{bmatrix} 1 & c_{12} & c_{13} & \cdots & c_{1n} \\ 0 & c_{22} & c_{23} & \cdots & c_{2n} \\ 0 & c_{n2} & c_{n3} & \cdots & c_{nn} \end{bmatrix} \begin{bmatrix} x_1 \\ x_n \end{bmatrix} = \begin{bmatrix} d_1 \\ d_n \end{bmatrix} \tag{A.39}$$

The second equation is now divided through by its diagonal term (c_{22}) and the resulting equation used to eliminate the x_2 term from all other equations. The process is continued in the same manner. In a typical step, the ith step of the procedure, the ith equation is divided through by its diagonal term and then used to eliminate the x_i terms from equations both above and below the ith.

After four stages of elimination, the equations have the appearance

$$
\begin{bmatrix}
1 & & & & e_{15} & \cdots\cdots & e_{1n} \\
& 1 & & & e_{25} & & \\
& & 1 & & e_{35} & & \\
& & & 1 & e_{45} & & \\
\hline
& & & & e_{55} & & \\
& & & & e_{65} & & \\
& & & & \cdot & & \\
& & & & \cdot & & \\
& & & & \cdot & & \\
& & & & e_{n5} & & e_{nn}
\end{bmatrix}
\begin{bmatrix}
x_1 \\ \cdot \\ \\ \cdot \\ \hline \cdot \\ \cdot \\ \cdot \\ \\ \\ x_n
\end{bmatrix}
=
\begin{bmatrix}
f_1 \\ f_2 \\ \\ \\ \hline \\ \\ \\ \\ \\ f_n
\end{bmatrix}
\qquad (A.40)
$$

With successive steps, the unit matrix in the top left-hand corner grows in size, until eventually the equations have the form

$$IX = G \qquad (A.41)$$

The equations are then solved since each element of x is equal to the corresponding element of G. In effect, G is $A^{-1}B$.

If, in the original equations A.38, the matrix B contains several columns, the procedure is unaltered. Matrices D, F and G will contain the same number of columns as B. The elements of the first column of G will represent the solutions corresponding to the values in the first column of B and so on.

It should also be borne in mind that the equations can be taken in any order without altering their validity in any way. Thus when we have reached the stage shown in equation A.40 any equation below the dotted line may be regarded as the fifth equation. This fact is of importance if the element e_{55} happens to be zero. In that event some other equation is moved up into fifth position.

The significance of the various submatrices in the array of equations A.40 can be elucidated if we first divide the original equations into submatrices of size corresponding to those of equations A.40.

$$
\begin{bmatrix}
A_{11} & A_{12} \\
\hline
A_{21} & A_{22}
\end{bmatrix}
\begin{bmatrix}
X_1 \\
\hline
X_2
\end{bmatrix}
=
\begin{bmatrix}
B_1 \\
\hline
B_2
\end{bmatrix}
\qquad (A.42)
$$

We now operate on these two matrix equations by a process similar to that above, but using matrix operations. The first matrix equation of A.42 is premultiplied by A_{11}^{-1}, which is equivalent to dividing through the first equation by its initial coefficient:

$$\left[\begin{array}{c|c} I & A_{11}^{-1}A_{12} \\ \hline A_{21} & A_{22} \end{array}\right]\left[\begin{array}{c} X_1 \\ \hline X_2 \end{array}\right] = \left[\begin{array}{c} A_{11}^{-1}B_1 \\ \hline B_2 \end{array}\right]$$

To eliminate A_{21} from the second matrix equation, we premultiply the first equation by A_{21} and subtract from the second.

$$\left[\begin{array}{c|c} I & A_{11}^{-1}A_{12} \\ \hline A_{21} - A_{21}I & \\ = 0 & A_{22} - A_{21}A_{11}^{-1}A_{12} \end{array}\right]\left[\begin{array}{c} X_1 \\ \hline X_2 \end{array}\right] = \left[\begin{array}{c} A_{11}^{-1}B_1 \\ \hline B_2 \\ -A_{21}A_{11}^{-1}B_1 \end{array}\right] \quad (A.43)$$

This form is similar to that of equations A.40 and, by comparison, the submatrices of E and F are appreciated as functions of the original matrices A and B.

As mentioned above, B may have as many columns as desired. If for B we adopt a square matrix I, then as the elimination process reduces the matrix A to a unit matrix on the left of the equation, the I matrix on the right of the equation is reduced to A^{-1}. In this way the elimination process can be used for matrix inversion.

The Gauss-Jordan procedure is virtually the same as the transformation process described in Section A.10. Each step of the Gauss-Jordan elimination corresponds to premultiplication by a further transformation matrix T.

A.14 TRANSPOSITION AND INVERSION OF PRODUCTS

Suppose that matrices A and B are of order $(l \times m)$ and $(m \times n)$ respectively, so that they can form a product AB. The transposed matrices A^T and B^T are of order $(m \times l)$ and $(n \times m)$ respectively and can therefore form a product $B^T A^T$. The product $A^T B^T$ is not possible unless $n = l$. Because of the interchange of columns and rows when a matrix is transposed it can easily be shown that the product $B^T A^T$ is the transpose of the product AB. This fact is illustrated in Fig. A.6.

$$C = AB$$

and $$D = B^T A^T$$

Furthermore, d_{ji} is equal to c_{ij} since they are both formed by the inner

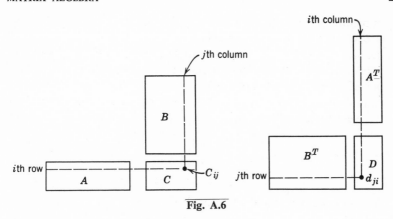

Fig. A.6

products of the same elements.   Hence

$$D = C^T$$

and $$B^T A^T = (AB)^T$$

The rule can easily be extended to the form

$$(ABCD)^T = D^T C^T B^T A^T \qquad (A.44)$$

The transposition of the product of n matrices is the product of the transposes taken in the reverse order.   A similar reversal of order occurs when the product of n matrices is inverted.   The product

$$
\begin{aligned}
(ABCD)(D^{-1}C^{-1}B^{-1}A^{-1}) &= ABC(DD^{-1})C^{-1}B^{-1}A^{-1} \\
&= AB(CC^{-1})B^{-1}A^{-1} \\
&= A(BB^{-1})A^{-1} \\
&= AA^{-1} \\
&= I
\end{aligned}
$$

Hence $$(ABCD)^{-1} = D^{-1}C^{-1}B^{-1}A^{-1} \qquad (A.45)$$

A.15 IMPROVEMENT OF THE ACCURACY OF AN INVERSE MATRIX

Suppose that it is required to find the inverse of a matrix B, and suppose also that a reasonable approximation, A^{-1}, to this inverse is known.   It is possible to adjust the matrix A^{-1} to obtain a closer approximation to B^{-1}, and hence to approach B^{-1} by iteration.

The problem can be formulated from two different standpoints.   First, a matrix A might be inverted correctly to yield A^{-1}.   It may then be required to make slight modifications to the elements of A.   In a structural problem such a variation might result from the alteration of the size of certain member of a frame. In this way the matrix A is changed to the matrix B whose inverse is now required.

In the second place the inverse of B might be incorrectly determined as A^{-1} instead of B^{-1}. If the error is not large it can be adjusted. Two methods of adjustment are discussed.

Suppose that A and ΔA are two square matrices of the same order, and that the elements of ΔA are small compared with those of A. We can write

$$B = A + \Delta A$$
$$= A + AA^{-1}\Delta A$$
$$= A(I + A^{-1}\Delta A) \qquad (A.46)$$

Then, using the theorem of equation A.45,

$$B^{-1} = (I + A^{-1}\Delta A)^{-1}A^{-1} \qquad (A.47)$$

It can be shown that the binomial theorem applies to matrix expressions provided that the order of the terms is preserved. Expanding the right-hand side of equation A.47 in this way, we have

$$B^{-1} = [I - (A^{-1}\Delta A) + (A^{-1}\Delta A)^2 - (A^{-1}\Delta A)^3 \ldots]A^{-1} \quad (A.48)$$

Provided that this expansion converges rapidly it can be used to obtain B^{-1} from A^{-1} and ΔA.

Suppose that it is required to find the inverse of the matrix

$$B = \begin{bmatrix} 4 & 4 & 8 \\ 1 & 2 & 1 \\ 2 & 6 & 16 \end{bmatrix}$$

while the inverse of the matrix

$$A = \begin{bmatrix} 4 & 4 & 8 \\ 1 & 2 & 0 \\ 2 & 6 & 16 \end{bmatrix}$$

is known to be

$$A^{-1} = \begin{bmatrix} +0.400 & -0.200 & -0.200 \\ -0.200 & +0.600 & +0.100 \\ +0.025 & -0.200 & +0.050 \end{bmatrix}$$

In this case the variation ΔA is

$$\Delta A = \begin{bmatrix} 0 & 0 & 0 \\ 0 & 0 & +1 \\ 0 & 0 & 0 \end{bmatrix}$$

It should be noted that in general ΔA might contain small variations of all the elements, but for simplicity only one element is varied here.

The product $A^{-1} \Delta A$ is formed.

$$A^{-1} \Delta A = \begin{bmatrix} 0 & 0 & -0.200 \\ 0 & 0 & +0.600 \\ 0 & 0 & -0.200 \end{bmatrix}$$

When only the first two terms of the binomial expansion are used, equation A.48 gives

$$B^{-1} = \begin{bmatrix} 1 & 0 & +0.200 \\ 0 & 1 & -0.600 \\ 0 & 0 & +1.200 \end{bmatrix} \begin{bmatrix} +0.400 & -0.200 & -0.200 \\ -0.200 & +0.600 & +0.100 \\ +0.025 & -0.200 & +0.050 \end{bmatrix} = \begin{bmatrix} +0.405 & -0.250 & -0.190 \\ -0.215 & +0.720 & +0.070 \\ +0.030 & -0.240 & +0.060 \end{bmatrix}$$

$\quad\quad\quad (I - A^{-1} \Delta A) \quad\quad\quad\quad A^{-1}$ $\hfill$ (A.49)

If the first three terms of the binomial expansion are to be used, the matrix $(A^{-1} \Delta A)$ is squared and added to the matrix $(I - A^{-1} \Delta A)$. We then have

$$B^{-1} = \begin{bmatrix} 1 & 0 & +0.240 \\ 0 & 1 & -0.720 \\ 0 & 0 & +1.240 \end{bmatrix} \begin{bmatrix} +0.400 & -0.200 & -0.200 \\ -0.200 & +0.600 & +0.100 \\ +0.025 & -0.200 & +0.050 \end{bmatrix} = \begin{bmatrix} +0.406 & -0.248 & -0.187 \\ -0.219 & +0.744 & +0.064 \\ +0.031 & -0.248 & +0.062 \end{bmatrix}$$

$[I - (A^{-1} \Delta A) + (A^{-1} \Delta A)^2] A^{-1}$ $\hfill$ (A.50)

The approximations to the inverse B^{-1} as obtained in equations A.49 and A.50 should be compared with the true value, which is (correct to three decimal places)

$$B^{-1} = \begin{bmatrix} +0.406 & -0.250 & -0.188 \\ -0.219 & +0.750 & +0.062 \\ +0.031 & -0.250 & +0.062 \end{bmatrix} \quad\quad (A.51)$$

An alternative method of adjustment can be derived by putting

$$B^{-1} = A^{-1} + \Delta A^{-1} \quad\quad (A.52)$$

Premultiplication of this equation by B gives

$$I = BA^{-1} + B \Delta A^{-1}$$

and, upon rearrangement,

$$B \Delta A^{-1} = I - BA^{-1}$$

Premultiplication by A^{-1} now gives

$$(A^{-1}B) \Delta A^{-1} = A^{-1}(I - BA^{-1})$$

Since $A^{-1}B$ is approximately equal to I, we therefore have

$$\Delta A^{-1} \approx A^{-1}(I - BA^{-1})$$

and by substituting this value in equation A.52 we obtain

$$B^{-1} \approx A^{-1} + A^{-1}(I - BA^{-1})$$

$$\approx A^{-1}(2I - BA^{-1}) \tag{A.53}$$

Given A^{-1} as an approximate value of B^{-1}, equation A.53 provides a means of determining a closer approximation. If necessary this can then be used as a new value of A^{-1} so that B^{-1} is approached by iteration. Using this procedure on the same example as before, we commence with the values

$$B = \begin{bmatrix} 4 & 4 & 8 \\ 1 & 2 & 1 \\ 2 & 6 & 16 \end{bmatrix} \text{ and } A^{-1} = \begin{bmatrix} +0.400 & -0.200 & -0.200 \\ -0.200 & +0.600 & +0.100 \\ +0.025 & -0.200 & +0.050 \end{bmatrix}$$

By equation A.53, a closer approximation to B^{-1} is

$$B^{-1} = [A^{-1}] \left\{ \begin{bmatrix} 2 & 0 & 0 \\ 0 & 2 & 0 \\ 0 & 0 & 2 \end{bmatrix} - \begin{bmatrix} 4 & 4 & 8 \\ 1 & 2 & 1 \\ 2 & 6 & 16 \end{bmatrix} \begin{bmatrix} +0.400 & -0.200 & -0.200 \\ -0.200 & +0.600 & +0.100 \\ +0.025 & -0.200 & +0.050 \end{bmatrix} \right\}$$

$$= [A^{-1}] \begin{bmatrix} 1 & 0 & 0 \\ -0.025 & +1.200 & -0.050 \\ 0 & 0 & 1 \end{bmatrix}$$

$$= \begin{bmatrix} +0.405 & -0.240 & -0.190 \\ -0.215 & +0.720 & +0.070 \\ +0.030 & -0.240 & +0.060 \end{bmatrix} \tag{A.54}$$

If this is considered as a new value of A^{-1}, a repetition of the procedure yields the value

$$B^{-1} = \begin{bmatrix} +0.406 & -0.250 & -0.188 \\ -0.219 & +0.749 & +0.063 \\ -0.029 & -0.250 & +0.062 \end{bmatrix} \tag{A.55}$$

The approximations given in equations A.54 and A.55 should be compared with the true value of B^{-1} given in equation A.51.

Answers to Problems

For reasons of space, only partial answers are given to some problems but these sh
be sufficient to provide a check.

CHAPTER 4

4.1. $N^x = -2.39$ kips $\quad N^y = -13.91$ kips $\quad M^z = +4.15$ kip-feet

$$u_0 = \frac{921}{EI} \quad \text{(units = kips, feet)}$$

4.2.
$$\begin{bmatrix} u_D \\ u_E \end{bmatrix} = \begin{bmatrix} -36 & 13 & 48 \\ 157 & 183 & 66 \end{bmatrix} \begin{bmatrix} W_1 \\ W_2 \\ W_3 \end{bmatrix}$$

$$\begin{bmatrix} M_G \\ M_H \end{bmatrix} = \begin{bmatrix} 3.19 & 1.08 & -0.92 \\ -1.81 & -1.92 & -0.92 \end{bmatrix} \begin{bmatrix} W_1 \\ W_2 \\ W_3 \end{bmatrix}$$

4.3.
$$\begin{bmatrix} N^x \\ N^y \\ M^z \end{bmatrix} = \begin{bmatrix} -15.01 & -10.21 & 1.90 \\ -0.01 & 0.56 & 1.62 \\ 0 & 14.59 & -5.32 \end{bmatrix}$$

4.4. $5.12\dfrac{L}{EA}$; $\quad$ 0.509 millimeter towards the left.

4.5. $M_A = -52.5$; $\quad M_B = 6.7$; $\quad M_C = -22.7$;
$M_D = -56.9$; $\quad M_E = 83.6$
(kip, foot units, + indicates compression outside).

4.6. $N^x = -0.450$; $\quad N^y = 0.667$; $\quad N^z = 0.200$ kip
$M^x = 0.800$; $\quad M^y = 0.400$; $\quad M^z = -0.467$ kip-feet.

4.7.

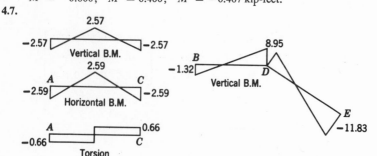

303

4.8.

Col.	N^x	N^y	N^z	M^x	M^y	M^z
AB	11.539	5.615	0.102	−0.080	−0.043	49.618
CD	3.362	−5.552	−0.053	0.530	0	33.618
EF	0.099	−0.063	−0.049	0.488	0	0.989

Units: kips, feet.
At each joint x is in the direction BD and y is vertically upwards.
4.9. 0.73 inch downwards.
4.11. (a) −74.5 lb-feet   (b) 3.27 kip-feet.
4.12.

Member	Force	Member	Force	Member	Force
1	−0.56	5	−0.56	9	0.79
2	−0.56	6	0.56	10	0
3	0.79	7	0	11	0.56
4	0.79	8	0.79	12	0.56
				13	0.56

Unit = kips.

4.13.

Member	Force	Member	Force	Member	Force
1	1.39	5	1.85	9	18.07
2	1.85	6	−9.45	10	−14.45
3	−2.31	7	−14.45	11	10.84
4	−2.31	8	18.07		

Unit = kips

CHAPTER 5
5.1. {−2.41 9.91 −5.00 −78.76 −5.72 −3.30}
5.2. In each case

$$R = \begin{bmatrix} \lambda & 0 \\ 0 & \lambda \end{bmatrix}$$

(i) $\lambda = \begin{bmatrix} 0.9397 & 0.3420 & 0 \\ -0.3420 & 0.9397 & 0 \\ 0 & 0 & 1 \end{bmatrix}$ (ii) $\lambda = \begin{bmatrix} 0.9848 & 0 & -0.1736 \\ 0 & 1 & 0 \\ 0.1736 & 0 & 0.9848 \end{bmatrix}$

5.3. $A = \begin{bmatrix} 0 & -1 & 0 \\ 1 & 0 & 0 \\ 8 & -3 & 1 \end{bmatrix}$

5.4. $\{-0.4 \quad 0 \quad -12.8 \quad 26.8 \quad -91.0 \quad -2.4\}$

5.5.
$$\begin{bmatrix} 0.853 & -0.492 & 0.174 & 0 & 0 & 0 \\ 0.500 & 0.866 & 0 & 0 & 0 & 0 \\ -0.150 & 0.087 & 0.985 & 0 & 0 & 0 \\ -0.279 & -1.042 & -1.583 & 0.853 & -0.492 & 0.174 \\ 0 & 0 & 6 & 0.500 & 0.866 & 0 \\ -1.583 & -5.909 & 0.279 & -0.150 & 0.087 & 0.985 \end{bmatrix}$$

5.6. $\{0.4706 \quad 0.4100 \quad 0.2392 \quad 0 \quad -0.0032 \quad -0.0025\}$

5.7. $\bar{u} = \begin{bmatrix} \lambda & 0 \\ 0 & \lambda \end{bmatrix} u$ where $\lambda = \begin{bmatrix} 0 & -1 & 0 \\ 0 & 0 & 1 \\ -1 & 0 & 0 \end{bmatrix}$

5.8. True $u_B = \quad -2.541 \quad 0.314 \quad +20°$
Error $= \quad 0.215 \quad 0.001 \quad 0$

CHAPTER 6

6.1. $f_{DD} = 10^{-7} \begin{bmatrix} 2.133 & & & & & \\ & 6068.148 & & & & 63.210 \\ & & 2184.533 & & -22.756 & \\ & & & 1.369 & & \\ & & -22.756 & & 0.493 & \\ & 63.210 & & & & 1.370 \end{bmatrix}$

Units = inches, pounds.

6.2. $f_{QQ} = \dfrac{1}{G} \begin{bmatrix} 0.904 & & & & & 5.87 \\ & 960 & & & & \\ & & 2721 & & -14.41 & \\ & & & 0.12 & & \\ & & -14.41 & & 0.108 & \\ & 5.87 & & & & 0.059 \end{bmatrix}$

Units = inches.

6.3. (a) $f_{BB} = \dfrac{1}{G} \begin{bmatrix} 6.67 & & & & & \\ & 5109 & & & & 830 \\ & & 3112 & & -347 & \\ & & & 178 & & \\ & & -347 & & 55.5 & \\ & 830 & & & & 188 \end{bmatrix}$

Units = feet.

(b) $f_{BB} = \dfrac{1}{G} \begin{bmatrix} 5109 & 830 \\ 830 & 188 \end{bmatrix}$

(c) $u_B = \dfrac{1}{G}\begin{bmatrix} -66,264 \\ -7,152 \end{bmatrix}$ At A $p_2 = +51$ kips, $p_6 = +284$ kip-feet.
     At B $p_2 = +24$ kips, $p_6 = -67.9$ kip-feet.

Units = feet, kips.

6.4. $f_{BB} = \begin{bmatrix} 1668.324 & -31.374 & 1034.297 & 0.676 & -12.027 & -2.127 \\ -31.374 & 2962.024 & 674.329 & 12.293 & -1.901 & 14.887 \\ 1034.297 & 674.329 & 1193.176 & 3.508 & -12.263 & 1.225 \\ 0.676 & 12.293 & 3.508 & 0.216 & -0.003 & -0.013 \\ -12.027 & -1.901 & -12.263 & -0.003 & 0.180 & -0.011 \\ -2.127 & 14.887 & 1.225 & -0.013 & -0.011 & 0.209 \end{bmatrix}$

x clockwise from A to B in plan, y obliquely upward.
z radially inward.

6.5. $u_0 = \{-7950, \quad -21,760, \quad -9973, \quad -130, \quad 52, \quad -26\}$

CHAPTER 7

7.1. (a) $\begin{bmatrix} 17.68 & -10.19 & -10.56 \\ -10.19 & 5.89 & 6.10 \\ -10.56 & 6.10 & 84.62 \end{bmatrix}$ (b) $\begin{bmatrix} 4340.90 & -1209.11 & -604.55 \\ -1209.11 & 336.48 & 169.24 \\ -604.55 & 169.24 & 84.62 \end{bmatrix}$

7.2. $\begin{bmatrix} 3446.4 & -138.4 & -982.6 & -9.2 & 160.5 & -68.7 \\ -138.4 & 1358.7 & -1049.7 & -141.5 & 1.8 & 39.9 \\ -982.6 & -1049.7 & 797.0 & 62.3 & -50.5 & 4.7 \\ -9.2 & -141.5 & 62.3 & 9.0 & 0 & 0.5 \\ 160.5 & 1.8 & -50.5 & 0 & 10.8 & 0.6 \\ -68.7 & 39.9 & 4.7 & 0.5 & 0.6 & 10.4 \end{bmatrix}$

7.3. $f_{BB} = \begin{bmatrix} 579.80 & -546.75 & -6.63 \\ -546.75 & 614.30 & 8.10 \\ -6.63 & 8.10 & 0.126 \end{bmatrix}$

$f_{AA} = \begin{bmatrix} 586.4 & 550.7 & -6.68 \\ 550.7 & 616.6 & -8.13 \\ -6.68 & -8.13 & 0.126 \end{bmatrix}$

7.4. $A_{AB} = \begin{bmatrix} 0 & 0 & 1 & 0 & 0 & 0 \\ 0 & 1 & 0 & 0 & 0 & 0 \\ 1 & 0 & 0 & 0 & 0 & 0 \\ -6 & -8 & 0 & 0 & 0 & 1 \\ -10 & 0 & -8 & 0 & 1 & 0 \\ 0 & 10 & -6 & 1 & 0 & 0 \end{bmatrix}$ $f_{AA} = (A_{AB}^{-1})^T f_{BB} (A_{AB}^{-1})$

7.5.

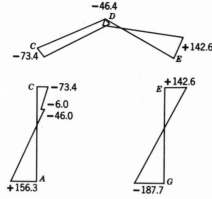

7.6. −3.28 k-ft.

7.7. (a) $f_{DD} = \begin{bmatrix} 1760 & -1960 & -160 \\ -1960 & 4138 & 323.3 \\ -160 & 323.3 & 30 \end{bmatrix}$

(b) If E is 12 feet above D and 6 feet to left of D,

$f_{EE} = \begin{bmatrix} 920 & -260 & 20 \\ -260 & 697 & -36.6 \\ 20 & -36.6 & 30 \end{bmatrix}$

If E is 11 feet above D and 5 feet to the left of D,

$f_{EE} = \begin{bmatrix} 910 & -233.5 & -10 \\ -233.5 & 655.4 & -6.7 \\ -10 & -6.7 & 30 \end{bmatrix}$

CHAPTER 8

8.1. 0.341 inches

8.2. (a) $\dfrac{1}{E} \begin{bmatrix} 5333.3 & -2000.0 & -300.0 \\ -2000.0 & 1666.7 & 200.0 \\ -300.0 & 200.0 & 30.0 \end{bmatrix}$

(b) $\dfrac{1}{E} \begin{bmatrix} 333.3 & 500.0 & 50.0 & -333.3 & 1000.0 & 50.0 \\ 500.0 & 1333.3 & 150.0 & -500.0 & 2000.0 & 100.0 \\ 50.0 & 150.0 & 20.0 & -50.0 & 200.0 & 10.0 \\ -333.3 & -500.0 & -50.0 & 333.3 & -1000.0 & -50.0 \\ 1000.0 & 2000.0 & 200.0 & -1000.0 & 5333.3 & 300.0 \\ 50.0 & 100.0 & 10.0 & -50.0 & 300.0 & 20.0 \end{bmatrix}$

(c) $\dfrac{1}{E} \begin{bmatrix} 13.3 & 0 & 33.3 & 3.3 & -3.3 & 0 \\ 0 & 0 & 0 & 0 & 0 & 0 \\ 33.3 & 0 & 666.5 & 33.3 & -33.3 & 0 \\ 3.3 & 0 & 33.3 & 13.3 & -3.3 & 0 \\ -3.3 & 0 & -33.3 & -3.3 & 6.7 & 1.7 \\ 0 & 0 & 0 & 0 & 1.7 & 3.3 \end{bmatrix}$

8.3. (a)

$$F = \frac{1}{G}$$

```
⎡ 533.33      0    400.00      0    -40.00 │     0    177.78  -533.33      0    -40.00      0 ⎤
⎢          5311.11     0     13.33      0   │ 520.00       0   5000.00   133.33      0   -13.00 ⎥
⎢                   444.44      0    -46.67 │     0    13.33   -400.00      0    -40.00      0 ⎥
⎢                             51.33      0  │   5.33       0        0     13.33      0    -1.33 ⎥
⎢                                    54.00  │     0        0     40.00        0        0      0 ⎥
⎢  ─────────────────────────────────────────────────────────────────────────────────────── ⎥
⎢                                           │ 177.78       0    500.00        0   -13.33    50.00⎥
⎢                                           │         5666.67   133.33     40.00       0   520.00⎥
⎢                                           │                  177.78         0   -20.00      0 ⎥
⎢                 symmetric                 │                            54.00     54.00      0 ⎥
⎢                                           │                                       2.67       0 ⎥
⎣                                           │                                               54.00⎦
```

(b)

$$F = \frac{1}{G}$$

```
⎡ 20577.78   10400.00   -66.67 │      0     6.67   1040.00 ⎤
⎢           5666.67   400.00   │  -20.00      0    560.00 ⎥
⎢                    6955.56   │  -93.33  -520.00      0   ⎥
⎢  ─────────────────────────────────────────────────────── ⎥
⎢                              │   53.33      0        0   ⎥
⎢        symmetric             │           52.67        0  ⎥
⎣                              │                     58.00 ⎦
```

(c)

$$F = \frac{1}{G}$$

87.04	118.24	−62.72	−6.65	9.60	8.87	−59.48	224.42	50.46	−11.26	−4.80	8.08
	2947.31	2406.40	−32.45	−232.93	294.06	−125.00	5434.70	−4776.80	54.76	236.39	267.47
		2553.85	−13.12	−256.93	239.58	0.32	4662.23	−4765.47	83.34	240.53	235.37
			52.79	0.35	−2.28	14.33	−76.07	−10.82	0.35	0.57	−3.56
				26.75	−23.64	−6.83	−448.24	489.99	−8.63	−24.75	−22.76
					31.13	−5.78	526.07	−491.36	5.72	24.33	25.98
						103.31	−283.60	−193.91	5.80	10.34	−12.03
							11160.28	−8974.96	108.83	444.77	563.25
								10354.01	−144.07	−521.14	−450.57
									54.05	7.53	5.85
										26.75	22.41
											29.87

symmetric

8.4.

$$F = \frac{1}{E}\begin{bmatrix} 216000 & 0 & -10800 & 67500 \\ 0 & 18900 & 0 & 0 \\ -10800 & 0 & 1080 & -2700 \\ 67500 & 0 & -2700 & 31320 \end{bmatrix}$$

8.5. $f_{QQ}^P =$

$$\begin{bmatrix} 3.0 & & & & & \\ & 682.5 & & & & 90.0 \\ & & 682.5 & & -90.0 & \\ \hline & & & 31.1 & & \\ & & -90.0 & & 21.0 & \\ & 90.0 & & & & 21.0 \end{bmatrix}$$

Shear deformations have been included in these values.

Stress resultants at midpoints of beams

Load (kips)

Beam	20	12	14
DJ	−0.019	−2.483	0
	−0.023	−3.000	0
	−1.472	0	0.835
	10.186	0	−5.433
	−5.562	0	10.538
	−0.050	−6.617	0
FJ	−8.492	−2.483	−3.212
	−6.005	−3.000	−3.134
	0	0	1.123
	0	0	−5.303
	0	0	11.628
	−37.886	−6.617	−8.678
HJ	−0.019	−2.483	0
	−0.023	−3.000	0
	1.472	0	−5.588
	−10.186	0	−38.218
	5.562	0	−13.737
	−0.050	−6.617	0
BJ	−11.436	−2.483	3.212
	6.051	−3.000	3.134
	0	0	1.123
	0	0	−5.303
	0	0	11.628
	38.188	−6.617	8.678

For each beam the x axis is towards J and the y axis is upward.

The horizontal displacements of F (for $E = 2.5$ k.s.f.) are:

6626 in the direction JF
2266 in the direction JD

These displacements are for all loads applied simultaneously.

8.6. The reactions at the base of each column are given in frame axes—x from A to E and y vertically upward. The member forces at the top of each beam are given in member axes; for each beam xy is the vertical plane, with x running up the axis of the beam.

(a)

Member	p_1	p_2	p_3	p_4	p_5	p_6
AB	−7.70	+16.61	+0.19	+3.24	+0.59	+103.94
CD	−0.79	+0.08	−0.03	+0.28	+5.6C	+11.81
EF	−15.51	+15.31	−0.16	−2.27	+0.72	+153.10
BG	−3.81	+22.09	−0.19	−0.62	−4.15	−30.29
DG	−0.07	−0.04	+0.79	−3.37	+11.32	+0.15
FG	−21.59	−2.94	−0.16	−0.28	−3.96	−20.80

Vertical deflection of G = 0.25 ft. downward.

(b)

Member	p_1	p_2	p_3	p_4	p_5	p_6
AB	−17.77	−3.86	+0.09	+0.71	+0.63	+161.44
CD	−0.56	−0.20	+0.08	−0.71	+3.92	+9.37
EF	−6.67	+4.06	−0.17	−3.22	+0.30	+77.49
BG	−3.47	+7.43	−0.09	+0.11	−2.65	−43.49
DG	+0.18	+0.11	+0.56	−1.56	+7.44	−0.39
FG	−7.77	+0.76	−0.17	−0.75	−3.15	−37.78

Vertical deflection of G = 0.64 ft. upward.

8.7. Top beam: $N = -1377$ kips; $M = 882$ kip-feet
Bottom beam: $N = 777$ kips; $M = 939$ kip-feet.

8.8. (i) horizontal deflections   (ii) forces at right-hand end of arches

	Loading (a)	Loading (b)	Loading (c)		Member	Loading (a)	Loading (b)	Loading (c)
B	0.40	0.57	0.65			−25.45	−22.50	−21.12
D	0.29	0.47	0.56		BD	5.09	9.02	10.85
F	0.22	0.47	0.57			65.67	−8.16	−42.09
H	0.18	0.36	0.48					
L	0.16	0.31	0.49			−17.98	−10.16	−6.28
N	0.14	0.28	0.42		DF	4.80	7.25	9.00
						33.86	−40.52	−89.58

Units: kips, feet, radians.

	−11.86	−22.94	−16.25
FH	3.75	6.13	8.31
	13.05	33.77	−38.52

Forces on curved members are
expressed in vertical axes:

	−6.90	−13.58	−3.75
HL	3.13	6.24	8.02
	−6.30	−13.00	−91.58

	−2.46	−4.82	−7.00
LN	3.24	6.36	8.82
	−36.84	−72.38	−105.01

8.9. For reasons of space, solutions are given only for (i) a single vertical load and (ii) wind load alone. There are 31 possible load combinations, solutions for which can be obtained by addition or rearrangement of the solutions given below. Many of these 31 solutions are not unique, being merely rearrangements of the values in other solutions on account of symmetry.

The x direction is taken in the direction of the wind.

The y direction is taken vertically upward.

The six forces at each column top are then numbered in the usual order.

(i) Load at point M only

Col.	p_1	p_2	p_3	p_4	p_5	p_6
A	−0.10	0.02	−0.10	−0.27	0	0.28
B	−0.22	−0.50	−0.88	3.11	0.08	−0.74
C	−0.06	−0.49	−1.15	3.53	−0.12	0.60
D	−0.01	0.15	−0.15	−0.60	−0.25	0.99
E	−0.88	−0.49	−0.22	0.74	−0.08	−3.11
H	0.93	−1.13	−0.70	1.70	−0.22	11.39
K	−1.15	−0.50	−0.71	0.06	0.12	−3.53
N	2.11	−3.28	−0.11	−0.86	−0.02	22.56
O	−0.15	0.15	−0.01	−0.99	0.25	0.59
P	−0.39	−1.13	0.93	−11.39	0.22	−1.39
Q	−0.11	−3.28	2.11	−22.56	0.02	0.86
R	0.02	0.46	0.02	−1.91	0	1.91

(ii) Wind load only

Col.	p_1	p_2	p_3	p_4	p_5	p_6
A	0.49	0.36	−0.01	0.05	0.64	−2.73
B	0.79	−0.33	−0.13	1.02	0.36	−0.33
C	0.79	0.33	0.13	−1.02	0.36	−0.33
D	0.49	−0.36	0.01	−0.05	0.64	−2.73
E	1.72	0.31	−0.01	0.08	0.49	−9.91
H	1.72	−0.31	0.01	−0.08	0.49	−9.91
K	1.72	0.31	0.01	−0.08	−0.49	−9.91
N	1.72	−0.31	−0.01	0.08	−0.49	−9.91
O	0.49	0.36	0.01	−0.05	−0.64	−2.73
P	0.79	−0.33	0.13	−1.02	−0.36	−0.33
Q	0.79	0.33	−0.13	1.02	−0.36	−0.33
R	0.49	−0.36	−0.01	0.05	−0.64	−2.73

CHAPTER 9

9.1. $F_{\alpha\alpha} = \dfrac{L^3}{12EI} \begin{bmatrix} 9 & 11 & 7 \\ 11 & 16 & 11 \\ 7 & 11 & 9 \end{bmatrix}$ $F_{\beta\beta} = \dfrac{L^3}{6EI} \begin{bmatrix} 4 & 1 & 0 \\ 1 & 4 & 1 \\ 0 & 1 & 4 \end{bmatrix}$

9.2. (a) $\begin{bmatrix} 26.38 & 3.38 \\ 3.38 & 26.38 \end{bmatrix}$ (b) $\begin{bmatrix} 46.89 & -40.89 \\ -40.89 & 81.78 \end{bmatrix}$

(c) $\begin{bmatrix} 16.88 & -2.70 \\ -2.70 & 26.38 \end{bmatrix}$ (d) $\begin{bmatrix} 46.89 & -30.67 \\ -30.67 & 46.00 \end{bmatrix}$

9.3. $\begin{bmatrix} 0 & -1 & 0 \\ 1 & 0 & 0 \\ -12 & -10 & 1 \end{bmatrix}$

9.4. $F_{\beta\beta} = \begin{bmatrix} 19.12 & -8.31 & 2.04 \\ -8.31 & 28.44 & -0.65 \\ 2.04 & -0.65 & 19.83 \end{bmatrix}$ $V = 0.33$ kips
$H = 1.05$ kips
$M = 8.88$ kip-feet

9.5. $F_{\alpha\alpha} = \begin{bmatrix} 666.7 & 0 & -100 \\ 0 & 1621.3 & 0 \\ -100 & 0 & 36 \end{bmatrix}$ $F_{\beta\beta} = \begin{bmatrix} 8.00 & 1.67 & -4.67 \\ 1.67 & 22.67 & 1.67 \\ -4.67 & 1.67 & 8.0 \end{bmatrix}$

$F_{\gamma\gamma} = \begin{bmatrix} 13.0 & -3.33 & 0.33 \\ -3.33 & 22.67 & -3.33 \\ 0.33 & -3.33 & 13.00 \end{bmatrix}$ $F_{\delta\delta} = \begin{bmatrix} 173.0 & -283.33 & 160.33 \\ -283.33 & 502.67 & -283.33 \\ 160.33 & -283.33 & 173.00 \end{bmatrix}$

$F_{\varepsilon\varepsilon} = \begin{bmatrix} 16673.0 & -32833.3 & 16660.3 \\ -32833.3 & 64702.6 & -32833.3 \\ 16660.3 & -32833.3 & 16673.0 \end{bmatrix}$

9.6. $F_{\alpha\alpha} = \begin{bmatrix} 1152 & 1440 & -144 & -576 & 1440 & 72 \\ 1440 & 7467 & -440 & -1440 & 4800 & 240 \\ -144 & -440 & 44 & 72 & -240 & -12 \\ 576 & -1440 & 72 & 1152 & -1440 & -144 \\ 1440 & 4800 & -240 & -1440 & 7467 & 440 \\ +72 & 240 & -12 & -144 & 440 & 44 \end{bmatrix}$

$F_{\beta\beta} = \begin{bmatrix} 688 & 0 & 0 & 237 & -327 & -33 \\ 0 & 3067 & 0 & 327 & -1200 & -120 \\ 0 & 0 & 44 & -33 & 120 & 12 \\ 237 & 327 & -33 & 688 & 0 & 0 \\ -327 & -1200 & 120 & 0 & 3067 & 0 \\ -33 & -120 & 12 & 0 & 0 & 44 \end{bmatrix}$

N.B.: Signs depend on directions assumed for redundants.

9.9. L.H. Support: $H = -0.396$ kips; $V = +4.692$ kips; $M = +3.470$ kip-feet.
R.H. Support: $H = -3.604$ kips; $V = +5.308$ kips; $M = +14.370$ kip-feet

CHAPTER 11

11.1. (a) $P_{B0} = +5.83$ kip-feet AB at end B: $+10$ kips -16.67 kip-feet
                                  BC at end B: $+5$ kips $+22.50$ kip-feet

    (b) $P_{B0} = +15$ kip-feet BE at end: $+5$ kips $+15$ kip-feet
         $P_{C0} = 0$
         hor. rest. $= -13$ kips

    (c) $P_{B0} = +6$ kip-feet AB at end B: 0, 0, 0.
         hor. rest. $= 0$ BC at end B: 0, $+3.5$ kips, $+14$ kip-feet
         vert. rest. $= +5.5$ kips DB at end B: 0, $+2.0$ kips, -8 kip-feet

    (d) (i) $P_{B0} = +7.5$ kip-feet BC at end B: $+2.5$ kips, $+7.5$ kip-feet
       (ii) $P_{B0} = +7.5$ kip-feet
        hor. rest. $= -1.77$ kips   member actions as for (d) (i)
        vert. rest. $= +1.77$ kips

Direction of member x axis indicated by order of lettering.

11.2. Beam CD: $M_C = +13.38$ $M_D = -25.88$
      Beam BE: $M_B = +64.23$ $M_E = -78.64$
      Column AB: $M_A = -111.75$ $M_B = +57.11$
      Column BC: $M_B = -7.31$ $M_C = +13.88$
      Column DE: $M_D = -25.88$ $M_E = +27.36$
      Column EF: $M_E = -51.28$ $M_F = 0$

    (+) denotes compression on the top of beams and on the outside of columns.
    Units: kip-feet.

11.3. $M_A = +25.4$; $M_B = -47.8$; $M_C = +3.8$; $M_D = -27.4$;
       $M_E = +45.8$.

    Units: kip-feet; tension inside +.

11.5.

$$P_0 = \begin{bmatrix} 0 \\ 66.7 \\ -66.7 \\ 66.7 \\ -66.7 \\ 66.7 \\ -66.7 \\ \hline 0 \\ 0 \end{bmatrix}$$

	A	B	C	D	E	F	G	2	1
	72	16		20				+6	−6
	16	104	16		20			+6	−6
		16	72			20		+6	−6
$K =$	20			116	18			+6	0
		20		18	152	18		+6	0
			20		18	152	18	+6	0
						18	76	0	+6
	+6	+6	+6	+6	+6	+6	0	3.6	−3.6
	−6	−6	−6	0	0	0	+6	−3.6	8.4

11.6.

	(1)		(2)		(3)		
Floor	Span M (kip-feet)	Floor	Support M	Floor	End couple ↰₊		
						Top	Bottom
9	27.6	9	−42.3	9-8		4.7	1.3
8	24.6	7	−39.5	8-7		12.5	7.4
7	24.4	5	−39.1	7-6		19.8	14.5
6	23.7	3	−38.1	6-5		28.2	12.6
5	23.9	1	−37.6	5-4		58.3	52.3
4	23.7			4-3		37.0	39.2
3	22.8			3-2		49.2	44.2
2	22.3			2-1		53.0	53.5
1	21.6			1-0		40.6	95.8

11.7. End moments (kip-feet) ↰ positive.

(*a*) Beams

	Vertical loading				Horizontal loading		
40.66	−54.24	25.67	0.47	−3.72	−3.18	−3.18	−3.72
1.86	−22.32	50.73	−52.03	−11.05	−9.87	−9.87	−11.05
50.30	−53.46	21.27	−0.25	−21.21	−18.69	−18.69	−21.21
0.41	−19.48	54.05	−52.54	−31.02	−27.74	−27.74	−31.02
52.72	−57.99	16.52	1.74	−35.47	−31.23	−31.23	−35.47

(*b*) Columns

	Vertical loading			Horizontal loading	
−40.66	28.57	−0.47	3.72	6.37	3.72
−4.17	−9.85	26.58	0.97	4.25	0.97
2.31	−18.56	25.46	10.08	15.49	10.08
−24.36	14.50	0.66	5.81	12.73	5.81
−25.94	17.69	−0.41	15.40	24.65	15.40
−1.41	−12.73	22.79	11.49	21.57	11.49
1.00	−21.84	29.75	19.53	33.91	19.53
−24.27	9.57	5.79	17.12	32.80	17.12
−28.45	31.90	−7.53	18.35	29.66	18.35
−12.19	17.99	−1.73	36.00	41.65	36.00

11.8. See 11.7.

11.9. (*a*) With no node at the point K, the stiffness matrix is: taking $E = 100$.

	A	B	C	D	E	F	G	H	I	J	L	M	N	O	P	Q	R	S	5	4	3	2	1	V
A	80	20			20														6	−6				−3
B	20	120	20	20	20														6	−6	−6			3
C		20	120	20		20													6	−6		−1.5		−3
D		20	20	80	20														6	−6		−6		3
E	20	20		20	120	20	20												6	−6		−6		
F			20		20	160	20	20	20										6	−4.5	6	6	−6	
G					20	20	120	20	20										6	6	6	4.5	−6	
H						20	20	100		20								10		1.5		6	−6	
I						20	20		120	20	20										6	6		
J								20	20	120	20	20						20			6	6		
L									20	20	120	160	20	20	20				6	1.5		6		
M										20	20	160	120	20	20	20			6			6		
N											20	120	120	20	20	20			−6	−6		6	−6	−3
O								10				20	20	100	20	20		20	−6	4.5		4.5	−6	3
P													20	20	120	20	20							
Q														20	20	160	20	20						
R															20	20	160	20						
S																20	20	120						
5	6	6	6	6	6	6	6				6	6	−6	−6					4.8	−4.8				
4	−6	−6	−6	−6	−6	−4.5	6	1.5			1.5		−6	4.5					−4.8	7.35	−2.4	−0.15		
3		−6				6	6		6	6										−2.4	4.8	−2.4		
2			−1.5	−6	−6	6	4.5	6	6	6	6	6	6	6						−0.15	−2.4	7.35	−4.8	
1						−6	−6	−6					−6	−6								−4.8	9.6	
V	−3	3	−3	3				3					−3	3										1.2

11.10. Horizontal displacement   = 0.078 inch at A and B
Vertical displacement at A = 0.206 inch upward
Vertical displacement at B = 0.206 inch downward

CHAPTER 12
12.1. See 11.6.
12.2. See 11.10.
12.3. See 11.6.
12.4. See 11.10.

12.5.

	A	B	C	D	E	F	G	H
Top	−83.5	−89.3	−32.4	15.5	76.8	113.8	39.2	−42.0
Bottom	−79.7	−87.4	−31.9	15.3	75.0	110.8	38.0	−38.8

12.6.

Load at	A	B	C	D	E	F	G
$M_{BB} =$	0	−1.12	−2.20	−1.79	−1.19	−0.60	0

CHAPTER 13
13.1. 225 kips/inch; −225 kips/inch.

13.2. $\begin{bmatrix} 26.32 & -73.31 \\ -73.31 & 198.68 \end{bmatrix}$ Units: kips, inches.

13.3. $\begin{bmatrix} 59.26 & 533.33 & -59.26 & 533.33 \\ 533.33 & 6400.00 & -533.33 & 3200.00 \\ -59.26 & -533.33 & 59.26 & -533.33 \\ 533.33 & 3200.00 & -533.33 & 6400.00 \end{bmatrix}$

Units = kips feet.

13.4. (*a*) $\begin{bmatrix} \binom{\infty}{15,014} & \binom{\infty}{8634} & -266.67 & \binom{-\infty}{-15014} & \binom{-\infty}{-8634} & -266.67 \\ \binom{\infty}{8,634} & \binom{\infty}{5044} & 461.87 & \binom{-\infty}{-8634} & \binom{-\infty}{-5044} & 461.87 \\ -266.67 & 461.87 & 6400 & 266.67 & -461.87 & 3200 \\ \binom{-\infty}{-15014} & \binom{-\infty}{-8634} & 266.67 & \binom{\infty}{15014} & \binom{\infty}{8634} & 266.67 \\ \binom{-\infty}{-8634} & \binom{-\infty}{-5044} & -461.87 & \binom{\infty}{8634} & \binom{\infty}{5044} & -461.87 \\ -266.67 & 461.87 & 3200 & 266.67 & -461.87 & 6400 \end{bmatrix}$

(b)

$$\begin{bmatrix}
\left({\infty \atop 20000}\right) & 0 & 0 & 0 & \left({-\infty \atop -20000}\right) & 0 \\[4pt]
0 & 59.26 & 533.33 & 59.26 & 0 & 622.22 \\[2pt]
0 & 533.33 & 6400 & 533.33 & 0 & 4000 \\[2pt]
0 & 59.26 & 533.33 & 59.26 & 0 & 622.22 \\[4pt]
\left({-\infty \atop -20000}\right) & 0 & 0 & 0 & \left({\infty \atop 20000}\right) & 0 \\[4pt]
0 & 622.22 & 4000 & 622.22 & 0 & 8133.33
\end{bmatrix}$$

(c)

$$\begin{bmatrix}
\left({\infty \atop 20000}\right) & 0 & 0 & 0 & \left({-\infty \atop -20000}\right) & \left({\infty \atop 60000}\right) \\[4pt]
0 & 59.26 & 533.33 & 59.26 & 0 & 533.33 \\[2pt]
0 & 533.33 & 6400 & 533.33 & 0 & 3200 \\[2pt]
0 & 59.26 & 533.33 & 59.26 & 0 & 533.33 \\[4pt]
\left({-\infty \atop -20000}\right) & 0 & 0 & 0 & \left({\infty \atop 20000}\right) & \left({-\infty \atop -60000}\right) \\[4pt]
\left({\infty \atop 60000}\right) & 533.33 & 3200 & 533.33 & \left({-\infty \atop -60000}\right) & \left({\infty \atop 186400}\right)
\end{bmatrix}$$

Assumptions of infinite and finite axial stiffness respectively, produce values shown in brackets.

13.5.
$$\begin{bmatrix}
14.815 & 266.667 & -14.815 \\
266.667 & 4800 & -266.667 \\
-14.815 & -266.667 & 14.815
\end{bmatrix}$$

13.6. $k_{QQ} = G \times$
$$\begin{bmatrix}
1.202 & & & & -0.291 \\
& 0.003 & & & \\
& & 0.001 & 0.158 & \\
& & & 8.850 & \\
& & 0.158 & 30.990 & \\
-0.291 & & & & 47.657
\end{bmatrix}$$

13.7. Using Simpson's rule with 10° segments.

$K_{AB} = 10^{-4} \times$

$$\begin{array}{cc}
\underbrace{\qquad\qquad K_{AA} \qquad\qquad}_{} & \underbrace{\qquad\qquad K_{AB} \qquad\qquad}_{}
\end{array}$$

$$\left[
\begin{array}{cccccc|cccccc}
-0.9 & -1.2 & & 9.3 & & & -0.6 & -1.4 & & -19.7 & & \\
& 0.5 & 8.4 & & 15.8 & & & -0.6 & -8.4 & & 15.8 & \\
& & 2.3 & -28.2 & & & 1.4 & 2.2 & 22.2 & & & \\
& & & 251.7 & 249.4 & & -8.4 & -35.0 & -189.9 & 124.4 & & \\
& & & & 501.9 & & -19.7 & -22.2 & -124.4 & 458.9 & & \\
& & & & & 531.1 & -15.8 & & & & & \\
\hline
& & & & & & 0.9 & 1.2 & & 9.3 & & \\
& & & & & & 0.5 & 8.4 & 28.2 & -15.8 & & \\
& & & & & & 2.3 & 251.7 & -249.4 & & & \\
& & & & & & & 501.9 & & & & \\
& & & & & & & 531.1 & & & &
\end{array}
\right]$$

$$\begin{array}{cc}
\underbrace{\qquad\qquad K_{BA} \qquad\qquad}_{} & \underbrace{\qquad\qquad K_{BB} \qquad\qquad}_{}
\end{array}$$

$P_A = \{0 \quad 30.0 \quad 0 \quad 70.3 \quad 0 \quad 467.4\}$

$P_B = \{0 \quad 30.0 \quad 0 \quad 70.3 \quad 0 \quad -467.4\}$

13.8.

$$10^{-5} \times \begin{bmatrix} 1.38 & & -3.11 & & 18.5 & & -2.00 & & -2.76 \\ & 0.73 & & 32.9 & & 19.0 & & -0.73 & \\ -3.11 & & -13.0 & & -197.0 & & 9.69 & & 9.19 \\ & 32.9 & & 1480 & & 854 & & -32.9 & \\ 18.5 & & -197.0 & & 4300 & & -162.0 & & -115.0 \\ & 19.0 & & 854 & & 493 & & -19.0 & \\ \hline -2.00 & & 9.69 & & -162.0 & & 7.39 & & 6.58 \\ & -0.73 & & -32.9 & & -19.0 & & 0.73 & \\ -2.76 & & 9.19 & & -115.0 & & 6.58 & & 96.8 \end{bmatrix}$$

13.9.

$$k_{BB} = \begin{bmatrix} 0.00136 & 0.00039 & -0.00096 & 0.00575 & 0.03348 & 0.02563 \\ 0.00039 & 0.00164 & -0.00206 & -0.03251 & -0.08810 & -0.08934 \\ -0.00096 & -0.00206 & 0.00603 & -0.07822 & 0.28504 & 0.08472 \\ 0.00575 & -0.03251 & -0.07822 & 9.46308 & -4.67186 & 2.83396 \\ 0.03348 & -0.08810 & 0.28504 & -4.67186 & 24.20114 & 6.56398 \\ 0.02563 & -0.08934 & 0.08472 & 2.83396 & 6.56398 & 11.45683 \end{bmatrix}$$

13.10. With y axis vertical,

$$p_A = \begin{bmatrix} -1.83 \\ 14.71 \\ 0.03 \\ 383.79 \\ 233.01 \\ -1013.02 \end{bmatrix} \qquad p_B = \begin{bmatrix} 1.83 \\ 11.66 \\ -0.03 \\ -88.12 \\ 118.05 \\ -569.07 \end{bmatrix}$$

13.11. Based on the stiffness from problem 13.7.

$$k_{FF} = 10^{-5} \times \begin{bmatrix} 22.7 & 0 & -11.8 & 0 & -262.1 & 0 \\ 0 & 5.8 & 0 & 21.3 & 0 & -169.3 \\ -11.8 & 0 & 9.1 & 0 & -213.7 & 0 \\ 0 & 21.3 & 0 & 1127.7 & 0 & -392.2 \\ -262.1 & 0 & 213.7 & 0 & 5648 & 0 \\ 0 & -169.3 & 0 & -392.2 & 0 & 6244 \end{bmatrix}$$

Actions at $D = \{4.23 \quad 3.24 \quad -0.67 \quad -57.52 \quad -28.06 \quad -1.47\} \times 10^{-6}$
Units: kips, feet.

CHAPTER 14

14.1. (*a*) Axes at both *B* and *C* are taken with x horizontal towards the right.

$$
K = \begin{array}{c} \\ B \\ \\ \\ C \\ \\ \end{array}
\left[
\begin{array}{ccc|ccc}
2.70 & 0 & 6.00 & -1.50 & 0 & 0 \\
0 & 3.15 & 1.50 & 0 & -0.15 & 1.50 \\
6.00 & 1.50 & 60.00 & 0 & -1.50 & 10.00 \\
\hline
-1.50 & 0 & 0 & 2.77 & -0.85 & 2.12 \\
0 & -0.15 & -1.50 & -0.85 & 1.42 & 0.62 \\
0 & 1.50 & 10.00 & 2.12 & 0.62 & 48.28
\end{array}
\right]
$$

(*b*) If the three restraints are taken as (i) horizontal along *BC*, (ii) rotation at *B*, and (iii) rotation at *C*, then

$$
K = \begin{bmatrix}
2.20 & 4.50 & 2.74 \\
4.50 & 60.00 & 10.00 \\
2.74 & 10.00 & 48.28
\end{bmatrix}
$$

14.2.
$$
K = 10^{-2} \times
\begin{array}{c}
\vec{B} \quad \overset{\curvearrowright}{B} \quad \overset{\curvearrowright}{C} \quad \vec{D} \quad \overset{\curvearrowright}{D} \\
\begin{bmatrix}
1.669 & 4.125 & 0 & -0.469 & 1.875 \\
4.125 & 60 & 10 & 1.875 & 0 \\
0 & 10 & 40 & 0 & 10 \\
-0.469 & 1.875 & 0 & 1.669 & 4.125 \\
1.875 & 0 & 10 & 4.125 & 60
\end{bmatrix}
\end{array}
$$

14.3.

(*a*)

	E1	E2	E3	E4	E5	E6	F1	F2	F3	F4	F5	F6
	25676	8970				360	−14400					
		7290				90		−36				540
			10430	−360	210				−16		−240	
				7617	−2492					−1129		
					12405				240		2400	
$K=$						17527		−540				5400
							25676	−8970				360
								7290				90
									10430	−360	−210	
										7617	2492	
											12405	
	symmetrical											17527

(*b*)

	EF	E4	E5	E6	F4	F5	F6
	579			−427			−427
		7617	−2492		−1129		
			12405			2400	
$K=$				17527			5400
					7617	2492	
						12405	
	symmetrical						17527

14.4. Assume direction of axes: x from B to D, y vertically upward.
Reactions at A: 2.05, 10.82, 0.46, 4.55, −0.55, −5.98
Reactions at C: −2.61, 9.44, 3.77, 20.95, 0.53, 9.58
Reactions at E: −5.44, 2.24, 3.77, 20.96, 1.53, 50.03.
Internal actions: at mid-point of BD, −2.05, 0.43, −0.46, 0.03, 11.11, 60.97.

14.5. With x towards the right and y vertically upward, the reactions on the bases of the columns are;

Col. base	(a) horiz.	(a) vert.	(a) couple.	(b) horiz.	(b) vert.	(b) couple.	(c) horiz.	(c) vert.	(c) couple.
A	14.69	38.68	−99.32	8.28	4.01	−74.37	−16.86	−2.77	62.60
C	11.80	93.07	−85.74	14.16	3.58	−104.16	−6.43	−0.10	47.17
E	−26.49	28.25	−30.05	−22.44	32.41	−75.64	−6.71	2.87	29.35

Units: kips, feet.

14.6. As for 4.4.

14.7.   Load case

Member	(a)	(b)	(c)	(d)	(e)	(f)
AB	0	0	0	0	0	0
BC	0	0	0	0	0	0
CD	0	0	0	0	0	0
AD	0	0	0	0	0	0
EF	−2.040	+0.266	−0.113	−0.852	−1.446	−1.061
FG	+0.620	−0.072	−1.292	−1.676	−0.031	−0.369
GH	+0.620	−1.687	+0.594	−0.144	−0.031	+0.322
EH	−2.040	−1.349	−1.292	−2.384	−1.446	−0.369
AE	−5.635	+0.834	+1.134	−5.792	−3.636	−7.320
BF	−0.189	−0.159	+1.134	−7.277	−7.668	−7.320
CG	−1.152	−8.153	−0.882	−9.824	−11.701	−0.349
DH	−0.189	+0.313	−0.882	−7.277	−7.668	−0.349
AF	+1.388	−0.037	+0.454	−2.311	+0.906	−3.440
BE	−5.050	+0.478	+0.454	−3.776	−6.577	−3.440
BG	+0.880	−3.883	+1.556	−3.005	−0.418	+0.590
CF	−1.100	+0.279	−2.186	−5.282	−7.901	−4.087
CH	−1.100	−1.952	−0.208	−6.715	−7.901	−0.057
DG	+0.880	−2.372	−0.208	−0.697	−0.418	−0.057
DE	−5.050	−1.753	−2.186	−6.085	−6.577	−4.087
AH	+1.388	+1.474	+1.556	−0.878	+0.906	+0.590
EG	−2.207	−1.099	−0.526	−0.156	−0.739	−0.369
FH	+0.787	−0.321	−0.526	−2.372	−0.739	−0.369

14.8. (a) $\begin{bmatrix} 0.1 & 0 & 0 \\ 0 & 1.6 & 0 \\ 0 & 0 & 0 \end{bmatrix}$ (b) $\begin{bmatrix} 0.475 & 0.650 & 0 \\ 0.650 & 1.225 & 0 \\ 0 & 0 & 0 \end{bmatrix}$

(c) $\begin{bmatrix} 0.850 & 0.750 & 0 \\ 0.750 & 0.850 & 0 \\ 0 & 0 & 0 \end{bmatrix}$

14.9.

(a) $10^3 \times \begin{bmatrix} 234.2 & 0 & 0 \\ 0 & 1.236 & 1.236c \\ 0 & 1.236c & 1.236c^2 \end{bmatrix}$

(b) $10^3 \times \begin{bmatrix} 176.0 & -100.9 & 0.62c \\ -100.9 & 59.5 & 1.07c \\ 0.62c & 1.07c & 1.236c^2 \end{bmatrix}$

(c) $10^3 \times \begin{bmatrix} 117 & -117 & 0.87c \\ -117 & 117 & 0.87c \\ 0.87c & 0.87c & 1.236c^2 \end{bmatrix}$

Index

323

$$P_1 = 2.38$$

$$P_2 \quad 13.92$$

$$P_6 \quad 59.89$$